PULMONARY SURFACTANT SYSTEM

SYMPOSIA OF THE GIOVANNI LORENZINI FOUNDATION
Volume 16

Other volumes in this series:

PULMONARY SURFACTANT SYSTEM

Proceedings of the International Symposium on the Surfactant System of the Lung held in Rome, Italy, March 2-4,1983

Editors:

Ermelando V. Cosmi

and

Emile M. Scarpelli

1983

ELSEVIER SCIENCE PUBLISHERS
AMSTERDAM–NEW YORK–OXFORD

iv

ISBN for this volume 0-444-80514-1
ISBN for the series: 0-444-80040-9

Published by:
Elsevier Science Publishers
P.O. Box 211
1000 AE Amsterdam, The Netherlands

Sole distributors for the USA and Canada:
Elsevier Science Publishing Company Inc.
52 Vanderbilt Avenue
New York, N.Y. 10017

Library of Congress Cataloging in Publication Data

International Symposium on the Surfactant System of the
    Lung (1983 : Rome, Italy)
    Pulmonary surfactant system.

    (Symposia of the Giovanni Lorenzini Foundation ;
v. 16)
    Bibliography: p.
    Includes indexes.
    1. Respiratory distress syndrome, Adult--Congresses.
2. Respiratory distress syndrome--Congresses. 3. Pulmonary surfactant--Congresses. I. Cosmi, Ermelando V.,
1937-   . II. Scarpelli, Emile M. III. Title.
IV. Series. [DNLM: 1. Pulmonary surfactant--Congresses.
2. Respiratory distress syndrome--Congresses.
3. Respiratory distress syndrome, Adult--Congresses.

W3 SY1056 v. 16 / WF 600 I614r 1983]
RC776.R38I57 1983   616.2'4   83-9040
ISBN 0-444-80514-1

Printed in The Netherlands

FOREWORD

The present volume contains the proceedings of the International Symposium on "The surfactant system of the lung", held in Rome on March 2-4, 1983 and organized by the Giovanni Lorenzini Foundation of Milan.

This scientific event represents a further step of the continuous effort of our Foundation in presenting to the international scientific community a balanced evaluation of the new discoveries in biological sciences of potential interest for clinical medicine.

The present Symposium on the surfactant system of the lung is a particularly good example of the positive results obtained by the joined efforts of lipid biochemists, pulmonary physiologists and two apparently distant groups of clinical scientists: obstetrics and specialists in respiratory diseases.

The results are of practical interest as well as of major significance for the understanding of many pulmonary disorders. The large participation of clinical and basic specialists of many different countries underlines the international interests for this new and rapidly growing field of medical research.

We are particularly grateful to professors E. Cosmi (Rome, Italy), E.M. Scarpelli (New York, USA) and M. Gaetani of the Institute De Angeli (Milan, Italy) for their efforts in organizing the meeting and to the publisher for a rapid and accurate publication of the proceedings of a timely conference.

Prof. Rodolfo Paoletti
President of the Giovanni Lorenzini
Foundation

PREFACE

The surfactant system of the lung, born in 1955 and christened in 1967, has now reached full maturity. This was celebrated at the international symposium held in Rome, from March 2 through 4, 1983.

Many were invited to speak and the words of those who accepted the invitation are the contents of this volume. Many others submitted communications and from these 65 were selected for presentation either in conferences or in poster sessions. This grand response from colleagues worldwide, reporting from all continents, was quite unexpected both by the Program Committee and the publishers. As a result, selected papers and posters are, regretably, not included in this volume. However, in recognition of the work of these scientists and to convey the universal activity in surfactant research, we list here the broad categories into which these communications may be classified, as well as the senior author and the city in which the work was done:

(1) Surfactant metabolism, content and conformation in the alveolar lining layer were reported by Drs. Aihara (Tokyo), Albergheria (Catania), Bourbon (Paris), Egberts (Leiden), Ignazi (Imola), Kawanami (Tokyo) and Seeger (Giessen).

(2) Fetal pulmonary maturation, its diagnosis and factors affecting surfactants both positively and negatively, were the topics of Drs. Arif (Karachi), Bourbon (Paris), Engle (Madison), Guerrini (Ferrara), Huovila (Helsinki), Knitza (Homburg), Lamedica (Genoa), Marin (Paris), Montoneri (Catania), Müller-Tyl (Vienna), Tolino (Naples), Vakhidov (Tashkent) and Zullo (Naples).

(3) Morphology, histochemistry and modification of the surfactant system is under study in the laboratories of Drs. Anyanwu (Münster), Chieco (Bologna), Franceschelli (Bologna), Hirohata (Tokyo), Leopardi (Milan) and Satoh (Tokyo).

(4) It is now clear that the surfactant system of both children and adults is modified in many disease states and by various airborne substances. Some of these were reported by Drs. Bacolla (Turin), Battacharyya (Calcutta), Dottorini (Perugia), Gullo (Trieste), Guzmán Blanco (LaCoruña), Hallman (Helsinki), Kato (Tokyo), Kobayashi (Tokyo), Maiorano (Bari), Michimata (Tokyo), Obladen (Bochum), Piazza (Sivilgliano), Prévost (Toulouse), Rotaru (Iassy), Santos Rosa (Coimbra), Wollman (Tübingen), Zanello (Bologna), Zarzar (Tashkent) and Zimmermann (Berlin).

(5) It is also clear that new therapies are being sought to stimulate production and to provide supplementation of surfactants in deficiency states. Ambroxol, which is receiving much attention, was reported by Drs. Chiara (Milan), Cocco (Naples), Delli Colli (Rome), Luerti (Milan), Lüstro (Siracusa), Mezzetti (Milan), Wiesemann (Essen) and Zsolnai (Budapest). Supplementation was reported by Drs. Kobayashi (Tokyo), Pettenasso (Padua) and Yoshida (Tokyo).

(6) Whereas the surfactant system is generally considered with regard to its alveolar functions, several studies indicate that it may serve an equally important role in airway function as reported by Drs. Morgenroth (Bochum), Rensch (Biberach) and von Seefeld (Biberach), by some of the authors included in this text, and in many of the studies of mucociliary stimulating drugs.

Equally overwhelming was the large attendance at the meetings of researchers and clinicians, who confirmed the universality of interest in the surfactants. Their participation and interaction with speakers and presenters proves that, as mature as it may be, the surfactant system of the lung has a long and challenging life ahead.

THE EDITORS

INTRODUCTION

The primary objective of the Symposium was to provide a structure for discussion and interaction among researchers in the many medical and basic scientific disciplines concerned with the field of pulmonary surfactants. The structure of the meetings is reflected in the organization of this text. Clearly, there is continuing interest in the mysteries of composition and in the new functional significance of the surfactant system (Part I) and in the disease state which for the last 14 years has been the focal clinical entity to which surfactant deficiency could be attributed, i.e., respiratory distress syndrome of the newborn infant (Part II). As knowledge of surfactants has expanded and as research curiosity has become more sophisticated, it is clear that the surfactant system must be dealt with in a number of other problems pertaining to alveolar function and malfunction, e.g., adult respiratory distress syndrome and exogenous insults (Part III). But beyond this, the word is beginning to be heard that the domain of the surfactant system reaches outside the alveolus to the airways and that, perhaps, a new story is soon to be written (Part IV).

E.V. Cosmi

CONTENTS

FUNCTIONAL SIGNIFICANCE AND COMPOSITION

© 1983, Elsevier Science Publishers B.V.
*Pulmonary Surfactant System, E.V. Cosmi
and E.M. Scarpelli eds.*

NEAR-ZERO SURFACE TENSION, INTRAPULMONARY FOAM AND LUNG MECHANICS

EMILE M. SCARPELLI[1,2], ASHOK KUMAR[2] AND BELLA C. CLUTARIO[1]
[1]Pulmonary Division, Department of Pediatrics, and [2]Department of Physiology and Biophysics, Albert Einstein College of Medicine, 1300 Morris Park Avenue, Bronx, New York 10461 (U.S.A.).

In 1955, Pattle (1) reported that stable bubbles could be expressed from normal lungs of both mature fetuses and adults, and from normal lungs that had been made edematous in the laboratory. In a series of papers (1-4), he described the physical characteristics of the films of these bubbles as highly resistant to chemical antifoams, permeable to atmospheric gases, and stable even after repeated washings with normal saline solution. He observed the bubbles under the microscope, noted that their size remained remarkably constant with time and calculated that surface tension (γ) of the bubble films was near zero, i.e., ~0.1 mN·m^{-1}. He assumed that the bubbles were produced as a result of his laboratory manipulations, i.e., that the surface lining was lifted from the alveoli directly in the process of bubble formation. Therefore, the normal alveolar lining was rich in these films and operated at near-zero γ. He interpreted the functional significance of this highly surface-active lining in terms of liquid balance at the alveolar/capillary level and said that near-zero γ was important in preventing intraalveolar liquid accumulation. To the extent that γ exceeded zero, liquid balance would be disrupted in favor of alveolar filling. This, in essence, is Pattle's antiedema theory of surfactant function.

Subsequently, Clements et al (5-8) reported that extracts from normal lungs were highly surface-active as measured in two-dimensional films in a modified Langmuir-Wilhelmy surface balance. They noted that upon compression, γ of these films varied directly with surface area and reached a lower limiting value of about 10 mN·m^{-1}. They concluded that analogous surface behavior at the alveolar level would stabilize these units during deflation and that the tension-area (TA) isotherms from the surface balance could explain the inflation-deflation curves of the volume-pressure (VP) diagram of normal lungs inflated from the "degassed" (airless) state. These concepts have been refined (9-11), but still underly the antiatelectasis theory of surfactant function.

In the years that followed, the essential role of surfactants in normal lung function was verified, as the physiological chemistry of surfactants was explored further: For example (1) Avery and Mead (12) showed that respiratory distress syndrome (RDS) of the immature newborn infant is related to, probably caused by a deficiency of surfactants; (2) maturation of the surfactant system prior to birth follows a strict developmental timetable (13), and functional maturity of the lungs depends on adequate concentrations of surfactants (14); (3) surfactants are synthesized directly by the fetal lung and secreted into the liquid milieu (15), fetal pulmonary fluid (FPF), that fills all potential airspaces prior to birth (16); (4) displacement of normal surfactants from the lungs results in severe respiratory distress in the newborn with inability to adapt to the air environment (17) and in extreme collapsibility of the adult lung in vitro with inability to maintain a residual volume (18); (5) dipalmitoyl phosphatidylcholine (DPPC) is the principal surfactant of the lung surfactant system (19) and other phospholipids of the system, particularly phosphatidylglycerol (20), are equally surface-active but present in lower concentrations than DPPC.

In this report, we present our studies on intrapulmonary foam formation: its relationship to fetal lung maturity, surfactants and near-zero γ; its central role in establishing the normal air-lung at birth; and its function as the basis for normal VP behavior of both neonatal and adult lungs. These studies substantiate and extend many of the seminal observations of Pattle and redefine conventional interpretations of the role of surfactants in lung stability and static mechanics.

MATURE FETAL/NEONATAL LUNG

We first observed foam in the airways of normal mature neonatal kids at the onset of breathing at birth and noted that when the normal surfactants of FPF had been displaced by a nonionic surfactant with relatively high γ, bubble formation virtually ceased (17). Subsequently, we looked into the possibility that foam formation is a regular and natural process at birth, understanding that this is a reasonable expectation as air enters surfactant-rich FPF through a system of conduits that branch successively as tube diameter becomes progressively smaller. In this respect the airways could serve as a natural sparger for dispersing inhaled air into FPF.

We have examined the lungs of mature rabbit fetuses, 30 days gestation, following spontaneous breathing after either vaginal or cesarean birth and during inflation and deflation of the lungs, in vitro, from the FPF-filled fetal state (21,22). We find that intrapulmonary foam formation is the central process in each of these conditions.

Rabbits delivered through uterotomy were allowed to breath air spontaneously for <1 to 15 min, then sacrificed and, following removal of the anterior thorax, examined at atmospheric pressure under a stereomicroscope (21). Bubbles were present in aerated terminal lung units (TLU) of all neonates. Foam was also present in the tracheas of those that were sacrificed earliest, while there was little or no tracheal foam in those that had breathed for the longest times. In all cases, however, bubbles were present in terminal airways and saccules (Figure 1). When the lungs of rabbits that had been sacrificed prior to air-breathing were inflated to maximal volume then deflated to atmospheric pressure in vitro, most of the TLU remained inflated as <50% of the inflation volume could be withdrawn and bubbles appeared in the major bronchi and trachea. During inflation, as air first entered the lung, bulk air displaced bulk FPF peripherally and as air entered the smallest airways a clear meniscus ("pre-bubble") could be seen. When air was withdrawn before the apparent bubble had

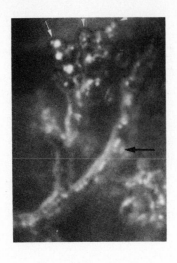

Fig. 1. Bubbles are seen in airways (e.g., horizontal black arrow). Bubbles also in periphery of TLU (short white arrows). x45. From reference 21 with permission

formed, the airway refilled with FPF. However, if inflation was continued, the saccules inflated and remained inflated. Bubbles could be seen moving freely toward the periphery of the TLU, expanding previously unexpanded areas of these units (Figure 1).

To confirm the formation of bubbles, we devised a method for producing micro-orifices in the epithelial surface of the lung by microdissection (22). After spontaneous breathing at birth or after inflation-deflation in vitro, and with the lungs at atmospheric pressure, formed bubbles could be delivered intact directly from the saccules and observed in air-equilibrated normal saline solution. These bubbles, formed in situ, retained virtually constant diameter during >30 min observation. Their size range (45-200 μm) and stability was the same as the bubbles studied by Pattle and we concluded that γ is the same, i.e., near-zero. By elevating distending pressure to 5-15 cm H_2O, additional formed bubbles were delivered through the micro-orifice. These were followed by new bubble formation from FPF at the micro-orifice, apparently when the population of formed bubbles had been exhausted. For each micro-orifice, the new bubbles were of uniform size; the size range from different micro-orifices was within the range of bubbles formed in situ. All bubbles were stable (near-zero γ). We randomly sampled TLU from each lobe for bubbles and found them in *all* sampled units that remained aerated at atmospheric pressure.

We were also able to harvest foam from the lungs of mature sheep and analyze

TABLE

	FPF	Foam Wet	Foam Dry
Albumin	+	+	+
SIgA	+	+	+
"Transferrin"	+	±	-
Other Proteins	2-4	±	-
Phosphatidylcholine	+	+	+
Phosphatidylglycerol	+	+	+
Phosphatidylethanolamine	?	?	?
Sphingomyelin	+	-	-
Lysophosphatidylcholine	±	-	-
Non-phospholipids	+	+	+

+ = present
- = absent
? = identity not confirmed

their films qualitatively for lipid and protein content (Table). We found that the bubble films contained phosphatidylcholine in highest concentration, plus phosphatidylglycerol, (?) phosphatidylethanolamine, non-phospholipids and traces of albumin and secretory immunoglobulin A. This composition might be considered as constituting the first analogue of the future alveolar lining layer of the air-lung.

We conclude from these studies that (1) FPF surfactants are incorporated into bubble films at the onset of breathing; (2) bubbles, which require relatively little pressure for their formation, establish a functional residual capacity immediately with the first breath; (3) bubble films are the first formed lining layer of the saccules (alveoli); (4) air-bubbles serve to dilate the normally constricted pulmonary arterioles as oxygen diffuses into these vessel walls directly under a high pressure gradient; (5) saccular and capillary oxygenation is sustained both during and between inspiratory efforts; (6) the conventional concept of the early neonatal lung being a two-phase system of bulk air and bulk FPF is untenable; (7) as bubble films collapse or rupture and FPF is absorbed rapidly after birth, establishment of the stable air-lung is facilitated by the bubble films of near-zero γ. It may be anticipated, therefore, that

deficiency of surfactants will result in inability to form bubbles and that consequent respiratory embarrassment is related to those functions attributed to
bubbles.

IMMATURE FETAL/NEONATAL LUNG

We have reported studies of immature rabbits of 27 days gestation (23-25)
similar to those described for the mature fetus (above). None of the fetuses
delivered from uterotomy lived longer than 3 hr outside the uterus: At postmortem examination we found airways and TLU generally filled with liquid and
very few TLU containing air. When the lungs were inflated to maximal volume in
vitro, all TLU were apparently aerated, whereas liquid refilled most TLU during
deflation and no stable bubbles were found. Clearly, the immature lung, which
is surfactant-poor (14) because accelerated synthesis and secretion of surfactants has not begun, is incapable of producing stable foam and, therefore, incapable of retaining an air-volume compatable with life after birth. The only
air retention was the result of air entrapment peripheral to liquid locks that
were formed in the samll airways during deflation.

Analysis of the functional anatomy of immature lungs, wherein stereomicro-
scopic examination was coupled with measurement of VP characteristics (Figure
2), clarified the basis of immature lung function during initial aeration: As
aeration begins and pressure is increased from atmospheric pressure (P0) to
approximately 25 cm H_2O (P25), only airways are inflated. Resistance to inflation in this pressure range is from recruitment of progressively smaller conduits, meniscus formation at the bulk air/liquid interfaces of these conduits,
high γ, distension of airways (airway volume may be 5 to 6 times greater than
resting volume at P25) and movement of FPF through the smallest airways peripherally. It is apparent that pressures of this magnitude would *not* be expected
to produce successful saccular aeration in vivo. When pressure is increased
above P25, in 5 cm H_2O increments and 120 sec pauses at each pressure step,

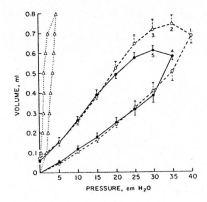

Fig. 2 (left). VP diagrams, immature rabbit fetal lungs. Mean ± SEM recorded 2 min at each step. P35 (●) and P40 (○) air diagrams; △ = liquid diagram. From reference 24 with permission.

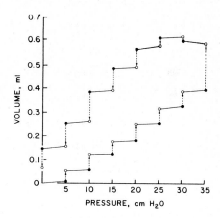

Fig. 3 (right). VP diagram, immature rabbit fetal lungs. Mean values. ● = immediate change after pressure step; ○ = 2 min at pressure step. From reference 25 with permission.

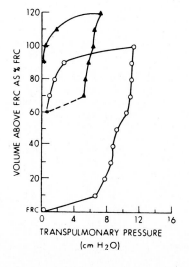

Fig. 4 (left). First (○—○) and second (▲—▲) air VP diagrams of mature lamb fetus. * = volume at which foam appears in trachea. From reference 21 with permission.

saccular recruitment begins. Saccular recruitment is very much pressure- and time-dependent, so that significant volume changes occur at each pressure step with time (Figure 3). These large volume changes not infrequently lead to rupture, generally of peripheral TLU, which are inflated first and therefore distended most, as pressure is either sustained or increased.

Early deflation (P40,35 to P30) is marked by negative compliance in which the processes of saccular inflation (recruitment) continue to some extent as the process of deflation begins. The latter is essentially the refilling of saccules with liquid as the bulk air/liquid configuration is sustained. Deflation to P0 is promoted by the reduction of pressure and recoil of previously distended airway walls. It is marked by central movement of the air/liquid column, some entrapment of air by liquid locks (above), and absence of stable bubble formation. Hysteresis in the VP diagram is *not* due to changing γ at the air/liquid interfaces, but to the visibly similar configurations of air-filled TLU (during deflation) and air-filled airways (during inflation) at the same pressure. Because the capacity of the system that includes TLU is much larger than that without TLU, volume is greater during deflation than during inflation. If stable bubbles had been produced, as in the mature lung, volume retention would also have been significantly greater at lower pressures during deflation, including P0 (Figure 4; compare with Figure 2). Thus, hysteresis in the *mature* lung includes the added contribution of stable bubble formation. This brings up an important point: In neither case (mature or immature) is hysteresis based on VP characteristics that might be calculated from conventional TA diagrams of lung extracts, as is commonly held (8). This also suggests a practical possibility: If surfactants are added to immature FPF, the mechanical properties of the lungs should change from the immature to the mature type (e.g., by broadening hysteresis at low pressures) as a consequence of the production of stable bubbles containing films of near-zero γ.

SURFACTANT SUPPLEMENTATION

The pioneering work of Enhörning, Robertson, Adams and Fujiwara (26-29) has verified the first premise of the possibility just mentioned, i.e., that surfactant supplementation into immature lungs changes their mechanical behavior toward that of mature lungs. They have shown that injection of a liquid surfactant preparation directly into the airways (trachea and posterior pharynx), either prior to the first breath or after breathing has begun, produces remarkable changes in lung mechanics both in vivo and in vitro and in related cardiopulmonary function in vivo. The excitement of using supplementary surfactants for the treatment of RDS that followed the first report of Fujiwara et al (29) is now universal. Our own work in this area (22) has verified the second premise of the possibility, i.e., that the mechanism by which supplementary surfactants operate is through the production of stable intrapulmonary bubbles with near-zero γ. In this respect, supplementation puts the lung in a state analogous to that of the mature lung with surfactant-rich FPF at the start of breathing.

We (22) injected dispersions of surfactants in liquid, prepared and administered according to the schedule of Adams et al (28), into the trachea of the FPF-filled lungs of immature fetal rabbits (27 days gestation), then inflated and deflated the lungs between P0 and P40 according to our usual protocol (24, 25). At end-deflation, few peripheral saccules retained air, whereas central (perihilar) airspaces contained stable bubbles. When peripheral saccules were microdissected, there was no evidence for stable bubble production. However, when the lungs were cycled through 3 to 5 additional inflations and deflations, stable bubbles were present both in peripheral and central TLU and residual volume was increased significantly. These experiments revealed that addition of surfactants to immature FPF effectively induces lung stability and mechanical properties like those of mature lungs as a consequence of the production of stable foam with films of zero or near-zero γ. We also learned that proper distribution of the surfactants is required to achieve optimal effect. We speculate that this effect was achieved in newborn infants with RDS by Fujiwara et al (29) by positioning the infants and by subsequent ventilation after injection of surfactants.

We (22) also compared the relative effectiveness of sustained positive distending pressure with administration of supplementary surfactants. When untreated immature lungs were inflated to P40 and pressure was sustained for 6 min or more, the volume accommodated by the lungs was much greater than without sustained pressure. This reflects the combined effects of pressure *plus* time, as discussed above and as reported recently (25). It also relates to the clinical observation (30,31) that elevation of *mean* airway pressure improves aeration of infants with RDS. However, administration of surfactants was more effective because it produced comparable maximal volumes without prolongation of the time during which maximal pressure was applied and, equally importantly, it resulted in significantly higher volumes at the lowest pressures, to P0. Therefore, the conclusions that we had drawn from our studies of mature lungs were reinforced by these experiments. They can be summarized as follows: (1) γ cannot be calculated accurately from standard VP diagrams. (2) Hysteresis of the VP curves cannot be explained by the hysteresis of conventional TA diagrams of films of lung surfactants in a surface balance. (3) Bubble formation and retention are central mechanisms which must be taken into account in analyses of the static mechanical properties of the neonatal lung.

ADULT AIR-LUNG

Faridy and Permutt (32,33) reported foam in the airways of excised normal adult lungs that had been inflated from the degassed state. It was assumed that bubbles had been formed from surfactants in the lining of the airspaces and that they might produce airway obstruction. Macklem et al (34) produced menisci in small bronchioles of excised lungs and suggested that these airways, like the alveoli, are lined with a surfactant film that operates to maintain airway stability. Recently, Frazer et al (35-37) deduced that meniscus formation occurs regularly during expansion of degassed lungs. They noted that residual volume increased with each cycle after the first and that residual volume was related inversely to end-deflation pressure. They concluded that the lower end-deflation pressure, the greater the opportunity for apposition of the walls of airspaces and, therefore, the greater the chances for meniscus formation during subsequent inflation. If, however, end-deflation pressure was too high (e.g., >5-6 cm H2O), wall-to-wall distance would be too large to permit formation of a meniscus. [Note: Although the terms "menisci" and "foam" are sometimes used interchangeably, it is apparent to us that the difference is only one of semantics: It is not reasonable to assume that isolated menisci exist as such in the normal lung, since they must be continuous with the "wet" linings of the airspaces. In this case the "meniscus" would be a segment of a continuous film, e.g., a sphere or cylinder, i.e., a bubble. See reference 38 for further discussion].

It is reasonable to conclude from the preceding observations that the *inflation* curve of the adult VP diagram (recorded from the degassed state) includes forces required to form menisci or bubbles as well as to expand TLU in which menisci or bubbles are not sustained (e.g., due to film rupture). The expected negative compliance as volume increases does not materialize because of recruitment of progressively smaller TLU (which require progressively higher pressures) and development of progressively greater resistance within the fibrous network of the lungs. This is a close to literal interpretation of the analogy of blowing bubbles that was given by Mead (39); we look at it as the blowing of bubbles into a fibrous net.

Two major processes describe *deflation* from maximal volume: (1) Flow of free air under the driving forces of retraction of the connective tissue network (from maximal volume to residual volume) and (2) entrapment of the air bubbles within the lungs (residual volume). Indeed, when tissue forces - as measured

and extrapolated from data on length-tension characteristics of lung parenchyma - are subtracted from interfacial plus tissue forces (which constitute the
conventional air VP diagram)(Figure 5), it is apparent that interfacial forces
are consistent with bubble formation during inflation and with near-zero γ during deflation and that the fibrous network accounts for *most* of the force of
retraction in the VP diagram. Clearly, γ does not account for 67% to 75% of
the total force of retraction as has been commonly accepted. Our interpretation of the VP diagram, which has been presented elsewhere in detail (38), is
an essential modification of traditional concepts (8,40). Since it includes
the mechanism of intrapulmonary bubble production, we (41) have investigated
this possibility in normal adult rabbit lungs by the same techniques that we
have used in our studies of fetal lungs.

After degassing, adult lungs were inflated and deflated through four complete
cycles (41), according to the protocol of Frazer et al (37), and alveolar epithelial surfaces were microdissected at end-deflation (PO). From each alveolus
that had retained air at PO and was examined by this technique, we were able to
deliver an intact, stable bubble of estimated near-zero γ. Our working conclusion is that intrapulmonary bubble production is as integral to normal mechanics
and stability of the adult lung as it is to the newborn lung.

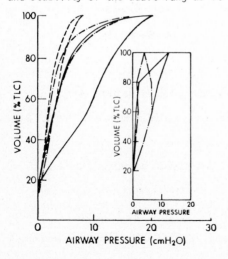

Fig. 5. VP diagrams of adult lungs
inflated *from minimal volume*.
--- liquid; -·- tissue: calculated
(reference 40) from alveolar wall
length-tension curves from data reported in reference 42; —— air. From
reference 40. INSET: -·- air minus
tissue VP diagram; —— air minus liquid
VP diagram. Calculated by present
authors. From reference 38 with
permission.

ACKNOWLEDGEMENTS

The authors' research has been supported by grants #HL 23995 and #HL 07060 from the National Heart, Lung and Blood Institutes, National Institutes of Health and #1749 and #1771 from the New York State Health Research Council.

REFERENCES

1. Pattle, R.E. (1955) Nature, 175, 1125.

2. Pattle, R.E. (1956) J. Pathol. Bacteriol., 72, 203.

3. Pattle, R.E. (1958) Proc. Roy. Soc. (London), B148, 217.

4. Pattle, R.E. (1960) Phys. Med. Biol., 5, 11.

5. Clements, J.A. (1957) Proc. Soc. Exptl. Biol. Med., 95, 170.

6. Clements, J.A., Brown, E.S. and Johnson, R.P. (1958) J. Appl. Physiol., 12,262.

7. Clements, J.A., Hustead, R.F., Johnson, R.P. and Gribetz, I (1961) J. Appl. Physiol., 16, 444.

8. Clements, J.A. (1962) Physiologist, 5, 11.

9. King, R.J. and Clements, J.A. (1972) Am. J. Physiol., 223, 707.

10. King, R.J. and Clements, J.A. (1972) Am. J. Physiol., 223, 715.

11. King, R.J. and Clements, J.A. (1972) Am. J. Physiol., 223, 727.

12. Avery, M.E. and Mead, J. (1959) Am. J. Dis. Child., 97, 517.

13. Gluck, L. and Kulovich, M.V. (1973) Am. J. Obstet. Gynecol., 115, 539.

14. Brumley, G.W., Chernick, V., Hodson, W.A., Normand, C., Fenner, A. and Avery, M.E. (1967) J. Clin. Invest., 40, 863.

15. Scarpelli, E.M. (1967) Pediatrics, 40, 951.

16. Adams, F.H., Fujiwara, T. and Rowshan, G. (1963) J. Pediat., 63, 881.

17. Scarpelli, E.M., Agasso, E.J. and Kikkawa, Y. (1971) Resp. Physiol., 12,110.

18. Yoshida, A. (1962) Am. J. Physiol., 203, 725.

19. Morgan, T.E., Finley, T.N. and Fialkow, H. (1965) Biochim. Biophys., 106, 403.

20. Hallman, M. and Gluck, L. (1974) Biochem. Biophys. Res. Commun., 60, 1.

21. Scarpelli, E.M. (1978) Pediat. Res., 12, 1070.

22. Clutario, B.C., Mautone, A.J., Baum, J. and Scarpelli, E.M. Submitted for publication.

23. Scarpelli, E.M., Clutario, B.C. and Traver, D. (1979) Pediat. Res., 13, 1285.

24. Scarpelli, E.M., Kumar, A., Doyle, C. and Clutario, B.C. (1981) Respir. Physiol., 45, 25.

25. Kumar, A., Clutario, B.C., Doyle, C. and Scarpelli, E.M. (1983) Respir. Physiol., 51,000 (In press).

26. Enhörning, G. and Robertson, B. (1972) Pediatrics, 50, 58.

27. Enhörning, G., Grossman, G. and Robertson, B. (1972) Biol. Neonate, 22, 126.

28. Adams, F.H., Towers, B., Osher, A.B., Ikegami, M., Fujiwara, T. and Nosaki, M. (1978) Pediat. Res., 12, 841.

29. Fujiwara, T., Chida, S., Watabe, Y., Maeta, H., Morita, T. and Abe, T. (1980) Lancet, 1, 55.

30. Boros, S.J. (1979) J. Pediat., 94, 114.

31. Reynolds, E.O.R. (1971) Arch. Dis. Childh., 46, 152.

32. Faridy, E.E. and Permutt, S. (1971) J. Appl. Physiol., 30, 319.

33. Faridy, E.E. (1973) J. Appl. Physiol., 34, 597.

34. Macklem, P.T., Proctor, D.F. and Hogg, J.C. (1970) Respir. Physiol., 8, 191.

35. Frazer, D.G. and Weber, K.C. (1976) J. Appl. Physiol., 40, 915.

36. Frazer, D.G. and Weber, K.C. (1979) Respir. Physiol., 37, 173.

37. Frazer, D.G., Stengel, P.W. and Weber, K.C. (1979) Respir. Physiol., 36,121.

38. Scarpelli, E.M. and Mautone, A.J. (1983) in: van Golde, L.M.G., Batenburg, J.J. and Robertson, B. (Eds.), Pulmonary Surfactants, Elsevier/North Holland Biomedical Press, Amsterdam, in press.

39. Mead, J. (1961) Physiol. Rev., 41, 281.

40. Hoppin, F.G., Jr. and Hildebrandt, J. (1977) in: West, J.B. (Ed.) Bioengineering Aspects of the Lung (Volume 3 Lung Biology in Health and Disease), Marcel Dekker, New York, pp. 83-162.

41. Clutario, B.C., Saitto, C., Mautone, A.J. and Scarpelli, E.M. (1983) Personal observations.

42. Sugihara, T., Martin, C.J. and Hildebrandt, J. (1971) J. Appl. Physiol., 30, 874.

© 1983, Elsevier Science Publishers B.V.
Pulmonary Surfactant System, E.V. Cosmi
and E.M. Scarpelli eds.

BIOPHYSICS OF THE SURFACTANT SYSTEM OF THE LUNG

BRIAN A. HILLS

The University of Texas Medical School at Houston, Department of Anesthesiology,
6431 Fannin Street, Houston, Texas 77030, U.S.A.

The clinical evidence leaves no doubt that surfactant is vital to the well-
being of the lung and, possibly, to many other organs. However, to understand
its role, it is essential to have the most appropriate physical model for the
alveolus and this is where we need to take a very critical look at the bubble
concept on which conventional respiratory physiology has been based for several
decades (1).

Just like most other surfactants, pulmonary surfactants reduce surface energy
although, until recently (2), only their ability to do so at liquid-gas interfaces has been considered. Most physiological texts depict the simple action

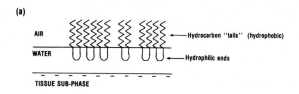

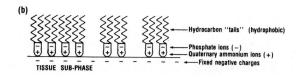

Fig. 1. Depicting (a) how detergents locate at air-water interfaces when, by orientating the molecules with the hydrophilic
moiety in the water and hydrophobic moiety in the air, they
reduce surface tension and (b) how amphoteric surfactants can
also reduce surface energy - but of a solid - by direct
adsorption to the tissue sub-phase, their being a net force
of attraction between the fixed charge of the membrane and
the dipole of the zwitterion.

of detergents in reducing surface tension whereby the molecules are orientated
with their hydrophilic "heads" in the aqueous phase and their hydrocarbon
"tails" in the air - see Fig. 1a. Thermodynamically, it is equally acceptable
for surfactants to reduce the surface energy of solids which they can do by
direct adsorption provided the total energy of the overall system is lowered.

In this presentation it is intended to point out how, by direct adsorption (Fig. 1b), surfactants with the same functional moieties indogenous to the lung can impart many highly desirable properties to *solid* surfaces (3) and to review the evidence for their pulmonary "cousins" doing much the same at the alveolar wall. These properties, emanating from the hydrocarbon surfaces which they impart - as seen in Fig. 1b - have been greatly exploited commercially for the last 2-3 decades, their efficacy being well proven even if some of the under-lying molecular mechanisms are still subject to debate by physicists.

To return to the all-important issue of the alveolar model, the emphasis upon the liquid-air interfaces has been derived from studies in which liquid filling greatly increases the compliance (4) of the lung and almost eliminates compliance hysteresis (5). These observations have been very easy to interpret by the conventional approach by claiming that the liquid simply fills the inside of the bubble, eliminating the air-aqueous interface and, hence, the pressure (ΔP) with which any concave surface tends to collapse in accordance with the Laplace equation:

$$\Delta P = 2\gamma/r \qquad . \quad . \qquad . \quad . \qquad (1)$$

where γ is the surface tension and r is the bubble radius, positive values of r representing a curvature which is *concave* with respect to air. The above expression then provides a very simple expression by which simple detergent theory (Fig. 1a) - readily quantifiable on the Langmuir trough - can be so easily related to collapsing pressure by Equation 1; but convenience must not influence our assessment of its validity.

Teleologically, the simple detergent/bubble model of the alveolus is hard to believe since a continuous liquid lining would, in effect, be adding to a

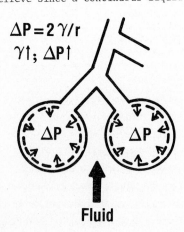

$$\Delta P = 2\gamma/r$$
$$\gamma\uparrow; \Delta P\uparrow$$

ΔP ΔP

Fluid

Fig. 2. Illustrating the conventional bubble concept of the alveolus in which a continuous liquid lining provides a continuous aqueous hypophase for surfactant to locate at an air-aqueous interface; but this then introduces a collapsing pressure (ΔP).

blood-air barrier for gas exchange which has been reduced by evolution to an effective thickness of only 0.7 μm (6). Moreover the concave nature of the aqueous-air interface in the bubble model (r positive in Equ. 1) means that there is a tendency to collapse ($\Delta P > 0$). Not only is this undesirable by mechanically opposing inflation but, by considering two adjacent interconnected bubbles (Fig. 2), the model itself introduces the problems of alveolar instability (7) and the tendency to suck fluid into the intervening space as interstitial oedema (8). Traditionally, surfactant is then claimed to exert a beneficial role by reducing surface tension (γ in Equation 1) and, hence, the tendency for bubbles to collapse (ΔP).

If there were no continuous hypophase, however, then there would be no collapsing pressure when the resistance to inflation and the accompanying hypothetical problems of alveolar instability and interstitial oedema due to collapse would not exist - at least, not in the normal physiological state.

Another teleological aspect which causes one to question the simple detergent/bubble model of the alveolus is why the body would locate a surfactant at any air-aqueous interface to produce such a large hysteresis in surface tension versus area if, as conventionally accepted (1), this makes such a substantial contribution to P:V hysteresis and, hence, to the work of breathing - see Fig. 3. In other words, it makes no sense to have a substance present which

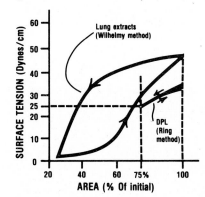

Fig. 3. The traditional loop depicted in conventional texts (1) for surface tension versus area of lung extracts cycled between 100% and 25% of initial area under laboratory conditions where surface tension was measured by the Wilhelmy method. Also shown is the corresponding relationship for DPL cycled between 100% and 75% of initial area under simultaneously simulated physiological conditions using a method independent of contact angle (9). Note the virtual absence of hysteresis

would make the body work harder. However, when the surface surfactants are studied under simultaneously simulated physiological conditions (9) and allowance is made for errors due to contact angle inherent in the Wilhelmy method (10), then surface tension:area (γ:A) hysteresis is negligible - see Fig. 3. This restores ones confidence in the body to select an efficient surfactant system. In justifying this divergence from limits traditionally used on the Langmuir trough, it is very difficult to envisage how ventilation could cause changes of 75-80% in lung surface area - which is the order of magnitude needed to induce the wide γ:A loops often presented in standard texts (1, 7). This departure from conventional theory then leaves unanswered the question of what actually causes the wide pressure:volume loops seen in excised lungs. It can now be attributed to the contortions clearly visible (11) as part of a general geometric irreversibility due to the additional degrees of freedom (12) provided by excision (13) and, therefore, of modest proportions *in vivo* - as seen when monitoring oesophageal pressure.

It can also be seen in Fig. 3 how the minimum value of surface tension (25 dynes/cm) corresponding to a maximum surface compression of no more than 25% (9) for normal ventilation is much higher than that recorded under less physiological conditions (1). This raises the question of compatibility with the bubble concept for which the substitution of γ = 25 dyne/cm and r = 148 μm for man (15) in Equ. 1 gives ΔP = 2.5 mmHg. However, for small mammals (16) such as the bat (r = 14.5 μm) or shrew (r = 16 μm), the values of ΔP reach ridiculous values (>25mmHg) if the lining is continuous (2). These values are calculated assuming the alveolus to be a sphere and are, therefore, the most conservative. It has often been pointed out (17, 18), however, that the curvature of any continuous liquid lining would be much greater at the septal corners (r much smaller in Equ. 1). In fact all of the other functional arguments also put forward (17) as reasons why the alveolus needs a low surface tension backfire and cast doubt upon the validity of the bubble model if this higher value (25 dyne/cm) is accepted for minimum surface tension - a value compatible with other studies (19).

The above discussion leaves no doubt that it is desirable to minimise hysteresis from the standpoint of work of breathing, but raises the question of whether there would be any functional advantage in stopping surface tension at 25 dyne/cm and not proceeding to the lower values possible with non-physiological compressions - see Fig. 3. Surfactant is generally assumed to "make breathing easy" by reducing the surface tension on each bubble surface, thus requiring less pressure to inflate the lung as a whole - an argument which could also be applied to a discontinuous liquid lining (Fig. 6a) since surface forces are reduced by liquid inflation whatever the model.

The above reasoning, however, ignores the fact that the lungs are normally inflated within the chest wall with which they come into mechanical equilibrium at FRC. Upon inflation, the chest wall is allowed to recoil, decreasing its potential energy, while that of the lung increases - and vice versa upon deflation. There is thus an exchange of potential energy just as occurs between an elevator and its counterweight which need to be well balanced - see Fig. 4. If the counterweight is too heavy or too light, the motor will need to work

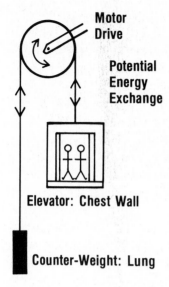

Motor Drive

Potential Energy Exchange

Elevator: Chest Wall

Counter-Weight: Lung

Fig. 4. A cartoon depicting an elevator simulating the chest wall and a counterweight simulating the lungs whose alveolar surface tension needs to be not too high nor too low- just as the counterweight needs the right value to reduce the work load on the motor to a minimum.

harder. In much the same way, the lung needs the correct surface tension - not too high and yet not too low that it no longer possesses the capacity to store potential energy as surface energy (2).

Another aspect of the conventional detergent/ bubble concept which needs closer examination is its application to the role of surfactant in alveolar oedema. There can be little doubt that "pores" or some other form of channel must exist between the epithelial lining and deeper structures for alveolar flooding to be possible under pathological conditions. Surfactant has been claimed to exert a favourable role by reducing surface tension and, hence, the tendency to suck fluid out of deeper structures just as it re- duces the height to which fluid rises in a simple capillary tube - see Fig. 5. This argument, however, can

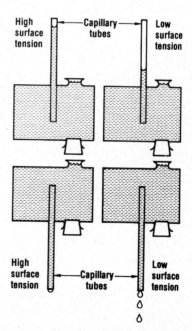

High surface tension — Capillary tubes — Low surface tension

High surface tension — Capillary tubes — Low surface tension

Fig. 5. Illustrating how fluid with a higher surface tension will rise to a higher level in a verti- cal capillary tube but how, upon inversion, the fluid with the *lower* surface tension will be more likely to emerge from the capillary tube simulating the alveolar "pore".

be literally turned upside down because not all pores will face upwards. They can be expected to have all orientations *in vivo* but, in those facing downwards (Fig. 4), fluid is less likely to leak out if the surface tension is *higher*. Hence, this would provide a second reason why surface tension should not be too low.

This and the previous aspects cast doubt upon the validity of the detergent/ bubble model of the alveolus and raise the basic question of whether the alveolar surface is essentially dry or, at least, has dry patches. If this were the case, alveolar homeostasis could be induced simultaneously by two mechanisms – one for the dry patches and another for the intervening pools – see Fig. 6(b).

Over the *dry* areas, fluid could be retained in deeper structures by water repellency. When hydrophilic substances such as cotton fabric are carboxylated to simulate a porous membrane and a drop of fluid placed on its surface, this rapidly wets the fibres and passes through. However, when a pulmonary surfactant such as dipalmitoyl lecithin (DPL) or dipalmitoyl phosphatidylethanolamine (DPPE) is deposited on the surface in an amount adequate to give an adsorbed monomolecular layer, then it does not block the channels yet prevents water from wetting the surface and penetrating the loose matrix of fibres. In fact, a head of 58 cms of water pressure can be maintained indefinitely without penetration (20) – a figure well in excess of normal pulmonary arterial pressure. It has therefore been proposed (20) that water repellency induced by surfactant on the dry patches could be making a significant contribution to the pressure threshold for alveolar flooding of 25mmHg – or "safety factor" as Guyton et al. (18) have termed it. It is difficult to assign more than 10mmHg of this threshold to colloid osmotic pressure (18), especially when recent studies have shown how solutions of 14% macromolecular protein with an oncotic pressure of 140mmHg can be adsorbed across the alveolar wall (21). The ideal conditions for water repellency are a large contact angle and a high surface tension (3). It has been demonstrated how monolayers of pulmonary surfactants can induce contact angles of up to 85° on otherwise hydrophilic surfaces such as glass (22) and also on tissue coated with it artificially (23) or naturally – as in the stomach (24). The enhancement of water repellency by higher surface tension is compatible with minimum values of 25 dyne/cm measured under physiological conditions (9) by comparison with values of 2-5 dynes/cm recorded under less physiological conditions (1), and needed (17) to satisfy the bubble model. A value of 25 dyne/cm may seem low by comparison with that for water at 37°C (69 dyne/cm), but the penetration threshold of 15-25mmHg needed to provide the safety factor for alveolar oedema is very modest by comparison with values

of 1,800mmHg which can be induced by commercial cationic surfactants (3).
While water repellency would seem to offer a novel explanation for homeostasis
over the dry patches, the next question concerns the wet areas.

For there to be dry patches, there must be an edge to the intervening wet
areas or "pools" which can now assume a *convex* profile with respect to the air.
With r now having a negative value in Equation 1, ΔP becomes negative. In
other words, forces due to surface curvature will now be tending to return
fluid to deeper structures – again maintaining homeostasis and aided in doing
so by a moderate surface tension. Even the minimum surface tension of
25 dyne/cm applied to surface droplets with the curvature seen in e.m.s. (25)
is adequate (2) to resolve the macromolecular protein solutions described
earlier.

This line of reasoning leads to the concept of a hydrophobic lining to
the alveolus (Fig. 6a) which is diametrically opposite to the conventional

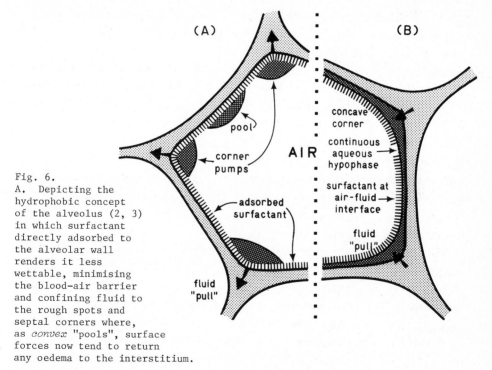

Fig. 6.
A. Depicting the
hydrophobic concept
of the alveolus (2, 3)
in which surfactant
directly adsorbed to
the alveolar wall
renders it less
wettable, minimising
the blood–air barrier
and confining fluid to
the rough spots and
septal corners where,
as *convex* "pools", surface
forces now tend to return
any oedema to the interstitium.

B. Depicting the conventional detergent/bubble model of the alveolus in
which surfactant acts only at an air–liquid interface of an aqueous hypophase
presumed to line the lung as a continuous layer whose *concave* profile now
causes surface forces to suck fluid into the air spaces.

detergent/bubble model (Fig. 6b). The vital questions are, therefore, whether pulmonary surfactant can be directly adsorbed to the epithelial wall and, if likely on theoretical and indirect experimental grounds, then what direct evidence is there to support such a claim in the lung itself?

The first lesson one learns in adsorption is that it occurs more often than theoretically predicted. For instance, cationic surfactants, i.e. those with a positively charged hydrophilic moiety, will be strongly adsorbed to a surface with negative charges but an anionic surfactant (negative moiety) will sometimes bind to the same surface - although less strongly - despite the predicted repulsion of like charges (26). Sometimes multivalent cations form bridges (26). Thus with the common lung surfactants being zwitterions, and the presence of Ca^{++} in vivo, it is easy to put forward many mechanisms for adsorption - whatever the relative orientation of the positively charged quaternary ammonium ion of the choline group and the negatively charged phosphate group relative to the two straight fatty-acid chains. Taking the simplest case with the orientation of charges shown in Fig. 1b - as supported by X-ray diffraction studies (27) - the dipole of the zwitterion would experience a net force of attraction for the fixed negative charges inherent (28) in all biological membranes. This configuration is ideal for pointing the two fatty-acid chains outwards where they can then close-pack with those of adsorbed neighbours to form a dense hydrocarbon layer not unlike polyethylene. Close packing might be enhanced by hydrogen bonding between the phosphate groups (3) and is certainly not hindered

TABLE 1

HYDROPHOBICITY (RELATIVE NON-WETTABILITY) OF VARIOUS SURFACES AS INDICATED BY THE CONTACT ANGLE

LIQUID	SOLID	CONTACT ANGLE	REFERENCE
WATER	GLASS	0°	56
WATER	GRAPHITE	86°	56
WATER	POLYETHYLENE	94°	56
WATER	PARAFFIN WAX	106°	56
WATER	TEFLON	108°	56
HEXANE	TEFLON	48°	56
BENZENE	TEFLON	48°	56
SALINE	OXYNTIC TISSUE	85°	24
SALINE	TRACHEAL EPITHEL'M	0°	23
SALINE	TREATED TRACHEA*	67°	23
SALINE	TREATED GLASS*	up to 95°	22

*Solid sub-phase coated with a pulmonary surfactant (DPL)

by steric factors since the hydrophilic moiety has a cross-sectional area equal to that of both chains, viz. 40Å^2 (2). The ability to form such a thin yet dense hydrocarbon outer surface is demonstrated by the manner in which totally wettable, hydrophilic surfaces such as glass (22) or tracheal epithelium (23) can be rendered hydrophobic by the surface application of lung surfactants to give contact angles comparable to those of polyethylene - see Table 1.

While the above studies indicate that the same surfactants found in the lung and their mixtures have the capability to produce very hydrophobic surfaces *in vitro* and *in vivo*, it still does not mean that they necessarily do so at the alveolar wall. This raises the subject of morphological studies which, from the start, have largely failed to demonstrate a continuous aqueous hypophase - even as pointed out by some proponents (29) of the bubble model. The latest electron micrographs show an essentially dry alveolar surface with fluid pushed aside from the primary gas exchange surfaces into the rough areas and septal corners as the "pools" described by Weibel and Bachofen (30). Many physiologists are apt to dismiss such studies as too prone to preparation artefact but two facts would tend to dispel this attitude. The first is that fixatives tend to destroy any hydrophobic surface (31) in facilitating the entry of water soluble substances. Thus they would tend to promote wetting and, if anything, favour the bubble model in preference to the hydrophobic concept proposed here. Secondly, when the same investigators take e.m.s. of amphibian lungs known (32) to be devoid of surfactant, then they do show the continuous aqueous hypophase (33) absent in mammalian pictures. One can see many drops of fluid sitting on the surface as though this were very hydrophobic (25, 30, 34). Even electronmicrographs produced to challenge this concept still show large alveolar areas which are free of fluid (35).

Any preparation artefact should be avoided in studying fresh untreated lung tissue by freeze fracture. Such studies (31) have shown that some of the minor detail has been smoothed out by a lining layer but that this is not water, nor covering an aqueous hypophase, since it is not sublimable. This has been presumed to be phospholipid (31) and would correspond to the adsorbed layer in Fig. 6a.

Other experiments sometimes cited in support of a continuous aqueous hypophase - although primarily designed for other purposes - are those of Schürch & McIver (36) and Rienfenrath (37). Fluorocarbon drops are found to spread after limited expansion of the alveolar surface (36) and it could be argued that they should have spread immediately if the dry patches were hydrophobic. However fluorocarbons and hydrocarbons do not readily wet each others' surfaces as demonstrated by the contact angle of 46° for hydrocarbons on Teflon - see

Table 1. Hence the data of Schürch & McIver would seem equally compatible with either a continuous or discontinuous aqueous hypophase. There is the additional argument that anything contacting the dry patches would automatically create an aqueous hypophase just as touching the inside of a tent in the rain starts a drip as depicted in the cartoon in Fig. 7. This argument would also apply to anyone trying to use the data from the ingeneous microanalysis technique of Reifenrath (37) for any purpose other than the surfactant identification for which it was intended. The microprobes had a liquid film at the tip and would have produced an aqueous hypophase even if the part of the wall which they first touched were not a "pool".

Fig. 7. Cartoon of a water-repellent tent in the rain, depicting how (a) touching the inside (b) starts a drip and how (c) a drip running down the inside recruits more wetted area to accelerate the flooding just as expansion of "pools" on an otherwise dry alveolar surface (Fig. 6a) could recruit the flow of oedema from more "pores" in the pathological lung.

The simple analogy with the tent can be taken further in that, for whatever reason alveolar flooding is started, it will accelerate if the cause is not removed. For instance, if alveolar capillary pressure is held above the safety factor or threshold of 25mmHg, the fluid content of the lung rises exponentially (38). This would correspond to enlargement of the pools in Fig. 6a whose spread over the alveolar surface would wet the dry ends of more pores and recruit flow from them – just as the drip running down the inside of the tent in Fig. 7c increases the rate of flooding. This is also compatible with the finding that creatures without surfactant have "wet" lungs in which fluid filtration through the alveolar walls is 10–20 times that found in mammals (39). When alveolar flooding exceeds a certain pressure in some animals, it cannot be reversed however much capillary blood pressure is lowered (38). This would correspond to the state where the pools in Fig. 6a had enlarged to the point where they merged and form a continuous liquid hypophase which is now *concave* and, therefore, sucking more fluid into the air spaces. In other words, flooding has progressed to the point of creating the conventional bubble model but as a pathological state and *not* the normal physiological state as conventional theory (1) would have us believe.

The same problems should arise if the hydrophobic lining imparted by surfactant directly adsorbed to the wall is removed by a solvent and this may explain the massive pulmonary oedema arising when liquid ether is aspirated due to incorrect use of an anaesthesia machine (40). The opposite should apply if surfactants which are good water repellents, e.g. silicones, are instilled into the alveoli to augment the natural hydrophobicity even though, ostensibly, they were added as "antifoams". This may explain why they were found to protect against pulmonary oedema (41) even though they failed to break alveolar foam to which they were added *in vitro* (29). Conversely, if wetting agents are applied to the dry patches on the alveolar wall, then these should create the continuous liquid lining of the conventional model and, hence, the collapsing pressure and its associated problems discussed earlier. Thus it is interesting to find alveolar oedema, interstitial oedema and alveolar instability arising in animal lungs after the instillation of Tween 20 (42) – a detergent sold industrially as a powerful *wetting* agent.

It would seem most pertinent that the undesirable properties associated with a continuous liquid lining only seem to occur in practice under pathological or other abnormal conditions where the conventional bubble model is more likely to apply. Much experimental evidence therefore seems to support the concept of an essentially *dry* alveolus with the minimum resistance to gas transfer and where the mechanical and homeostatic aspects of bubble collapse and alveolar instability introduced by the bubble model are non-problems because there really is no bubble in the first place – at least, in the normal physiological state.

Many of the other basic features of lungs are also compatible with the hydrophobic concept. For instance the large expansion of alveolar surface area associated with a sigh would cause fluid to recede from the dry patches and so restore contact angles at the edge of the "pools" (22). Some recent studies have shown that compliance hysteresis of the excised lung is not so easy to explain by surface tension alone (43) and a better correlation has been claimed on the basis of the hysteresis in contact angle which pulmonary surfactants have been shown to impart *in vitro* (22). On this hydrophobic model (Fig. 6A), liquid filling increases compliance and decreases compliance hysteresis simply by eliminating the pools and their edges.

The question which usually arises is how a dry alveolar surface could be regenerated after flooding since, if we were to take the cartoon of the tent too seriously, there would appear to be no way to restore water repellency until the rain stops. There is a phenomenon, however, by which a thin layer of fluid over a hydrophobic surface can rupture spontaneously and we have recently shown that lung surfactants can impart that property to hydrophilic surfaces *in vitro*. The liquid layers break up when their thickness is still several fold greater than the alveolar diameter (2, 22). In physical systems in general, this phenomenon has been attributed to the disjoining pressure (44) and is observed in everyday life as the dry patches which form on the bottom when removing water from a Teflon-lined pan and appear long before the pan is empty. This phenomenon can also be invoked in the clinic to explain the remarkable rise in arterial P_{O_2} upon placing patients on positive end-expired pressure (PEEP), the rise occurring long before there is any resolution of the total volume of oedema fluid (45). It is proposed that the thinning of the liquid layer of the flooded alveolus (Fig. 6a) upon expansion causes the aqueous hypophase to rupture spontaneously with fluid receding into the corners and restoring dry patches over most of the gas transfer surface, i.e. restoring the system to that shown in Fig. 6a.

The concept of an alveolus whose surfaces are maintained dry by an adsorbed layer of surfactant would therefore seem compatible with the evidence so far raised and would certainly have more appeal than the conventional bubble model teleologically.

If one accepts the concept of surfactant adsorption, then there are many other properties equally as desirable as water repellency which that hydrocarbon surface can impart. One of these is boundary lubrication (46) which is experienced in everyday life as the slipperiness remaining after touching a bar of wet soap and squeezing the water from between one's fingers. The common surfactants have been shown to reduce the coefficient of kinetic

friction by 80-99% and could facilitate ventilation by promoting better sliding
of the structural components of the parenchymal lung tissue as well as the
pleurae (47). In the latter case, an adsorbed boundary lubricant would seem to
offer a better explanation than the alternative - hydrodynamic (fluid film)
lubrication - because, for the fluid film to be hydrodynamically continuous,
the hydrostatic pressure at different points in the pleural cavity would need
to differ by the vertical head separating them. However, this does not appear
to be the case in practice (48). Surfactants have also been identified and the
phospholipids and their extracts shown to be good lubricants in other parts of
the body where sliding occurs under high load-bearing conditions, these including the synovium, the gastrointestinal tract (49) and several other locations.

Other desirable properties of an adsorbed surfactant layer is the ability of
surfaces to release from each other and this has been put forward (50) as a
possible reason for surfactant in the Eustachian tubes (51) or why the pleurae
separate so easily when air is introduced. Simple mechanical failure of surfaces to release could explain why serous otitis has remained an enigma (50).
If surfactant is also adsorbed onto bacteria this could render them more
hydrophobic - a property which renders them more conducive to invagination by
phagocytes (52), at least, when it occurs naturally.

Yet another application of the dense yet thin hydrocarbon lining which surfactant can lay down is its ability to protect a surface against acid attack -
just as the industrial "cousins" of mammalian surfactants are used industrially
as corrosion inhibitors (24). Phospholipids very similar in composition to
lung surfactants have been identified in the stomach which has been shown to
have a contact angle almost as high as polyethylene when the mucus is removed -
see Table 1. Moreover, known barrier breakers such as bile salts and aspirin
virtually eliminate the natural hydrophobicity (24). This may help to explain
the strong clinical correlation found between ARDS and peptic ulceration and,
in the newborn, between RDS and necrotising enterocolitis (53). If the ability
of bile salts to remove the hydrophobic lining of the stomach (24) also applies
to the alveolar lining, then this could explain both the pulmonary problem
arising in the newborn following aspiration of meconium in utero known (54) to
contain many of those salts, and the "chemical" nature of the insult seen
pathologically (55).

There are many other desirable properties which adsorbed surfactant can
impart to a solid surface and these would appear to extend far beyond the
vital roles played by these compounds in the lung.

REFERENCES

1. Clements, J.A. and Tierney, D.F. (1965). Alveolar instability associated with altered surface tension. In: Fenn, W.O., Rahn, H. (Eds.), Handbook of Physiology: Respiration, Vol. II, pp. 1565-1583. Washington: American Physiological Society.

2. Hills, B.A. (1982). What forces keep lung air spaces dry? Thorax, 37:713-717.

3. Hills, B.A. (1981). What is the true role of surfactant in the lung? Thorax, 36:1-4.

4. Von Neergaard, K. (1929). Neue Auffasungen über einen Grundbegriff der Atemmechanik die Retraktionskraft der Lunge, abhängig von der Oberflächenspannung in den Alveolen. Z. ges. exp. Med., 66:373-394.

5. Radford, E.P. (1957). Recent studies of mechanical properties of mammalian lungs. In: Remington, J.W. (Ed.), Tissue Elasticity. Washington: Amer. Physiol. Soc.

6. Weibel, E.R. (1971). Morphometric estimation of pulmonary diffusion capacity. Respirat. Physiol., 11:54-75.

7. Clements, J.A., Hustead, R.F., Johnson, R.P. and Gribetz, I. (1961). Pulmonary surface tension and alveolar stability. J. Appl. Physiol., 16:444-450.

8. Staub, N.C. (1974). Pulmonary edema. Physiol. Rev., 54:678-811.

9. Barrow, R.E. and Hills, B.A. (1979). Surface tension induced by dipalmitoyl lecithin *in vivo* under physiological conditions. J. Physiol., 297:217-227.

10. Barrow, R.E. and Hills, B.A. (1979). A critical assessment of the Wilhelmy method in studying lung surfactants. J. Physiol., 294:217-227.

11. Mead, J. (1968). Mechanical properties of the lung. In: Liebow, A.A., Smith, D.E. (Eds.), The Lung. Baltimore: Williams & Wilkins, Ch. 5, pp. 48-53.

12. Hills, B.A. (1977). Geometric irreversibility and compliance hysteresis in the lung. Respirat. Physiol., 13:50-61.

13. Barrow, R.E. and Hills, B.A. (1983). Surface and tissue compliance hysteresis in lungs liquid filled in situ. Fed. Proc. (in press).

14. Pattle, R.E. (1977). The relation between surface tension and area in the alveolar lining film. J. Physiol., 269:591-604.

15. Dunnill, M.S. (1962). Postnatal growth of the lung. Thorax, 17:329-333.

16. Tenney, S.M. and Remmers, J.E. (1963). Comparative quantitative morphology of the mammalian lung. Nature, 197:54-56.

17. Tierney, D.F. (1974). Lung Metabolism and Biochemistry. Ann. Rev. Physiol., 36:209-231.

18. Guyton, A.C., Taylor, A.E., Drake, R.E. and Parker, J.C. (1976). Dynamics of subatmospheric pressure in the pulmonary interstitial fluid. In: Lung Liquids. Ciba Foundation Symp. 38, Amsterdam: Elsevier.

19. Morgan, T.E. (1971). Biosynthesis of pulmonary surface-active lipid. Arch. Intern. Med., 127:401-407.

20. Hills, B.A. (1982). Water repellency induced by pulmonary surfactants. J. Physiol., 325:175-186.

21. Matthay, M.A., Landolt, C.C. and Staub, N.C. (1981). Effect of 14% albumin in alveolar fluid on the rate of liquid removal from the air spaces of sheep. Fed. Proc., 40:447.

22. Hills, B.A. (1982). Contact angle hysteresis induced by pulmonary surfactants. J. Appl. Physiol.: Respir. Environ. Exercise Physiol. (in press).

23. Hills, B.A. and Barrow, R.E. (1979). The contact angle induced by DPL at pulmonary epithelial surfaces. Respirat. Physiol., 38:173-183.

24. Hills, B.A., Butler, B.D. & Lichtenberger, L.M. (1983). Gastric mucosal barrier: the hydrophobic lining to the lumen of the stomach. Amer. J. Physiol., GI & Liver Physiol. (in press).

25. Kisch, B. (1958). Electron microscopy of the lungs in acute pulmonary edema. Exp. Med. Surg., 16:17-28.

26. Zecher, D.C. (1975). Corrosion inhibition by surface-active chelants. Paper 145, Proc. Internat. Corrosion Forum: Protection & Performance of Materials. Houston: Nat. Assn. Corrosion Engrs.

27. Lininger, A.L. (1976). Biochemistry, 2nd. ed., p. 289. New York: Worth.

28. Davson, H. (1964). A Textbook of General Physiology. (3rd edn.). London: Churchill.

29. Pattle, R.E. (1966). Surface tension and the lining of the lung alveoli. In: Caro, C.G. (Ed.), Advances in Respiratory Physiology, pp. 83-105. Baltimore: Williams & Wilkins.

30. Weibel, E.R. and Bachofen, H. (1979). Structural design of the alveolar septum and fluid exchange. In: Fishman, A.P., Renkin, E.M. (Eds.), Pulmonary Edema. Washington: American Physiological Society.

31. Untersee, P., Gil, J. and Weibel, E.R. (1971). Visualization of extracellular lining layer of lung alveoli by freeze-etching. Respirat. Physiol., 13:171-185.

32. Clements, J.A. (1962). Surface tension in the lungs. Scientific American, 207:121-130.

33. Hughes, G.M. and Weibel, E.R. (1978). Visualization of layers lining the lung of the South American lungfish (Lepidosiren Paradoxa) and a comparison with the frog and rat. Tissue & Cell, 10:343-353.

34. Dermer, G.B. (1969). The fixation of pulmonary surfactant for electron microscopy: I. The alveolar surface lining layer. J. Ultrastructure Res., 27:88-104.

35. Gil, J. (1983). Alveolar surface, intra-alveolar fluid pools and respiratory volume changes. J. Appl. Physiol.: Respirat. Environ. Exercise Physiol., 54:321-323.

36. Schürch, S. and McIver, D.J.L. (1981). Surface tension at low lung volumes: dependence on time and alveolar size. Biophys. J., 33:201a.

37. Reifenrath, R. (1973). Chemical analysis of the lung alveolar surfactant obtained by alveolar micropuncture. Respir. Physiol., 19:35-46.

38. Drake, R.E., Smith, J.H. and Gabel, J.C. (1980). Estimation of the filtration coefficient in intact dog lungs. Am. J. Physiol. 238 (Heart Circ. Physiol. 7):H430-H438.

39. Burggren, W.W. (1982). Pulmonary blood plasma filtration in reptiles: A "wet" vertebrate lung? Science, 215:77-78.

40. Guedel, A.E. (1953). Inhalation Anesthesia, p. 108. New York: MacMillan.

41. Luisada, A.A. and Cardi, L. (1956). Further studies with antifoaming agents in experimental pulmonary edema. Circulation Res., 3:510-513.

42. Nieman, G.F., Bredenberg, C.E., Clark, W.R. and West, N.R. (1981). Alveolar function following surfactant deactivation. J. Appl. Physiol.: Respirat. Environ. Exercise Physiol., 51:895-954.

43. Bachofen, H., Hildenbrandt, J. and Bachofen, M. (1970). Pressure-volume curves of air- and liquid-filled lungs excised lungs - surface tension in situ. J. Appl. Physiol., 29:422-431.

44. Deryaguin, B.V., Kusakov, M. and Lebedeva, L. (1939). Range of molecular action of surfaces and multimolecular solvate (adsorbed) layers. Doklady Akad. Nauk. USSR, 23:671-673.

45. Miller, W.C., Rice, D.L., Unger, K.M. and Bradley, B.L. (1981). Effect of PEEP on lung water content in experimental noncardiogenic pulmonary edema. Critical Care Med., 9:7-9.

46. Hardy, W.B. (1936). Collected Papers of Sir William Hardy. Cambridge: Cambridge U.P.

47. Hills, B.A., Butler, B.D. and Barrow, R.E. (1982). Boundary lubrication imparted by pleural surfactants and their identification. J. Appl. Physiol.: Respirat. Exercise Environ. Physiol., 53:463-469.

48. Agostoni, E., Miserocchi, G. and Bonnanni, M.V. (1969). Thickness and pressure of the pleural liquid in some mammals. Respir. Physiol., 6:245-256.

49. Butler, B.D., Lichtenberger, L.M. and Hills, B.A. (1983). Distribution of surfactants in the canine GI tract and their ability to lubricate. Amer. J. Physiol.: GI & Liver Physiol. (in press).

50. Hills, B.A. (1983). Aural barotrauma and surfactant. Aviat. Space & Environ. Med., (in press).

51. Birken, E.A. and Brookler, K.H. (1972). Surface tension lowering substance of the canine Eustachian tube. Ann. Otol., 81:268-271.

52. Van Oss, C.J., Gillman, C.F. and Neumann, A.W. (1975). Quoted by Neumann, A.W. (1978). Contact angles. In: Padday, J.F. (Ed.), Wetting, Spreading and Adhesion, pp. 28-30. Oxford: Academic Press.

53. Amoury, R.A. (1980). Necrotizing enterocolitis. In: Holder, T.M., Ashcraft, K.W. (Eds.), Pediatric Surgery, p. 378. Philadelphia: Saunders.

54. Lester, R., Pyrek, J.S., Stezycki, R. and Adcock, E.W. (1982). Short chain bile acids in meconium. Ped. Res., 16:169.

55. Auld, P.A.M. (1978). Respiratory distress syndrome of the newborn. In: Scarpelli, E.M., Auld, P.A.M. & Goldman, H.S. (Eds.), Pulmonary Disease of the Fetus, Newborn and Child, pp. 499-500. Philadelphia: Lea & Febiger.

56. Adamson, A.W. (1967). Physical chemistry of surfaces. 2nd. edn., pp. 352-367. New York: Wiley.

THE COMPONENTS OF ALVEOLAR SURFACTANT OF THE HUMAN LUNG IN NORMAL AND IN
PATHOLOGICAL STATES.

ERNESTO CATENA[1], SERGIO MARCATILI[1], CARLO MARZO[1], ANTONIO MARTIN[2] AND
ELEONORA ROGLIANI[2]

[1]Istituto di Clinica Tisiologica e Malattie dell'Apparato Respiratorio
(Director: Prof. E. Catena), c/o Ospedale "V.Monaldi", Via Leonardo Bianchi,15,
80131 Napoli and [2]Istituto di Chimica Biologica (Director: Prof. G. Della
Pietra), Via Costantinopoli, 16 , 80100 Napoli, 1^Facoltà di Medicina e
Chirurgia dell'Università di Napoli (ITALY)

INTRODUCTION

In the respiratory apparatus, alveolar cavities make up an area which is
commonly labelled with the term "deep lung". It has become increasingly evident that this territory represents a real "bronchiolo-alveolar microenviron-
ment" for a whole series of specific functional activities which take place
there alone.

Among these activities, in addition to respiratory exchanges, attention
should be paid both to the defence mechanisms against exogenous aggression
and the maintenance of mechanical stability in the alveolar cavities.

This last function is taken care of, as is well known, by a thin film com
posed mainly of phospholipids (surfactant), stratified on the endoalveolar
surface, a part of which rises into the small airways through ventilation.

The composition of surfactant is by now sufficiently clear and understood
following research carried out on animals but our knowledge is not quite so
clear regarding man.

Up to now, research carried out in the human field, has been concerned
with mainly physiopathological cases regarding foetal lung maturation (1,2,3)
and pathological conditions in the newborn and during early childhood (4,5,6),
whereas there have been very few observations regarding adults. However in the
last few years further observations have been made thanks to the extensive use
of new techiniques adopted in the study of the "deep lung", the composition
of endoalveolar surfactant and its possible modification in certain pathological conditions and under pharmacological treatment, still remains a field
which has yet to be defined. (7,8,9,10,11,12,13).

This paper relates the data from a series of research carried out according to three lines of study conducted on both broncho-alveolar lavage fluid
(BAL) and bronchial lavage fluid (BL) with the aim of getting to know the

various fractions of phospholipids.

In a first group of patients affected by different types of broncho-pulmonary diseases, the BAL was examined with the aim of finding out the behaviour of some of the most significant phospholipidic fractions of the surfactant during the course of the various pathological conditions.

In a second smaller group of patients, titration of the phospholipidic fractions was carried out not only at broncho-alveolar level, but also on lavage fluid taken from bronchi of large and medium calibre (BL), to ascertain a possible displacement of endoalveolar phospholipids into proximal tracts of the airways.

Finally, in a third group of patients, titration of phospholipidic fractions was performed in the BAL after treatment with a drug which is experimentally capable of influencing the production of endoalveolar surfactant (Ambroxol) (14,15,16).

MATERIALS AND METHODS

Study population. The number of studied patients is shown in Table 1.

There were in all 74 patients ranging from the age of 9 to 72: 44 were males, 30 females: 14 were smokers; 20 chronic bronchitis; 9 pneumoconiosis; 8 extrinsic allergic alveolitis; 7 with other broncho-pulmonary diseases and 16 were normal controls.

Technique for obtaining BL and BAL during fiberbronchoscopy. All the patients underwent BAL and 10 of them also underwent BL. Furthermore, 8 patients also underwent both BL and BAL, before and after therapy with ambroxol at a dose of 120 mg/day for a period of two weeks.

BL was carried out by instillation at the orifice of the main bronchus of 40 ml. of 0.9% saline divided up into two fractions and immediately re-aspirated.

BAL has been performed in accordance with the commonly used techiniques already described in previous works (17,18). The total volume of aspirated lavage fluid was noted; then it was filtered immediately through gauze to remove mucus and centrifugated at 500 g for 10 min. at 4°C. to sediment the respiratory cells.

The supernatant fluid was stored at -30°C until analyzed.

Phospholipid analysis. After a total lipid extraction from the supernatant lavage fluid according to Bligh and Dyer (19), phospholipid constituent were separated by thin layer chromatography (TLC) as previously described (20). The phospholipid amounts were calculated as dipalmitoyl-lecithine, dipalmitoyl cephaline and lignoceryl-sphingomyelin (PC, PE and S respectively).

RESULTS

In table 1 is shown the behaviour of the phospholipidic fractions studied in the BAL taken from subjects suffering from various pathological disorders.

TABLE 1

PHOSPHOLIPIDS IN BAL FLUID

Subjects	N	PC%	PE%	S%	PC/PE+S	PE/S
NORMAL CONTROL	16	61.4	18.1	20.5	1.59	0.88
SMOKERS	14	54.2	19.1	26.2	1.20	0.72
CHRONIC BRONCHITIS	20	58.8	16.2	24.7	1.43	0.65
PNEUMOCONIOSIS	9	71.4	9.3	19.1	2.51	0.48
EXTRINSIC ALL. ALVEOLITIS	8	44.3	30.1	25.5	0.79	1.18
OTHER RESP. DISEASE	7	50.2	21.5	28.0	1.0	0.76
TOTAL	74					

PC = PHOSPHATIDIL-CHOLINE
PE = PHOSPHATIDIL-ETHANOLAMINE
S = SPHINGOMYELIN

- PC is always the component represented by a greater percentage in respect to the others, both in the normal controls and in the pathological cases; however it reaches the lowest values in the course of E.A.A.

- PE increases considerably in E.A.A., but, on the contrary, it appears reduced in the pneumoconiosis.
- sphingomyelin appears increased among the smokers and in the E.A.A.
- the ratio between PC and the other phospholipidic fractions results particularly high in the pneumoconiosis and low in the E.A.A.
- the ratio between PE/S is increased in the E.A.A. and reduced in the pneumoconiosis.

In table 2 is reported the behaviour of the phospholipidic fractions studied in BAL and BL in cases of chronic bronchitis.

TABLE 2

BEHAVIOUR OF PHOSPHOLIPIDS IN THE BAL AND BL FLUID (10 Cases Chr. Bronchitis)

BAL FLUID

PC%	PE%	S%	PC/PE+S	PE/S
59.1±9	15.4±8	25.5±10	1,45	0,60
BL FLUID				
61.3±9.6	19.8±9.9	18.5±9.8	1,06	1,07

From this it can be shown that:
- sfingomyelin, which is present in BAL at the percentage of 25.5% on average,
is present with the percentage value of 18.5% in BL.
- consequently, the ratio PE/S, which in BAL is 0.60, increases to 1.07 in BL.

In table 3 are reported the data concerning the behaviour of phospholipidic
fractions in BAL and BL before and after therapy with Ambroxol in cases of
chronic bronchitis. It can be shown that:

TABLE 3

BEHAVIOUR OF PHOSPHOLIPIDS IN BAL AND BL FLUID BEFORE AND AFTER AMBROXOL THERAPY
(8 Cases Chr. Bronchitis)

	BAL FLUID					BL FLUID				
	PC%	PE%	S%	$\frac{PC}{PE+S}$	$\frac{PE}{S}$	PC%	PE%	S%	$\frac{PC}{PE+S}$	$\frac{PE}{S}$
BEFORE	61,6	13,3	25,1	1,60	0,52	60,7	21,9	16,8	1,56	1,30
AFTER	65,8	12,2	22,0	1,92	0,55	58,0	20,0	22,0	1,38	0,90

- in BAL no significant modifications are observed in the different phospholipidic fractions and in the ratios among them before and after treatment.
- in BL it seems that after treatment the percentage of spingomyelin increases
  (from 16.8% to 22%) and consequently the ratio PE/S is modified, passing from
  1.3 before to 0.9 after treatment.

COMMENT

The study hitherto carried out allows us to suggest the following:
- in the various broncho-pulmonary disorders there is nearly always the participation of the surfactant system with variations in the quantitative relationships among the various components;
- regional differences in the various fractions are shown, at both the alveolar and bronchial level, where the sphingomyelin appears to be significantly reduced;
- after therapy with ambroxol an increase in sphingomyelin at the level of the
  proximal bronchial tree is noted.

The interpretation of these results still remains difficult. In fact the
sampling techiniques, although being standardized in theory, do not in practi-

ce go uncriticized, especially in respect to various diseases, in which different quantities of recuperable material can be taken.

On the other hand, it is also necessary to quantify in absolute the phospholipidic fractions by establishing also a relationship with the protein level, which are suctioned at the same time as the phospholipids. Hitherto this has been done only in certain pathological cases and the relative observations are still being developed.

REFERENCES

1. Gluck, L., Kulovich, M.V., Borer, R.C., Brenner, P.H., Anderson, G.G. and Spellacy, W.N. (1971) Amer. J. Obstet. Gynec.: 109, 440

2. Nelson, G.H. (1972) Amer. J. Obstet. Gynec.: 112, 827.

3. Evans, J.J. (1975) New. Engl. J. Med.: 292, 1113.

4. Brumley, G.W., Hodson, W.A. and Avery M.E. (1967) Pediatrics: 40, 13.

5. Müller, K. and Tiller, R. (1981) Zent.für Gynäk. 18, 1070.

6. Luerti, M. and Zavattini, G. (1982) Gaz. Med. Ital. 141, 207.

7. Finley, T.N. and Ladman, A.J. (1972) New Engl. J. Med.: 286, 223.

8. Von Wichert, P. and Kohl, F.V. (1977) Intensive Car Med.: 3, 27.

9. Petty, T.L., Reiss, O.K., Paul, G.W., Silvers, G.W. and Elkins, N.D. (1977) Amer. Rev. Resp. Dis.: 115, 531.

10. Sahu, S. and Lynn, W.S. (1977) Amer. Rev. Resp. Dis.: 115, 233.

11. Valenti, S., Crimi, P., Ferrari, A. and Scordamaglia, A. (1979) INSERM: 84, 93.

12. Jouanel, P., Motta, C., Brun, J., Roche, G., Dastugue, B., Molina,C., (1979) INSERM: 84, 73.

13. Hallman, M., Spragg, R., Harrell, J. H., Moser, K.M. and Gluck, L. (1982) J. Clin. Invest.: 70, 673.

14. Curti, P.C. (1972) Pneumologic: 142, 62.

15. Elemer, G. and Kapanci, Y., (1981) Prog. Resp. Res.: 15, 234.

16. Loewenberg, E., Jimenez, L., Martinez, M. and Pommier, M. (1981) Prog. Resp. Res.: 15, 240.

17. Reynolds, H.Y., Fulmer, J.D., Kazmierowski, J.A., Roberts, W.C., Frank, M.M. and Crystal, R.G. (1977) J. Clin. Invest.: 59, 165.

18. Daniele, R.P., Altose, M.D. and Rowlands, D.T. (1975) J. Clin. Invest.: 56, 986.

19. Bligh, E.G. and Dyer, W.G. (1959) Canad. Journ. Bioch. Physiol.: 37, 911.

20. Catena, E., Marcatili, S., Borrelli, G., Abbruzzese, A., Motta, G., Rogliani, E. and Della Pietra, G.(1980) Pneumologica: 21, 37.

© 1983, Elsevier Science Publishers B.V.
Pulmonary Surfactant System, E.V. Cosmi
and E.M. Scarpelli eds.

DOSAGE OF PHOSPHOLIPIDS IN HUMANS BY PULMONARY LAVAGE:
REPRODUCIBILITY AND DRUG-INDUCED CHANGES

SALVATORE VALENTI,PAOLO CRIMI,SIMONETTA ZUPO AND VITO BRUSASCO
Istituto di Medicina e Chirurgia Broncopolmonare, Università
di Genova, Via Mosso 8, 16132 Genova (ITALY)

INTRODUCTION

The role of pulmonary surfactant for maintaining the mechanical
properties of the lung has been well established (1). Animal
studies (2,3) showed that lung surfactant obtained from different
species has an almost identical composition and contains more
than 80 % phospholipids. Among these, saturated phosphatidylcholine is the most abundant, and is responsible for the peculiar
surface activity of the alveolar lining layer (4), while phosphatidylglycerol is thought to be essential for improving the
efficacy of surfactant (5). The role of the other phospholipids
in the lung is still uncertain. The number of studies on the
composition of pulmonary surfactant of adult live humans is
relatively small because the procedures for obtaining specimens
were of great discomfort until recently, when the flexible bronchofiberscope was introduced in clinical routine.

METHODOLOGY

Technique of Bronchoalveolar lavage (BAL) during fiberbronchoscopy (FBS). The tip of a flexible bronchofiberscope is wedged
in a segmental bronchus, generally of the middle lobe; 100 ml
of normal saline, warmed at 37°C are injected and gently suctioned 30 to 60 seconds post injection. The lavage procedure is
repeated after 3 to 5 minutes wait.

Technique of Bronchial lavage (BL) during FBS. The bronchofiberscope is passed just beyond the orefice of a main-stem
bronchus, generally of the left lung; 20 ml of normal saline,

warmed at 37°C, are injected and almost immediately suctioned.

Limitations. Several sources of variance are connected with the experimental procedures described above. The amount of fluid recovered may vary depending on several random variables like morphological differences, local pathological changes, mode of suctioning, time elapsed between injection and suction, respiratory cycle. The composition of the fluid recovered may vary consequently because of the variability of the area and the structures of the washed surface, the time available for dilution, and the flux between blood and lining layer. For these reasons, the reproducibility of some indices derived from the chromatographic (6) analysis of pulmonary phospholipids may be conceivably poor.

Reproducibility. We have studied 8 healthy volunteers in order to assess the reproducubility of some indices which can be used to express lung phospholipid content in BAL fluids, namely the concentrations of total lung phospholipids and phosphatidylcholine, their ratio, and the lecithin to sphingomyelin ratio.

The coefficients of variation within subjects studied twice at a fortnight interval are shown in table 1.

TABLE 1

REPRODUCIBILITY OF PHOSPHOLIPIDS IN BAL

Percent Coefficient of Variation (CV) within subjects (2 trials)

Index	CV
Total phospholipids, ug/100 ml	21
Phosphatidylcholine, ug/100 ml	23
Phosphatidylcholine / total phospholipids	8
Lecithin/ Sphingomyelin	33

It appears from these data that the indices which are more likely to be influenced by the variables connected with the experimental procedure, i.e., phospholipid and phosphatidyl-

choline concentrations, are less reproducible than the ratio
phosphatidylcholine to phospholipids which,in theory, should
be less affected by these variables.

The poor reproducibility of the ratio lecithin to sphingomyelin
is attributable to a rather large variability of sphingomyelin,
which is scarsely present in BAL fluids from healthy subjects
(7). This ratio, which has been found clinically meaningful
when determined in the amniotic fluid seems, by contrast, of
limited usefulness when determined in adults' BAL fluid.

Another index recently proposed (8) for evaluating the content
of phosphatidylcholine in BAL fluid is its ratio to albumin or
to total proteins. We did not study systematically the reproducibility of this index in healthy subjects, but we found in
three patients with chronic obstructive pulmonary disease that
its coefficient of variation within subjects was very large,
about 70%. Since the ratios of other proteins, e.g.,immunoglob-
ulins and antiprotease, to albumin has been successfully used
for clinical purposes (9), we interpret the poor reproducibility
of phosphatidylcholine to albumin as due to the different physical and chemical properties of lipids and proteins, which may
therefore have different solubilities.

COMPOSITION OF BAL AND BL

Fluids obtained by BAL and BL show clear-cut differences after
light centrifugation (500 g x 15 minutes): the BAL pellet is
formed by a large amount of cells, mainly macrophages, that of
BL only by a mucofibrillar network; the BAL fluid shows a thicker
foamy layer at the surface of its supernatant. In 7 healthy
subjects we found some significant differences between the composition of BAL and BL fluids: namely, in BL the fraction of
phosphatidylcholine was constantly smaller, while the fractions
of spingomyelin and phosphatidylserine-phosphatidylinositol were
constanly larger. Nevertheless, as in BAL, posphatidylcholine

was the largest fraction, about 40 %, of total phospholipids
also in BL (figure 1).

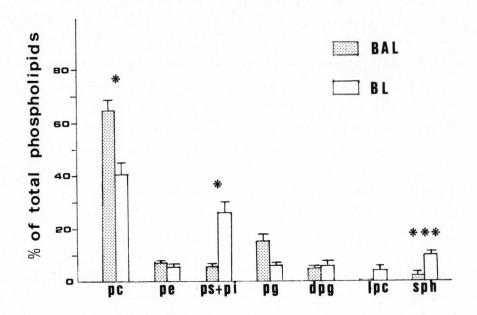

Fig.1. Phospholipid composition of Broncho-Alveolar Lavage (BAL)
and Bronchial Lavage (BL) in 7 healthy humans. pc: phosphatidylcholine; pe: phosphatidylethanolamine; ps+pi: phosphatidylserine-
phosphatidylinositol; pg:phosphatidylglycerol; dpg: diphosphatidyl-
glycerol; lpc: lysophosphatidylcholine; sph: sphingomyelin.
Heights of bars represent mean values and brackets 1 S.E.
* p < 0.05, *** p < 0.001.

If phospholipids found in BL are produced by bronchial cells or
originate in the alveolar zone and therefrom are moved toward
the bronchial conductive zone is still an open question (10).

In any case, their presence might help in stabilizing conductive
airways (11) and enhancing movements of mucous glycoproteins,
which in turn make the mucociliary clearance more effective.

EFFECT OF BENZYLAMINES ON BAL COMPOSITION

The clinical usefulness of BAL for evaluating the surfactant components in human respiratory distress syndrome has been demonstrated (7). Nevertheless, there are some clinical conditions, like chronic obstructive pulmonary disease, in which, even if the surfactant does not show gross abnormalities, an increase in its surface activity might be of some advantage. Animal studies have fecently shown that some benzylamines, and particularly Ambroxol, are able to stimulate alveolar tipe II cells (12) Clara's cells (13) and increase the content of phospholipids in BAL (14).

We have studied 18 patients suffering from chronic bronchitis with none or moderate degree of bronchial obstruction (forced expiratory volume in one second larger than 60% of predicted). We did not find any significant difference in phospholipid composition between BALs from healthy subjects and patients; these findings are consistent with those reported by Hallman et al. (7). These Authors, however, reported a significantly lower concentration of total phospholipids in BAL from patients with chronic obstructive pulmonary disease in respect to normal controls.

In our group of patients the mean of total phospholipids cocentrations was 1500 ± 183 S.E. ug/100ml, not significantly different from that we have observed in normals (2004 ± 594 S.E. ug/100ml). Nevertheless, the concentration of the total phospholipids in patients was significantly ($t=2.27; p < 0.05$) increased after 12-15 days of treatment with benzylamines (figure2).

This change was not accompanied by any change in the fraction of phosphatidylcholine (figure 3).

Our data do not enable us to confirm what others observed in animals (12,13,14), since it is difficult to say if the increased concentration of phospholipids found in BAL is due to the increase of their production or to an easier removal of the lining layer following a more efficient mucociliary clearance (15).

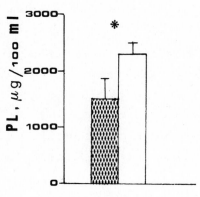

Fig.2. Effects of benzylamines on phospholipids (PL) concentration. Heights of bars represent mean values and brackets 1 S.E. Stippled bars represent pretreatment data.

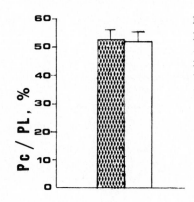

Fig.3. Effects of benzylamines on phosphatidylcholine to total phospholipids (Pc/PL). Heights of bars represent mean values and brackets 1 S.E. Stippled bars represent pretreatment data.

CONCLUSIONS

Pulmonary lavage via fiberoptic bronchoscopy is a useful and easy way to study the components of lung surfactant in adult humans. We have shown that the ratio of phosphatidylcholine to total phospholipids is well reproducible, while the concentration of total phospholipids, even if less reproducible, can be significantly modified by drugs like benzylamines.

An interesting finding is that phosphatidylcholine is the most abundant phospholipid not only in fluids recovered from small airways and alveoli, but also in fluids obtained by lavage of large airways. Further studies on BL are needed to learn more about the

origin of bronchial phospholipids and to see if their content
too is sensitive to pharmacological interventions.

ACKNOWLEDGEMENTS

We are grateful to Pr. G.N. Lamedica and Dr. N. Marchese for
their help in the chromatographic analysis of specimens.

This work was supported in part by a C.N.R. grant. (155 CT/
81.0087.04/115.6823).

REFERENCES

1. Von Neergard,K.Neue (1929) Auffassungen uber einen Grundbegriff der Atemmechanik. Z. Ges. Exp. Med.,66,pp 373-394.

2. King,H.R. (1982) Pulmonary Surfactant. J.Appl.Physiol.:Respirat.
   Environ.Exercise Physiol.: 53,pp 1-8.

3. Van Golde,L.M.G. (1976) Metabolism of phospholipids in the
   lung.Am. Rev. Respir. Dis.,114,pp 977-999.

4. Clements,J.A. and Tierney,D.F. (1964) Alveolar instability
   associated with altered surface tension. In: Handbook of
   Physiology Respiration, Am. Physiol. Soc., Washington, 1964,
   Sect. 3, Vol. II, Chapt. 69,pp 1565-1583.
5. Hallman,M. and Gluck,L. (1976) Phosphatidylglycerol in lung
   surfactant.III Possible modifier of surfactant fuction. J.
   Lipid Res. 17,pp 613-617.

6. Lamedica,G.M. and Canini,S. (1975) Nuovo metodo cromatografico
   per la valutazione della maturità polmonare fetale. Annuali
   di Ostetricia e Ginecologia Medicina Perinatale,6,pp 407-417.

7. Hallman,M.,Spregg,R.,Harrel,J.H.,Moser,K.M. and Gluck,L.(1982)
   Study of Bronchoalveolar lavage phospholipids. Surface activity
   Phospholipase activity and plasma myoinositol. The American
   Society for Clinical Investigation,70,pp 673-683.

8. Bladier,D.,Pre,J.,Georges,R.,Saumon,G.,Turbie,Ph,Mahe,C. and
   Battesti,J-P. (1979) Intérêt du rapport Lecithines/proteines
   dans les liquides de lavage broncho-alveolaire en pathologic
   pulmonaire intertielle. In:Les Colloques de l'INSERM,84,pp 85-
   92.

9. Low,R.B.,Davis,G.S. and Giancola,M.S. (1978)Biochemical
   Analysès of Broncoalveolar lavage fluids of healthy human

volunteer smokers and nonsmokers. Am.Rev.Resp.Dis.,118,1978

10. Fisher,H.K.,Hyman,M.H. and Ashcraft S.J.(1979) Alveolar
    surfactant phospholipids are not cleared by trachea.Federation
    Proc.,1979,38,p 1373.

11. Lopez-Vidriero,M.T. (1981) Airways Mucus; production and
    composition.Chest,80 suppl.,pp 799-804.

12. Sepulveda,J. and Velasquez,B.J. (1982)Study on the influence
    of Na-872 (Ambroxol) and Dexamethasone on the differentiation
    of Clara cells in albine mice. Respiration,43,pp 363-368.

13. Velasquez,B.J. and Sepulveda,J.(1982) Influence of Trans-
    placental Na-872 and Dexamethasone therapy on fetal and
    newborn mouse lung. Respiration,43,pp 389-400.

14. Prevost,M.,Soula,G. and Douste-Blazy,L. (1979) Biochemical
    Modifications of pulmonary surfactant after Bromexin derivate
    injection. Respiration,37,pp 215-219.

15. Iravani,J.,Melville,G.N. (1974) Wirkung von Bromexin-metabolit
    VIII und einem neun adrenergen stoff auf die mukoziliare
    funktion des respirationsstraktes.Arzneim-Forsch,24,pp 849-
    855.

16. Valenti,S.,Crimi,P.,Ferrari,A. and Scordamaglia,T. (1979)
    Etude des fractions phospholipidiques et du surfactant dans
    le lavage broncho-alveolaire chez l'homme. In:Les Colloques
    de l'INSERM,1979,84,pp 93-104.

© 1983, Elsevier Science Publishers B.V.
*Pulmonary Surfactant System, E.V. Cosmi
and E.M. Scarpelli eds.*

FRACTIONATION OF ALVEOLAR SATURATED PHOSPHATIDYLCHOLINE IN THE RABBIT

ALDO BARITUSSIO[1], RAFFAELE CARRARO[1], LUCIA BELLINA[1], ALBERTO ROSSI[1],
GIULIANO ENZI[1], MARTHA MAGOON[2], ISABELLA MUSSINI[3]

[1]Department of Internal Medicine, University of Padua (Italy); [2]1238 Lorell
SW, North Canton, Ohio, 44720 (U.S.A.); [3]National Research Council Unit
for Muscle Biology and Physiopathology, Department of General Pathology,
Padua (Italy)

INTRODUCTION

The authors who study the incorporation into alveolar surfactant of labelled precursors administered intravenously assume that mixing of label within
the alveolar spaces is instantaneous (1, 2), implying that the different
form of alveolar surfactant (tubular myelin, common myelin, monolayer of
phospholipids at the air-water interface) behave as components of a single
compartment. However, this assumption has never been tested experimentally.

In this report we present our attempts to fractionate alveolar saturated
phosphatidylcholine (SPC), the most abundant phospholipid species of lung
surfactant, by differential and density gradient centrifugation of lung
lavage.

We show that SPC of lung lavage ("A") can be separated into different fractions. One fraction ("B") contains 46.0±5.9% (M±SD) of lavage SPC, and corresponds for composition and sedimentability to what is usually defined
purified alveolar surfactant. A second fraction ("C") is identified by the
fact that it does not sediment after centrifugation of lung lavage at 80,000
g for 90 min. This fraction has never been extensively studied before, although it contains 29.8±14.0% of lavage SPC. Finally, a third fraction ("D")
represents SPC associated with the cells of lavage and contains less than
5% of SPC of lung lavage.

After i.v. injection of ^{3}H-palmitate we found that fraction "C" incorporates
the label with a small delay with respect to fraction "B" and that the label
enters fraction "B" in a sequence in which components of "B" with the highest
density and the lowest phospholipid to protein ratio are labelled first.

These findings do not support the assumption that mixing of label within
the alveolar spaces is instantaneous after i.v. injection of a labelled
precursor. The possible significance of fraction "C" is discussed.

MATERIALS AND METHODS

Collection and fractionation of alveolar SPC. Male New Zealand rabbits weighing 1.5-2.2 Kg were killed with i.v. sodium penthiobarbital and their lungs were isolated, degassed and subjected to alveolar lavage at 4°C with a medium containing 0.15 M NaCl, 10 mM TRIS·HCl, 1.25 mM $CaCl_2$, 1.00 mM $MgCl_2$, pH 7.4. The lavage was done by recycling 4 times in each lung an amount of medium sufficient to distend the airways completely.

The lavage fluid was then filtered through gauze and brought to 60 ml with medium. 20 ml of filtered lavage ("A") were used to make a discontinuous gradient by laying them over a cushion of 0.75 M sucrose. 38 ml of filtered lavage were used as such to fill a second centrifuge tube. Both tubes were then centrifuged at 80,000 g for 90 min in a SW 28 rotor.

The material banding over 0.75 M sucrose was collected, suspended in medium, sedimented at 80,000 g for 1 hour and called "B". The material found at the bottom of the 0.75 M sucrose solution was directly suspended in medium and called "D". The supernatant of the second tube, where no floating material was visible at the end of the run, was collected by gently inverting the tube and called "C".

In 6 experiments fraction "B" was brought to 0.75 M sucrose concentration, overlaid with a continuous gradient of sucrose (from 0.75 to 0.25 M) and centrifuged to isopicnic density in a SW 28 rotor for 36 hours at 80,000 g. At the end aliquots of 0.6 ml were taken from the gradient starting from the bottom.

In 6 experiments subfractions of "B" were obtained by discontinuous density gradient centrifugation. 6 ml of fraction "B" brought to 1.00 M sucrose concentration were overlaid with 5 ml of 0.70 M, 9 ml of 0.55 M, 9 ml of 0.45 M and 9 ml of 0.30 M sucrose solutions. The tube was then spun for 9 hours at 80,000 g in a SW 28 rotor. The resulting bands were collected by peristaltic pump, diluted 3 times with medium and sedimented at 80,000 g for 60 min.

Composition analysis. On the isolated fractions we determined proteins (3), phospholipid phosphorus (4), phospholipid profile (5), saturated phosphatidylcholine (6), total cholesterol (7), DNA (8).

Morphology. Negative staining was done on carbon coated grids (300 mesh, Formwar) using a Phillips EM 301 electron microscope.

Tracer experiments. We injected via an ear vein 12 rabbits fed ad libitum with ^{3}H-palmitate (100 µCi/Kg, S.A. 590 µCi/mMole). We killed them 2.5-70 hours after the injection of label.

Aliquots of saturated phosphatidylcholine isolated by the osmium tetroxide method from fractions "B", "C", and "D" were analyzed for phosphorus content and for radioactivity. Counts were corrected for quenching by external standard channels ratio method. Specific activity is expressed as DPM per micromole of phospholipid phosphorus.

RESULTS

Yield and composition. As shown in Table 1, after centrifugation of lung lavage at 80,000 g for 90 min, the greatest amount of SPC is found at the top of 0.75 M sucrose solution (fraction "B"), a consistent aliquot of SPC remains in the supernatant (fraction "C"), a small amount of it sediments at the bottom of 0.75 M sucrose (fraction "D").

TABLE 1
RECOVERY OF SATURATED PHOSPHATIDYLCHOLINE AFTER FRACTIONATION OF RABBIT ALVEOLAR SURFACTANT
The content of saturated phosphatidylcholine in original lavage was assumed to be 100%

Original lavage	100.0
Lavage subfraction:	
B[a]	46.0 ± 5.9
C[a]	29.8 ±14.0
D[a]	2.8 ± 1.6
Lost during filtration[b]	10.5 ± 2.5

a: data from 9 experiments
b: data from 4 experiments
M±SD

The cells of lavage sediment at the bottom of 0.75 M sucrose, where more than 98% of lavage DNA can be recovered (average of 3 experiments).

Fractions "B" and "C" have similar phospholipid composition, degree of saturation of phosphatidylcholine, and phospholipid/cholesterol ratio. Fraction "B" has the highest phospholipid to protein ratio, whereas low values are found in fractions "C" and "D". Fraction "D" has the lowest degree of saturation of phosphatidylcholine (Table 2 and 3).

TABLE 2

FRACTIONATION OF LUNG LAVAGE IN THE RABBIT: FRACTION'S YIELD AND COMPOSITION

Fraction	SPC (mg/gr lung)	SPC Phospholipids (%)	Phospholipid Protein (μMole/mg)	Phospholipid Cholesterol (molar ratio)
Original lavage	1.31±0.41	49.0±8.7	0.87±0.37	16.1±8.4
Lavage fraction				
B	0.58±0.16	58.1±7.4	11.64±3.10	22.7±12.1
C	0.41±0.27	58.8±8.7	0.43±0.21	23.6±11.5
D	0.03±0.01	10.1±4.3	0.30±0.04	7.4±2.5

M±SD, data from 12 experiments

TABLE 3

PHOSPHOLIPID COMPOSITION (%) OF FRACTIONS "B" AND "C"

Phospholipid	B	C
Front	2.0	1.6
Unknown phospholipids	4.4	3.5
Cardiolipin	1.5	1.2
Phosphatidylethanolamine	3.0	2.4
Phosphatidylglycerol	6.1	5.1
Phosphatidylcholine	81.4	83.1
Sphingomyelin	TR	TR
Phosphatidylserine + Phosphatidylinositol	0.4	TR
Lysophosphatidylcholine	TR	2.0
Origin	0.3	0.5

Average from 2 experiments
TR = traces

When fraction "B" is centrifuged to isopicnic density, fraction's SPC is recovered as a single band with an average density of 1.060±0.003 g/ml (M±SD, n = 6).

In fraction "B" the phospholipid to protein ratio is inversely related to density, as shown in the series of experiments in which subfractions of "B" were obtained by discontinuous density gradient centrifugation (Table 4).

TABLE 4

PHOSPHOLIPID/PROTEIN RATIO IN SUBFRACTIONS OF "B" OBTAINED BY DISCONTINUOUS SUCROSE DENSITY GRADIENT CENTRIFUGATION

Sucrose molarity	Phospholipid (μM)/protein (mg)
0.30-0.45	20.2±3.3
0.45-0.55	7.1±2.6
0.55-0.70	2.5±1.8

M±SD, data from 6 experiments

Morphology. In one experiment we purified "B" by centrifugation for 36 hours in a continuous density gradient of sucrose, collected fractions from the gradient at regular intervals of density and analyzed them by EM. We found large multilamellar vesicles or sheet-like structures uniformly distributed through the gradient. Tubular myelin was not recognizable in our preparation (Fig. 1: A and B).

Negative staining of fraction "C" showed a fairly uniform population of unilamellar vesicles with an average diameter of 34.8±13.7 nm (M±SD) (Fig. 1, C).

Tracer studies. As shown in Fig. 2, fractions "B" and "C" incorporate the ^{3}H-palmitate with a slightly different time-course, "B" having the highest specific activity up to 20 hours after the injection of label and then the lowest.

Fraction "B" does not represent a well mixed compartment. In fact, when "B" is purified by continuous density gradient centrifugation SPC specific activity is positively correlated with density 4 hours ($p < 0.001$), 5 hours ($p < 0.001$), and 60 hours ($p < 0.05$) after the injection of label. Only after 70 hours fraction "B" appears to be uniformly labelled with isothope (Fig. 3).

52

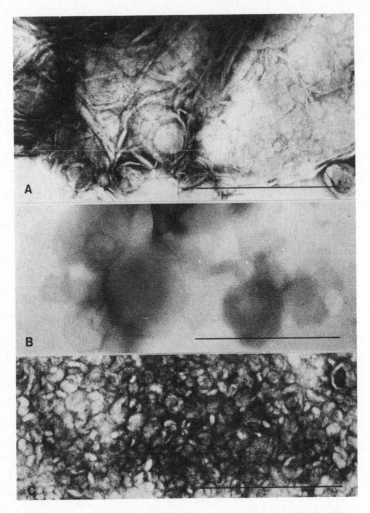

Fig. 1. Electron micrographs of fractions "B" and "C" (negative staining, 108.000x). Fraction "B" contained multilamellar vesicles and sheet-like structures (A,B). Fraction "C" contained, amidst amorphous material, a uniform population of small unilamellar vesicles (C). Calibration bar: 0.5 μm

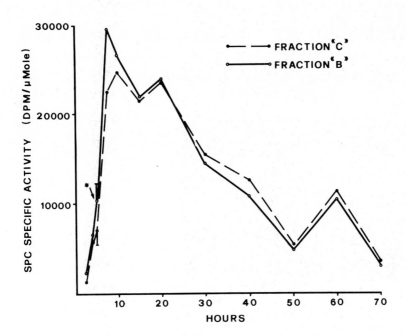

Fig. 2. Time-course of incorporation of ^{3}H-palmitate into SPC of fractions "B" and "C". Rabbits were killed at intervals between 2.5 and 70 hours after the injection of label. Each time-point represents 1 rabbit, except for 5 hours, when the experiment was done on 6 rabbits (M±SE). At 5 hours fraction "B" had a specific activity 32.0% higher than "C". This difference was statistically significant (p<0.01, paired "t" test).

DISCUSSION

The data presented show that SPC of lung lavage can be resolved into fractions differing for their sedimentability.

Fraction "B", for composition and sedimentability, is similar to what has been defined by others (9, 10) purified alveolar surfactant, contains enough SPC to provide the alveoli with a complete interfacial film at functional residual capacity (11), and is made by membranous material (large multila-mellar vesicles or sheet-like structures). The absence of tubular myelin (that we expected to find in this fraction (12)) could be due to the isola-

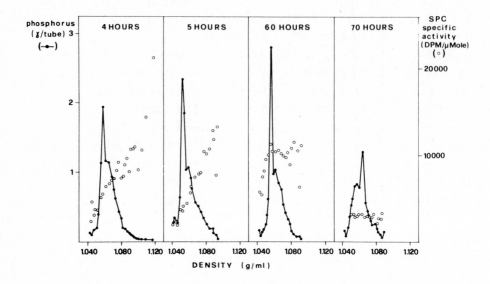

Fig. 3. Specific activity of SPC in fraction "B" purified by continuous density gradient centrifugation. Fraction "B" was isolated and centrifuged to equilibrium density in a continuous gradient of sucrose 4, 5, 60, and 70 hours after i.v. injection of ^{3}H-palmitate (100 μCi/Kg). Aliquots were taken from the gradient and tested for SPC specific activity. SPC specific activity and SPC phosphorus content per tube are plotted against density.

tion conditions or to structural rearrangements happened during negative staining.

Fraction "C" has never been clearly described. This fraction is similar to fraction "B" for phospholipid composition, degree of saturation of phosphatidylcholine, and cholesterol content and contains, amidst amorphous material, a fairly uniform population of small unilamellar vesicles. This fraction could be merely the result of structural rearrangements of alveolar surfactant happened during lavage, however, it is tempting to consider it as a surfactant component modified for reuptake by the alveolar cells. In fact, Oyarzun et al. (13) have shown that unilamellar vesicles of SPC,

40-60 nm in diameter, can be taken up by the cells of the alveoli through
a process that does not require stereospecificity. We feel that fraction
"C" deserves further investigation.

Fraction "D" is made by SPC associated with the cells of lavage, but at
present it is unclear if the SPC is extracellular, or is adsorbed to cells,
or is an integral component of cell membranes.

The tracer data show that the labelling of alveolar SPC is not instantaneous after i.v. injection of a radioactive precursor. In fact, fraction
"C" labels with a small delay with respect to fraction "B" (Fig. 2). Furthermore, fraction "B" incorporates the label in a sequence in which the
components with the highest density and the lowest phospholipid to protein
ratio are labelled first (Fig. 3). Taken together these findings are against
the view that alveolar SPC represents a well mixed compartment. On the contrary, they suggest the existence into the alveolar spaces of surfactant
related structures that undergo sequential transformations. In fact, the
pattern of incorporation of ^{3}H-palmitate is compatible with the existence
of a flow of SPC from fraction "B" to fraction "C".

REFERENCES

1. Baritussio A., Magoon M.W., Goerke J., Clements J.A. (1981) Precursor
    -product relationship between rabbit type II cell lamellar bodies and
    alveolar surfacie active material: surfactant turnover time. Biochim.
    Biophys. Acta 666: 382-393.

2. Jacobs H., Jobe A., Ikegami M., Jones S. (1982) Surfactant phosphatidyl-
    choline source, fluxes and turnover times in 3-day-old, 10-day-old,
    and adult rabbits. J. Biol. Chem. 257: 1805-1810.

3. Kashyap M.L., Hynd B.A., Robinson K. (1980) A rapid and simple method
    for measurement of total protein in very low density lipoproteins by
    the Lowry assay. J. Lipid Res. 21: 491-495.

4. Bartlett G.R. (1959) Phosphorus assay in column chromatography. J. Biol.
    Chem. 234: 466-468.

5. Poorthuis B.J.H.M., Yazaki P.J., Hostetler K.Y. (1976) An improved two
    dimensional thin-layer chromatography system for the separation of
    phosphatidylglycerol and its derivatives. J. Lipid Res. 17: 433-437.

6. Mason R.J., Nellenbogen J., Clements J.A. (1976) Isolation of disaturated
    phosphatidylcholine with osmium tetroxide. J. Lipid Res. 17: 281-284.

7. Gamble W.M., Vaughan M., Kruth H.S., Avigan J. (1978) Procedure for
    determination of free and total cholesterol in micro- or nanogram amount
    suitable for studies with cultures cells. J. Lipid Res. 19: 1068-1070.

8. Setaro F., Morley C.D., Colin G.D. (1976) A modified fluorometric method
    for the determination of microgram quantities of DNA from cell or tissue
    cultures. Anal. Biochem. 71: 313-317.

9. King R.J., Clements J.A. (1972) Surface active material from dog lung. I: Method of isolation. Am. J. Physiol. 223: 707-714.

10. Sueishi K., Benson J.B. (1981) Isolation of a major apolipoprotein of canine and murine pulmonary surfactant. Biochemical and immunochemical characteristics. Biochim. Biophys. Acta 665: 442-453.

11. Berlin Gail D., Steinkamp H., Massaro D. (1978) Interspecies variation in lung lavage and tissue saturated phosphatidylcholine. Respiration Physiol. 33: 289-297.

12. Gil J., Reiss O.K. (1973) Isolation and characterization of lamellar bodies and tubular myelin from rat lung homogenates. J. Cell Biol. 58: 152-171.

13. Oyarzun M.J., Clements J.A., Baritussio A. (1980) Ventilation enhances pulmonary alveolar clearance of radioactive dipalmitoylphosphatidyl-choline in liposomes. Am. Rev. Resp. Dis. 121: 709-721.

© 1983, Elsevier Science Publishers B.V.
Pulmonary Surfactant System, E.V. Cosmi
and E.M. Scarpelli eds.

TYPE II CELLS ISOLATED FROM ADULT AND FETAL RAT LUNG AS MODELS FOR STUDIES
ON THE FORMATION OF PULMONARY SURFACTANT

LAMBERT M.G. VAN GOLDE, MARTIN POST, ALFONS C.J. DE VRIES AND JOSEPH J.
BATENBURG
Laboratory of Veterinary Biochemistry, State University of Utrecht,
Biltstraat 172, 3572 BP Utrecht (The Netherlands)

INTRODUCTION

Pulmonary surfactant prevents alveoli from collapsing at low transpul-
monary pressure by lowering the surface tension at the alveolar surface
(1). Dipalmitoylphosphatidylcholine (dipalmitoyl-PC) is undoubtedly the
major surface-active component of pulmonary surfactant (2) although there
is evidence from clinical studies (3) that phosphatidylglycerol (PG) may
also be required for optimal functioning of this material. The deficiency
of pulmonary surfactant in patients with neonatal (4) and possibly in
those with adult (5) respiratory distress syndrome has been the impetus
for numerous biochemical investigations on the synthesis of surfactant in
the fetal and adult lung.

Most of the earlier investigations on the formation of pulmonary surfactant (for a review see ref. 6) were performed with preparations derived
from whole lung tissue and were, therefore, seriously handicapped by the
enormous heterogeneity of this tissue: It is known that the adult lung consists of approx. 40 different cell types whereas the production of pulmonary surfactant is confined to the alveolar epithelial type II cells (1,6,
7). Nevertheless, it became clear from studies with preparations derived
from whole lung that the major surfactant lipids are synthesized de novo
via the same pathways described for other tissues (8). The synthesis de
novo of phosphatidylcholine (PC) proceeds predominantly via the CDPcholine
route as outlined in Figure 1. Phosphatidic acid is synthesized by step-
wise acylation of glycerol-3-phosphate and converted either into diacylglycerol or into CDPdiacylglycerol. Diacylglycerol reacts, subsequently, with
CDPcholine to yield PC and CDPdiacylglycerol serves as common precursor in
the formation of phosphatidylinositol (PI) and PG.

A more detailed and precise insight into the formation of specific surfactant lipids may be obtained by investigations with preparations of
isolated alveolar type II cells. Methods to isolate this cell type from
both adult and fetal lung have become available in the past few years (for

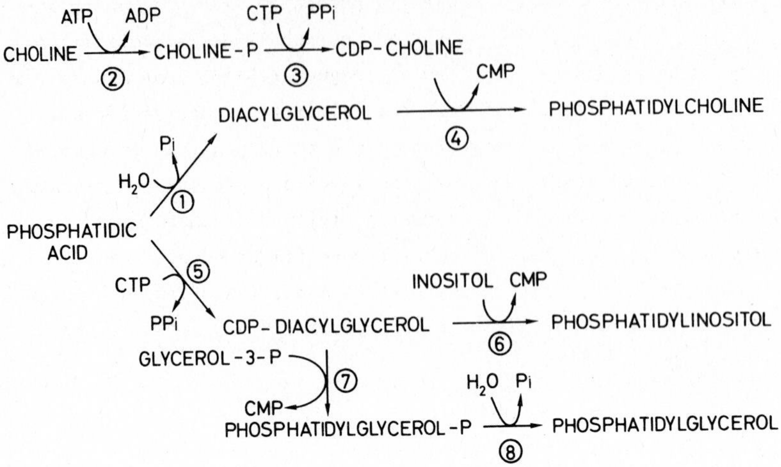

Fig. 1. Synthesis de novo of the major surfactant phospholipids.
Enzymes: 1: Phosphatidate phosphatase, 2: Choline kinase, 3: Cholinephosphate cytidylyltransferase, 4: Cholinephosphotransferase, 5: Phosphatidate cytidylyltransferase, 6: CDPdiacylglycerol-inositol phosphatidyltransferase, 7: Glycerolphosphate phosphatidyltransferase and
8: Phosphatidylglycerophosphatase.

reviews see refs. 7,9). In the following paragraphs we will describe some
of our recent studies with isolated alveolar type II cells focussing on
the formation of dipalmitoyl-PC, PG and PI and the regulation of these processes.

SYNTHESIS OF DISATURATED PC IN TYPE II CELLS ISOLATED FROM ADULT RAT LUNG

Earlier studies with preparations from whole lung had provided evidence
that direct synthesis de novo via disaturated diacylglycerol cannot be responsible for the formation of all pulmonary disaturated PC (which is predominantly dipalmitoyl-PC). Several investigators suggested that a part of
the disaturated PC is formed by remodeling of PC molecules containing an
unsaturated fatty acid at the 2-position. This remodeling could be accomplished by removal of the unsaturated fatty acid from the 2-position by
phospholipase A_2 and reesterification of the vacant OH-group by lysolecithin acyltransferase with palmitate (Figure 2, for a review see ref. 6).

We could demonstrate that such remodeling mechanism may play an important role in the synthesis of disaturated PC in type II cells isolated from
adult rat lung as described by Mason and colleagues (10-12). Upon incubation
of type II cells with radioactively labelled palmitate or acetate, the radioactivity was incorporated preferentially into the 2-position of disaturated PC. In disaturated diacylglycerol, the immediate precursor of disaturated PC in the synthesis de novo, the radioactivity distribution was strikingly different: Both the 1- and 2-position were almost equally labelled.
These observations (13) strongly suggested that a portion of the palmitate
at the 2-position of disaturated PC was incorporated via a mechanism by-
passing the CDPcholine route.

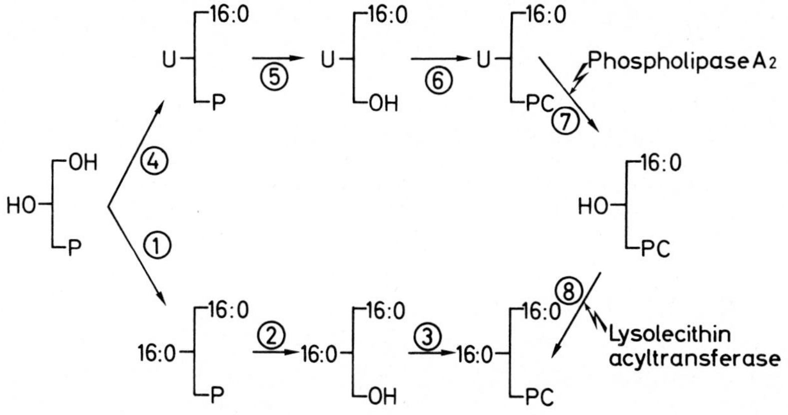

Fig. 2. Pathways operating in the type II cell for the synthesis of
dipalmitoyl-PC. U: unsaturated fatty acid; 16:0: palmitic acid.

Incubation of type II cells in the presence of phospholipase A_2 inhibitors such as 4-bromophenacylbromide or quinacrine led to a decreased synthesis of total PC from various labelled precursors but, interestingly, also led to an increased degree of unsaturation of PC synthesized by the
cells (13).

Although the results of the experiments with phospholipase A_2 inhibitors should be interpreted with caution because other effects of these compounds on the type II cells cannot be excluded, they do suggest that phospholipase A_2 is involved in the formation of disaturated PC by remodeling of 1-saturated-2-unsaturated PC. The saturated lyso-PC (predominantly 1-palmitoyl-lyso-PC) can subsequently be converted into disaturated PC by the enzyme lysolecithin acyltransferase. Interestingly, the specific activity of this enzyme is higher in type II cells than in whole lung homogenates and the type II cell enzyme displays a more pronounced preference for palmitate as substrate (14). Taken together, these findings do endorse the view that the type II cell possesses a deacylation-reacylation mechanism to transform unsaturated molecules synthesized de novo into disaturated PC (Figure 2, reactions 4-8).

We were also interested in the question as to whether direct synthesis de novo of disaturated PC may take place in the type II cell (Figure 2, reactions 1-3). Type II cell sonicates or whole lung homogenates were incubated with either CDP[Me-^{14}C]choline or CDP[2-^{14}C]ethanolamine using the endogenous diacylglycerols as substrates. Of the PC molecules synthesized by whole lung homogenates 20% appeared to be disaturated (see Table 1). Although the specific activity of cholinephosphotransferase was not higher in type II cells than in whole lung homogenates, it was intriguing to note that as much as 56% of the PC synthesized by the type II cell sonicates was disaturated. Interestingly, endogenous diacylglycerols were not utilized as

TABLE 1

FORMATION OF PC FROM ENDOGENOUS DIACYLGLYCEROLS IN SONICATES OF RAT LUNG TYPE II CELLS AND RAT LUNG HOMOGENATES

Type II cell sonicate (59 µg protein) or lung homogenate (68 µg protein) were incubated for 15 min in 0.15 ml medium of the following composition: 100 mM Tris-maleic acid (pH 8.0), 25 mM $MgCl_2$, 10 mM β-mercaptoethanol, 1 mM EDTA, and 0.5 mM CDP[Me-^{14}C]choline (spec. act. $4 \cdot 10^4$ dpm/nmol). For further details see ref. 13. Averages ± SE of three experiments, each carried out in triplicate, are presented.

Fraction	PC synthesized (pmol/h per mg protein)	Disaturated PC as % of total PC (label incorporated)
Type II cells	26 ± 6	56 ± 7
Lung homogenate	26 ± 2	20 ± 4

substrate by ethanolaminephosphotransferase which is in line with the observation that phosphatidylethanolamine of pulmonary surfactant hardly contains disaturated species (15).

The high percentage of labelled disaturated PC synthesized by the type II cells upon incubation with radioactively labelled CDPcholine should most likely be explained by a direct conversion of disaturated diacylglycerols into disaturated PC, although a rapid remodeling of unsaturated PC molecules synthesized by cholinephosphotransferase cannot be entirely excluded.

The studies described in this paragraph suggest that disaturated PC may be synthesized in the alveolar type II cell of adult rat lung both by direct synthesis de novo and by remodeling of 1-saturated-2-unsaturated PC (Figure 2). At present, it is difficult to establish the relative importance of these pathways.

THE RATE-LIMITING STEP IN THE SYNTHESIS DE NOVO OF PC IN TYPE II CELLS ISOLATED FROM ADULT RAT LUNG

Studies with a variety of mammalian tissues including the lung have supplied experimental evidence that cholinephosphate cytidylyltransferase (Figure 1, reaction 3) catalyses a rate-limiting step in the synthesis de novo of PC (16). As far as the lung is concerned the best evidence for this hypothesis was obtained in studies on the pool sizes of choline and its metabolites in developing rat and rabbit lung (17-19). The cholinephosphate pool was much larger than the CDPcholine pool which suggests that the formation of CDPcholine may be limited. Because these studies were performed with preparations of whole lung, the results are not necessarily applicable to type II cells.

We studied the uptake of [Me-^{14}C]choline and its incorporation into cholinephosphate, CDPcholine and PC over a period of 5 h by type II cells isolated from adult lung (20). At any time more than 90% of the water-soluble radioactivity extracted from the cells was associated with cholinephosphate. The much higher label incorporation into cholinephosphate as compared to that into intracellular choline indicated that the cholinephosphate pool is much larger than the intracellular choline pool. The incorporation of label into cholinephosphate was only slightly lower than that into PC but much higher than that into CDPcholine. These findings suggested that the cholinephosphate pool is much larger than both the choline and CDPcholine pool, which is consistent with the hypothesis that cholinephosphate cytidylyltransferase is rate-limiting in the formation of PC from choline (Figure 1, reactions 2-4).

This suggestion could be endorsed by pulse-chase studies. $[Me-^{14}C]$-choline taken up by the cells was rapidly converted into cholinephosphate during the pulse period. During the chase, the radioactivity disappeared rapidly from cholinephosphate and was recovered almost instantaneously in PC without affecting the labelling of CDPcholine. Inclusion of palmitate in the chase medium caused a twofold increase in the rate of disappearance of label from cholinephosphate and in the rate of incorporation into PC. Under these conditions the radioactivity associated with CDPcholine decreased, which indicated that cholinephosphate cytidylyltransferase cannot keep up with the increased utilization of CDPcholine in the last step of the pathway.

The effect of palmitate on the CDPcholine pathway was studied in more detail in the experiment shown in Figure 3. The type II cells were pre-labelled for 3 h with $[Me-^{14}C]$choline. At that point palmitate was added and the incubations were continued for an additional 3 h. The uptake of labelled choline by the type II cells and the incorporation into its metabolites were monitored at 1-h intervals after the addition of palmitate. The presence of palmitate led to an increased incorporation of choline into PC and a decreased labelling of cholinephosphate. The uptake of label into the intracellular choline pool and the incorporation into CDPcholine were not significantly affected by the addition of palmitate. The flux of radioactive choline through the choline kinase reaction, which was estimated by summation of the radioactivity in cholinephosphate, CDPcholine and PC was slightly increased in the presence of palmitate (not shown). These observations suggested that the decreased entry of choline into cholinephosphate was not due to a decreased activity of choline kinase but rather to an increased conversion of cholinephosphate into CDPcholine.

Addition of cyclic AMP instead of palmitate diminished the formation of PC from labelled choline and enhanced the entry of choline into cholinephosphate (Figure 3). The flux of radioactive choline through the pathway was not affected by cyclic AMP. These findings suggest that the decreased synthesis of PC in the presence of cyclic AMP may be due to a decreased activity of cholinephosphate cytidylyltransferase.

Since it has been shown that fatty acids suppress the formation of cyclic AMP in fat cells (22,23), it is tempting to speculate that the stimulatory effect of palmitate on cholinephosphate cytidylyltransferase is mediated via a decreased level of cyclic AMP in the Type II cell. The inhibitory effect of cyclic AMP on the activity of cholinephosphate cytidylyltransferase is in good agreement with a recent report (24) on the effect of

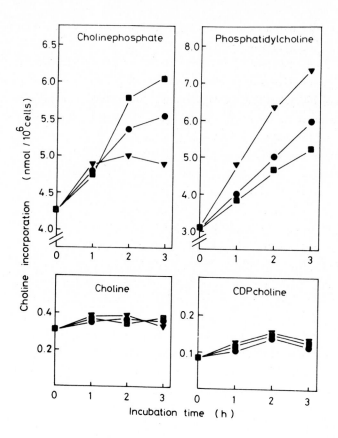

Fig. 3. The effect of the addition of palmitate or cyclic AMP on the uptake of [Me-^{14}C]choline into type II cells and its incorporation into cholinephosphate, CDPcholine and PC. The type II cells were preincubated with radioactive choline for 3 h. At this time (time zero) 0.2 mM palmitate or 0.25 mM cyclic AMP were added. ●——●, control; ▼——▼ with palmitate; ■——■ with cyclic AMP. For further details see refs. 20 and 21.

cyclic AMP on this enzyme in isolated hepatocytes. These authors suggested that the activity of the liver enzyme is regulated through a phosphorylation-dephosphorylation mechanism. In general, cyclic AMP-mediated protein phosphorylation results in stimulation of catabolic and inhibition of biosynthetic pathways. The effect of cyclic AMP on the formation of PC in type II cells and in hepatocytes would be consistent with this dogma. It should be emphasized, however, that more extensive studies are required to substantiate

the suggestion that cholinephosphate cytidylyltransferase may be regulated
in the type II cell by phosphorylation-dephosphorylation.

REGULATION OF PI AND PG SYNTHESIS IN TYPE II CELLS OF ADULT RAT LUNG

The production of surfactant in the fetal lung begins in the terminal
part of gestation (1,15). Initially, the percentage of PI increases con-
comitantly with that of disaturated PC whereas PG appears later (3,25).
The appearance of PG is accompanied by a decrease in the percentage of
PI. Several mechanisms have been proposed to regulate the shift from PI
to PG synthesis: 1. The increased PG synthesis is at least partly due to
an increased activity of microsomal glycerolphosphate phosphatidyltransferase (25). 2. The relative decrease of PI and the increase of PG are
caused by the decrease in serum inositol at the end of gestation (26).
This hypothesis was based on findings in rabbit lung microsomes that the
two enzymes which convert CDPdiacylglycerol into PI and PG-phosphate,
respectively (Figure 1, reactions 6 and 7) compete for the common substrate and that inositol enhanced PI synthesis at the expense of PG production. 3. The switch-over from PI to PG synthesis around term is caused
by the elevated level of CMP resulting from enhanced PC synthesis (27,28).
This suggestion was based on the observation that rabbit lung CDPdiacylglycerol-inositol phosphatidyltransferase catalyses a reversible reaction
and on the finding that CMP stimulated PG synthesis in lung microsomes by
providing CDPdiacylglycerol via a reverse reaction of CDPdiacylglycerol-
inositol phosphatidyltransferase (28). These three mechanisms were all
based on experiments with whole lung preparations. It was thought of interest, therefore, to investigate which of these mechanisms may regulate
the partitioning of CDPdiacylglycerol between PI and PG synthesis in type
II cells of adult rat lung.

Table 2 shows that the incorporation by intact type II cells of labelled glucose into PI is increased whereas the entry of glucose into PG is
decreased by addition of inositol to the incubation medium. The incorporation of glucose into PC was not affected. Similar results were obtained if glycerol was used as labelled substrate instead of glucose
(not shown). The effect of inositol on the synthesis of PI and PG became
apparent at concentrations higher than 0.1 mM inositol (29).

TABLE 2

EFFECTS OF INOSITOL AND CHOLINE ON THE INCORPORATION OF $[U-^{14}C]$GLUCOSE IN-TO PC, PG and PI BY INTACT TYPE II CELLS ISOLATED FROM ADULT RAT LUNG

The cells were incubated for 2.5 h in standard incubation medium supplemented with 5.6 mM $[U-^{14}C]$glucose and, where indicated, 5 mM inositol and/or 0.1 mM choline. The values in the table represent the ratio of the rate of incorporation under a certain condition over the rate in the control incubation (A). The data are the means ± SD of ratios observed in three experiments with three different cell preparations. For further details see ref. 29.

Incubation condition	Addition to medium	Incorporation condition A,B,C or D		
		Incorporation condition A		
		PC	PG	PI
A	None	1	1	1
B	Inositol	0.96 ± 0.06	0.28 ± 0.07[d]	7.74 ± 1.29[c]
C	Choline	1.80 ± 0.22[b]	1.16 ± 0.09[a]	1.35 ± 0.21[a]
D	Inositol + choline	1.81 ± 0.14[d]	0.33 ± 0.09[d]	8.63 ± 2.82[b]

Statistical significance was determined using Student's t-test; [a]$p<0.05$; [b]$p<0.025$; [c]$p<0.01$; [d]$p<0.005$

Figure 4 shows that inositol at concentrations >0.05 mM decreased the activity of the conversion of CDPdiacylglycerol into PG. The results shown in Table 2 and Figure 4 indicate that in type II cells of adult lung the enzymes glycerolphosphate phosphatidyltransferase and CDPdiacylglycerol-inositol phosphatidyltransferase compete for the same pool of CDPdiacyl-glycerols.

Our observations would favour the mechanism proposed by Hallman and colleagues (25,26) that the switch-over from PI to PG synthesis in the fetal lung may indeed be accomplished by a competition for CDPdiacylglycerol and a decrease in serum inositol concentration near term. In the present study we did not find evidence to support mechanism 3 (27,28). Addition of choline to the incubation medium increased the formation of PC from labelled glucose (Table 2) and, most likely, resulted in an increased CMP level (Figure 1, reaction 4). Although there was, indeed, a small increase in the rate of PG synthesis by the addition of choline, this increase was not accompanied by a depressed but rather by an enhanced PI formation. This finding strongly argues against the occurrence of mechanism 3, at least in type II cells of adult rat lung.

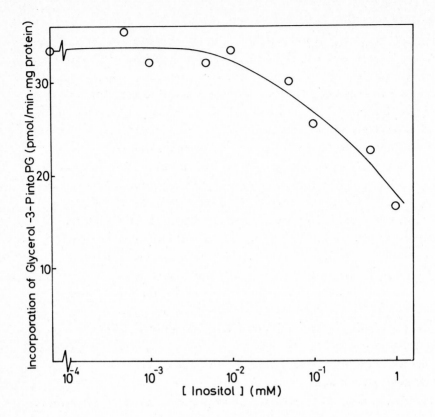

Fig. 4. Effect of inositol on the formation of PG from labelled glycerol-3-phosphate by a sonicate of type II cells from adult rat lung. The incubation medium (0.1 ml) contained 100 mM Tris-Cl (pH 7.4), 6 mM glutathion, 0.030 mM CDPdiacylglycerol (prepared from egg PC), 0.45 mM L-[U-^{14}C]-glycerol-3-phosphate (spec. act. $55 \cdot 10^3$ dpm/nmol), 5 mM MnCl$_2$ and sonicated type II cells (3.3 µg protein). After 15 min incubation radioactive product was separated from labelled precursor by the filter disk method (30).

EFFECTS OF AMBROXOL ON THE SYNTHESIS OF SURFACTANT LIPIDS BY ISOLATED TYPE II CELLS FROM ADULT RAT LUNG

   Primary cultures of type II cells from adult rat lung are a good model to investigate the effects of hormones and drugs on the production of pulmonary surfactant lipids. In an earlier paper (31) we could demonstrate that exposure of isolated type II cells from adult rat lung to cortisol led to an increased synthesis of the major surfactant lipids. These data indicated that corticosteroids may not only be involved in the regulation of surfactant synthesis in the fetal lung but may also play a role in the regulation of this process in the adult lung.

Pharmacological studies with Ambroxol (NA-872 or metabolite VIII of Bi-solvon, a bronchial secretolyticum) have demonstrated that this drug stimulates the production of pulmonary surfactant in the fetal lung (32-35). Recent experiments suggested that the drug has a specific effect on the alveolar type II cells (36,37). In view of these findings we designed experiments to investigate whether Ambroxol may also affect the formation of surfactant lipids by type II cells isolated from adult rat lung.

After the type II cells had been in culture for 20 h (31), the culture medium was replaced by fresh medium with and without Ambroxol (15 µg/ml) and the type II cells cultured for an additional 24 h. At the end of the 24-h period, the culture medium was replaced by a serum-free medium (31) containing Ambroxol (15 µg/ml) and one of the following combinations of labelled substrates to estimate the rate of lipid synthesis: 0.025 mM [Me-^{14}C]choline (plus 5.6 mM glucose and 0.2 mM palmitate); 5.6 mM [U-^{14}C]glucose (plus 0.05 mM choline); 0.1 mM [1(3)-^{3}H]glycerol (plus 0.2 mM palmitate and 0.05 mM choline); 1 mM [1-^{14}C]acetate (plus 5.6 mM glucose and 0.05 mM choline) and 0.2 mM [1-^{14}C]palmitate (plus 5.6 mM glucose and 0.05 mM choline). After a period of 5 h the incubations were terminated and the incorporation of the various labelled precursors into PC, disaturated PC and PG determined (31).

Ambroxol significantly stimulated the formation of total PC and disaturated PC from labelled choline and glycerol (Figure 5). It did not affect the formation of these lipids from labelled glucose and (not shown) acetate or palmitate. Ambroxol enhanced significantly the synthesis of PG from labelled glucose, glycerol and (not shown) acetate. These findings suggest that Ambroxol does not only stimulate the formation of surfactant lipids in the fetal lung but also in the adult lung. This suggestion is corroborated by our recent studies (to be published elsewhere) on the synthesis of surfactant lipids by the isolated perfused rat lung after pretreatment of the animals in vivo with Ambroxol. These studies indicated that Ambroxol may not only affect the synthesis but also the secretion of surfactant lipids by the adult lung.

SYNTHESIS OF DISATURATED PC IN TYPE II CELLS ISOLATED FROM FETAL RAT LUNG

Studies on the development and regulation of perinatal surfactant synthesis have sofar been carried out mainly with preparations derived from whole lung. Again, the results of such studies are not necessarily applicable to the producers of surfactant, the type II cells. Douglas and col-

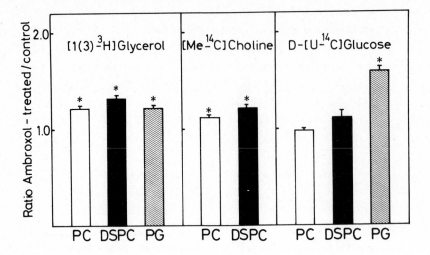

Fig. 5. Effects of Ambroxol on the synthesis of surfactant lipids by type II cells isolated from adult rat lung. The data are presented as ratios Ambroxol-treated/control which were calculated in each experiment. Averages ± S.E.M. (N=10) are presented. *: Statistically different from the controls (p<0.01).

leagues have developed a system for the organotypic culture of type II cells from fetal rat lung on a collagen sponge matrix (38,39). In these cultures the epithelial cells form alveolar-like structures. The percentage of type II cells in cultures initiated with cells of 19-days gestation, appeared to be 85-95% after 1 week in culture (40). Morphologic studies of Douglas and co-workers (41) demonstrated that the epithelial cells differentiate in the culture: When the culture is initiated with cells from rat lung at 16-days gestation, the epithelial cells lining the alveolar-like structure do not yet contain lamellar bodies. After a few days in culture lamellar bodies begin to appear in the cells. We could recently confirm these morphologic observations regarding the in vitro maturation of the type II cells in organotypic cultures (42), but we did not find evidence for biochemical maturation of the type II cells in the culture: e.g. no change took place in the percentage of PG nor in the ratio of disaturated PC to total PC. Nevertheless, the organotypic culture is a cell population strongly enriched in type II cells and could be an attractive model for studies on the pathways of surfactant formation and the regulation of these processes in the fetal lung.

TABLE 3

THE ACTIVITY OF LYSOLECITHIN ACYLTRANSFERASE AND LYSOLECITHIN:LYSOLECITHIN
ACYLTRANSFERASE IN HOMOGENATES AND TYPE II CELLS FROM FETAL RAT LUNG

Organotypic cultures were initiated with epithelial cells from fetal rat
lung at day 20 of gestation. The enzyme activities were measured in sonicates of type II cells that had been in culture for 2 days and in homogenates of whole fetal lung at day 20 of gestation. Lysolecithin acyltransferase was measured in 50 μl incubation medium of the following composition:
65 mM Tris-HCl (pH 7.4), 10 mM $MgCl_2$, 0.2 mM 1-palmitoyl-lyso-PC, 20 μM
$[1-^{14}C]$palmitoyl-CoA (spec. act 10^5 dpm/nmol) and either type II cell sonicate (10 μg protein) or whole lung homogenate (15 μg protein). Lysoleci-
thin:lysolecithin acyltransferase was measured in 50 μl of the following
medium: 0.4 mM 1-$[1-^{14}C]$palmitoyl-lyso-PC (spec. act. $5 \cdot 10^3$ dpm/nmol),
160 mM phosphate buffer (pH 6.0) and either type II cell sonicate (33 μg
protein) or whole lung homogenate (50 μg protein). For further details see
refs. 29 and 42.

Fraction	Lysolecithin acyltransferase	Lysolecithin:lysolecithin acyltransferase
	(nmol/min per mg protein)	
Whole lung homogenate	2.25	0.13
Type II cell sonicate	2.31	0.05

In the present study we investigated which mechanism could be responsible in the fetal type II cells for the remodeling of 1-saturated-2-unsatu-
rated PC synthesized de novo into disaturated PC. Two mechanisms have been
suggested (for reviews see refs. 6,7,43): 1. a deacylation-reacylation mechanism catalysed by phospholipase A_2 and lysolecithin acyltransferase, respectively and 2. a deacylation-transacylation process by the enzymes phospholipase A_2 and lysolecithin: lysolecithin acyltransferase, respectively.
Earlier studies (14,44) had shown that the second mechanism is not important for the biosynthesis of disaturated PC in the adult lung. This did not
preclude the possibility, however, that the deacylation-transacylation process may play a role in the formation of disaturated PC in the fetal lung,
particularly since there was evidence, albeit from studies with preparations
from whole lung, that the activity of lysolecithin:lysolecithin acyltransferase increases just before term in mouse and rat lung (see ref. 43 for a
review). We determined the activities of lysolecithin acyltransferase and
lysolecithin:lysolecithin acyltransferase in sonicates of fetal type II
cells and in homogenates from fetal lung (Table 3).

The activity of lysolecithin acyltransferase in fetal lung homogenate is comparable to that measured earlier in adult rat lung (29). Interestingly, the activity of this enzyme is not enriched in the fetal type II cell when compared to homogenate of whole fetal lung as had been observed for the type II cells of adult lung (29). The data of Table 3 show quite clearly that fetal lung homogenate contains very little lysolecithin:lysolecithin acyltransferase and that this enzyme is barely detectable in sonicates of fetal type II cells. These results strongly suggest that, like in the adult lung, the deacylation-transacylation process does not play an important role in the formation of disaturated PC in the type II cell of the fetal rat lung.

ACKNOWLEDGEMENTS

The authors wish to thank Mrs. W. Klazinga and Mrs. E.A.J.M. Schuurmans for excellent technical assistance. The investigations described in this paper were supported in part by the Netherlands Foundation for Chemical Research (S.O.N.) with financial aid from the Netherlands Organization for the Advancement of Pure Research (Z.W.O.), by the Dutch Asthma Foundation (Nederlands Astma Fonds) and by Dr. Karl Thomae, GmbH, Biberach, FRG.

REFERENCES

1. Goerke, J. (1974) Biochim. Biophys. Acta, 344, 241-261.

2. King, R.J. and Clements, J.A. (1972) Am. J. Physiol., 223, 715-726.

3. Hallman, M., Feldman, B.H., Kirkpatrick, E. and Gluck, L. (1977) Pediatr. Res., 11, 714-720.

4. Avery, M.E. and Mead, J. (1959) Am. J. Dis. Child., 97, 517-523.

5. Renovanz, H-D. and Von Seefeld, H. (1978) Prax. Pneumol., 32, 443-466.

6. Van Golde, L.M.G. (1976) Am. Rev. Resp. Dis., 114, 977-1000.

7. Batenburg, J.J. and Van Golde, L.M.G. (1979) in: Scarpelli, E.M. and Cosmi, E.V. (Eds.), Reviews in Perinatal Medicine, Vol. 3, Raven Press, New York, pp. 73-114.

8. Kennedy, E.P. (1961) Fed. Proc., 20, 934-940.

9. Batenburg, J.J. (1980) Lung, 158, 177-192.

10. Mason, R.J., Williams, M.C., Greenleaf, R.D. and Clements, J.A. (1977) Am. Rev. Resp. Dis., 115, 1015-1026.

11. Mason, R.J., Williams, M.C. and Dobbs, L.C. (1977) in: Sanders, C.L., Schneider, R.P., Dagle, G.E. and Ragan, H.A. (Eds.), Pulmonary Macrophage and Epithelial Cells, Series 43, Energy Research and Development Administration, Springfield, pp. 280-295.

12. Mason, R.J. and Williams, M.C. (1977) Am. Rev. Resp. Dis., 115, Suppl. 81-91.

13. Post, M., Schuurmans, E.A.J.M., Batenburg, J.J. and Van Golde, L.M.G. (1983) Biochim. Biophys. Acta, 750, 68-77.

14. Batenburg, J.J., Longmore, W.J., Klazinga, W. and Van Golde, L.M.G. (1979) Biochim. Biophys. Acta, 573, 136-144.

15. Ohno, K., Akino, T. and Fujiwara, T. (1978) in: Scarpelli, E.M. and Cosmi, E.V. (Eds.), Reviews in Perinatal Medicine, Vol. 2, Raven Press, New York, pp. 227-318.

16. Vance, D.E. and Choy, P.C. (1979) Trends Biochem. Sci., 4, 145-148.

17. Tokmakjian, S. and Possmayer, F. (1981) Biochim. Biophys. Acta, 666, 176-180.

18. Tokmakjian, S., Haines, D.S.M. and Possmayer, F. (1981) Biochim. Biophys. Acta, 663, 557-568.

19. Possmayer, F., Casola, P.G., Chun, F., MacDonald, P., Ormseth, M.A., Wong, T., Harding, P.G.R. and Tokmakjian, S. (1981) Biochim. Biophys. Acta, 664, 10-21.

20. Post, M., Batenburg, J.J., Schuurmans, E.A.J.M. and Van Golde, L.M.G. (1982) Biochim. Biophys. Acta, 712, 390-394.

21. Post, M. (1982) Thesis, University of Utrecht.

22. Burns, T.W., Langley, P.E., Terry, B.E. and Robinson, G.A. (1978) Metabolism, 27, 1755-1762.

23. Fain, J.R. and Shepherd, R.E. (1975) J. Biol. Chem., 250, 6586-6592.

24. Pelech, S.L., Pritchard, P.H. and Vance, D.E. (1981) J. Biol. Chem., 256, 8283-8286.

25. Hallman, M. and Gluck, L. (1980) Pediatr. Res., 14, 1250-1259.

26. Hallman, M. and Epstein, B.L. (1989) Biochem. Biophys. Res. Commun., 92, 1151-1159.

27. Quirk, J.G., Bleasdale, J.E., MacDonald, P.C. and Johnston, J.M. (1980) Biochem. Biophys. Res. Commun., 95, 985-992.

28. Bleasdale, J.E. and Johnston, J.M. (1982) Biochim. Biophys. Acta, 710, 377-390.

29. Batenburg, J.J., Klazinga, W. and Van Golde, L.M.G. (1982) FEBS Lett., 147, 171-174.

30. Goldfine, H. (1966) J. Lipid Res., 7, 146-149.

31. Post, M., Batenburg, J.J. and Van Golde, L.M.G. (1980) Biochim. Biophys. Acta, 618, 308-317.

32. Curti, P.C. (1972) Pneumologie, 147, 62-74.

33. Lorenz, U., Rüttgers, H., Fux, G. and Kubli, F. (1974) Am. J. Obstet. Gynecol, 119, 1126-1128.

34. Prevost, M.C., Soula, G. and Douste-Blazy, L. (1979) Respiration, 37, 215-219.

35. Van Petten, G.R., Mears, G.J. and Taylor, P.J. (1978) Am. J. Obstet. Gynec., 130, 35-40.

36. Cerutti, P. and Kapanci, Y. (1979) Respiration, 37, 241-251.

37. Velasquez, B.J. and Sépulveda, J. (1982) Respiration, 43, 389-400.

38. Douglas, W.H.J. and Teel, R.W. (1976) Am. Rev. Respir. Dis., 113, 17-23.

39. Douglas, W.H.J., McAteer, J.A. and Cavanagh, T. (1978) Tissue Culture Assoc. Manual, 4, 749-753.

40. Engle, M.J., Sanders, R.L. and Douglas, W.H.J. (1980) Biochim. Biophys. Acta, 617, 225-236.

41. Douglas, W.H.J., McAteer, J.A., Smith, J.R. and Braunschweiger, W.R. (1979) Int. Rev. Cytol, Suppl. 10, 45-65.

42. Batenburg, J.J., Funkhouser, J.D., Klazinga, W. and Van Golde, L.M.G. (1983) Biochim. Biophys. Acta, 750, 60-67.

43. Batenburg, J.J. (1982) in: Farrell, P.M. (Ed.), Lung Development: Biological and Clinical Perspectives, Vol. 1, Academic Press, New York, pp. 359-390.

44. Van Heusden, G.P.H., Vianen, G.M. and Van den Bosch, H. (1980) J. Biol. Chem., 255, 9312-9318.

RESPIRATORY DISTRESS SYNDROME OF NEWBORN

© 1983, Elsevier Science Publishers B.V.
Pulmonary Surfactant System, E.V. Cosmi
and E.M. Scarpelli eds.

DIAGNOSIS OF FETAL LUNG MATURITY

ERMELANDO V. COSMI AND GIAN CARLO DI RENZO
Second Department of Obstetrics and Gynecology, University of
Perugia, Perugia (Italy)

A number of substances of fetal origin in amniotic fluid (AF)
have been shown to change in concentration with advancing gestation and have been investigated as possible indices of fetal
maturity. In this report we will critically analyze those factors
which have been shown to be relevant in the assessment of fetal
lung maturity prior to birth. On the basis of his experiments in
fetal lambs Scarpelli was the first to suggest that analysis of
AF fluid phospholipids could provide an index of fetal lung
maturity and risk to respiratory distress syndrome (RDS),[1]
and Gluck et al.[2] were the first to demonstrate that the AF
lecithin/sphingomyelin (L/S) is, indeed, an extremely reliable
index of fetal lung maturity. On the basis of their careful and
detailed investigations in humans and animals they established
and validated what is now an universally-used clinical test.

In the following years a number of additional indices of lung
maturity have been proposed based on determination of constituent surfactants in AF.[3] Among the AF phospholipids (PL)
that might be related to lung maturation are lecithin (L), sphingomyelin (S), phosphatidylinositol (PI) and phosphatidylglycerol
(PG).

L and S concentrations are very low until 25 to 26 weeks of
gestation; S concentration is higher than L until about the 31st
week, when the two become equal. Thereafter, L concentration
increases rapidly until term. PI concentration is very low until
26 to 30 weeks; thereafter it increases, peaking at 36 weeks,

then decreasing to term. PG is first detected at 35 to 36 weeks,
and its level increases progressively to term. Other AF constituents related to lung maturation include lamellar bodies,
"lung specific" apoproteins and key enzymes in the pathways of
PL synthesis.

Various methods have been used to determine the levels of these
compounds in AF. The methods fall into two major categories:
biochemical and biophysical. The most commonly used are listed
in Tables 1 and 2.

TABLE 1

BIOCHEMICAL ASSAYS FOR LUNG MATURITY   CRITICAL VALUE

	IMMATURE	MATURE
Lecithin/sphingomyelin	< 1.5	⩾ 2
Total L concentration	< 2.5 mg/100 ml	⩾ 2.5 mg/100 ml
Disaturated L concentration	< 20 nM/ml	⩾ 35 nM/ml
Phosphatidylglycerol		
(pellet at 10,000 x g)	absent	present
(% of total phospholipids)	< 3%	⩾ 3%
(enzymatic determination)	< 3 nM/ml	⩾ 10 nM/ml
Palmitic acid concentration	< 0.072 mM/l	⩾ 0.072 mM/l
Palmitic acid/stearic acid	< 5.0	⩾ 5.0
Total PL concentration	< 1.5 mg/100 ml	⩾ 2.8 mg/100 ml
Total PL phosphorus	< 0.140 mg/100 ml	⩾ 0.140 mg/100 ml
PAPase	< 0.50	⩾ 0.50
Surfactant high-MW apoproteins	< 10% term pool	⩾ 30% term pool

BIOCHEMICAL METHODS

Phospholipids

The usual method for separating PL is to extract 1 volume of AF
with 3 volumes of chloroform/methanol (2:1, v/v). After mixing,
the sample is allowed to stand prior to centrifugation. The lower

organic phase is evaporated and dryed under nitrogen and the
residue is used for the various assays.

TABLE 2

BIOPHYSICAL ASSAYS FOR LUNG MATURITY   CRITICAL VALUE

	IMMATURE	MATURE
Compression-decompression of liquid surface	> 25 mN·m^{-1} $\bar{S} < 0.80$	$\leqslant 20$ mN·m^{-1} $\bar{S} \geqslant 0.85$
Foam stability test ("shake test")	negat at 1:1	posit at 1:2
Foam stability index	< 0.47	$\geqslant 0.47$
Capillary flow rate	< 40 sec	$\geqslant 66$ sec
Lipid globule formation test at	$\leqslant 340$ ul	$\geqslant 460$ ul
Fluorescence polarization (Microviscosity)	$\leqslant 0.320$	$\geqslant 0.340$
OD$_{650}$ nm	< 0.15	$\geqslant 0.15$

An important aspect is the speed and duration of centrifugation in which cells and cellular debris are removed from the
fluid. It seems that, regardless of the centrifugation force
and time, some PL are precipitated (including those adsorbed to
cells) and that more PL are lost at higher g.[4] For example,
the L/S is reduced as the centrifugal force is increased as
a result of a disproportionate loss of L. It is generally agreed
that centrifugation above 250 x g should be avoided, especially
if the sample is to be extracted immediately after collection.
Filtration of AF has a similar effect on the L/S because L is
more readily absorbed to filter paper than S; therefore, this
procedure is avoided in most laboratories.[4] Most investigators
suggest that the AF specimen be centrifuged at low speed ($<$250 x g)
and stored at 4°C for no more than 24 hours, or at -20°C for

longer periods. Storage at room temperature without centrifugation is not acceptable.[3] It is also important to mix the
supernatant before extraction. The mixing procedure should not
be performed too vigorously, since bubbles coated with PL may
be lost from the solution.[3,5]

Since a single extraction does not yield quantitatively all
PL, it is assumed that they are all extracted proportionately.
Some investigators, however, prefer to re-extract the aqueous/
methanol phase twice and combine all extracts.[3,4]

The site of amniocentesis may also affect results [6]: PL
concentration is higher in the fluid obtained near the fetal
mouth than in the fluid obtained close to the breech. In addition,
PL concentration varies inversely with AF volume.[7] Another
source of error is sample contamination with blood, meconium or
antiseptics.

Because concentration of L in the blood is approximately 10
times that in AF, contamination with either fetal or maternal
blood gives falsely high values for L.[8] Conversely, determination of AF PG is only slightly affected by blood contamination
since this compound is found in minimal amounts in the blood.[9]
Contamination with meconium, even if not visably detectable,
also alters the results because of the presence of bile salts,[3,4]
and antiseptics (e.g., chlorhexidine or cetrimide), or local
anesthetics (e.g., lidocaine) invalidate the analyses.[4,10]

Lecithin/Sphingomyelin (L/S)

The original procedure reported by Gluck et al.[2] comprises
isolation of PL, precipitation in cold acetone, separation of L
and S by thin-layer chromatography (TLC), and development and

measurement of lipid spots. The TLC plates employed are commercially available; it should be noted that the type of gel affects the L/S and that silica gel G is preferred. (Incorporation of ammonium sulfate in the gel as a charring agent alters the L/S). The solvent system consists of chloroform, methanol and water. Small amounts of ammonium hydroxide or acetic acid are added to aid in the separation of PI, avoiding its interference with the L/S determination.[11] L and S spots may be quantified by(1) gravimetry, whereby the compounds are either weighed or determined by phosphorus measurement; (2) color developing with bromothymol blue followed by planimetry; or (3) more precisely, by transmission or reflectance densitometry. From most reports, the planimetric or densitometric methods give equivalent L/S below 3.0.[8] The gravimetric method and the phosphorus measurement are most time consuming. High performance liquid chromatographic separation of PL also has been reported.[12]

The value of these semiquantitative methods rests on the facts that the S concentration remains rather constant throughout gestation, whereas around the 35th week there is a sharp rise in L concentration.Therefore, the S concentration provides a corrective factor for AF volume.

It is generally agreed that an L/S of 2 or greater indicates fetal lung maturity and negligible risk to RDS, whereas a ratio below 1.5 indicates lung immaturity and risk to RDS. (Fig.1)[14] With an intermediate ratio of 1.5 to 2.0 most, but not all, newborn infants escape the disease. In practice, however, standards must be established and validated in each laboratory.

Various modifications of the original procedure have been reported, the most common being the deletion of the cold acetone precipitation step which precipitates preferentially highly surface active L leaving non-surfactant PL in the supernate. The importance of this step has been highly debated. (2,13,15)

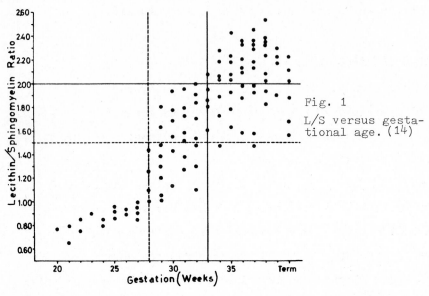

Fig. 1
L/S versus gestational age. (14)

Recently, two-dimensional TLC has been accepted as the preferred method for separation, because (1) it provides a better separation of PI and L and (2) reveals PG clearly. (13)

A high correlation has been found between the L/S of AF and that of tracheal or pharyngeal aspirates collected from newborn infants at birth. The L/S in these aspirates was found to predict accurately the risk and prognosis of RDS. (16)

The reported accuracy of a mature L/S in predicting the absence of RDS ranges between 95 and 98 percent, whereas reliability of immature ratios in predicting RDS varies from 22 to 92 percent. (3,17,18) To improve the reliability of the L/S, some have increased the critical value for maturity to 2.5 or greater. (19) However, this carries the disadvantage of increasing the percentage of falsely immature L/S.

Various modifications of the original method reflect the
feeling that the technique has some shortcomings.Data related
to the reproducibility of the L/S have been reported rarely.
The coefficient of variation ranges from 7 to 21%.[8]

Lecithin and other phospholipids

The concentration of L in the AF is usually determined by
measuring its phosphorus content after TLC separation. The same
applies to the measurement of total PL. Potassium permanganate
and periodate oxidation have been used to selectively oxidize
unsaturated L allowing determination of only disaturated L.[20]
This modification is advantageous for samples heavily contaminated with either blood or meconium. The recovery rate varies
between 67 and 98%. The main disadvantage of these methods is
that large variations in AF volume may give misleading results
because there is no"internal standard" in the procedures.

It has been suggested that when PG is present in the AF, RDS
does not occur even when the L/S is less than 2.[13] In addition,
it has been found that PG is more predictive of lung maturity
than the L/S in complicated pregnancies, especially by diabetes
mellitus.[21] In diabetic pregnancies associated with RDS, PG
was absent in the AF while PI concentration did not decline
until the 37th or 38th week. An early appearance of PG, even
before the L/S became mature, was observed in pregnancies associated with accelerated lung maturation and no RDS (e.g., class
F and R diabetes, chronic toxemia, or prolonged rupture of membra
nes).[3] It was also found that when the AF concentration of
PG is 3 percent or greater there is no risk of RDS regardless
of the severity of the underlying disease.[21] However, other
studies have indicated that the AF concentration of disaturated

L or the L/S are equally reliable or even better indices of fetal maturity than PG concentration.[22,23] Furthermore, lack of PG does not necessarily mean that the infant will develop RDS.

The "lung profile" (Fig. 2) has been advocated as the complete evaluation method: this includes determinations of L/S, PG, PI and percent disaturated L.[13,23-25]

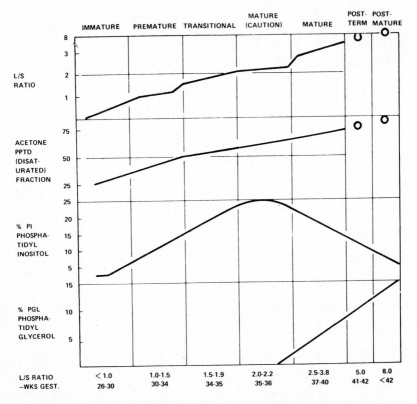

Fig. 2 The lung profile (24)

PG and PI are usually measured as percent of total PL. Methodology may influence the determination which must be standardized for each laboratory. In addition, the amount of PL applied to the plate can significantly affect the percentage of PG. It has been reported recently that isolation of the 10,000 x g pellet eliminates contaminating PL (e.g., from blood or meconium).[26]

A semiquantitative immuno-agglutination test for detecting PG is now available. A concentration of 2 ug/ml is considered by the manufacturer to be predictive of fetal lung maturity. However, there are no clinical reports of this method.

A fast and inexpensive procedure for the determination of PG using one-dimensional TLC and a phosphorus specific spray has been developed.[27] With this method it is possible to detect amounts of PG exceeding 1 ug/ml or 1.7% of PL.

More recently, an enzymatic method has been described for quantification of both L and PG.[28] It seems that AF contamination with meconium or bilirubin does not interfere with this assay.

Fatty Acids

About 75% of the total palmitic acid present in AF is esterified in the form of L. Its measurement by gas-liquid chromatography has been proposed as a method to assess fetal lung maturity.[29,30] The results are more reliable when the acyl components of L are expressed as a ratio of saturated (largely palmitate) to unsaturated (largely oleate and linoleate) fatty acids. The palmitic/stearic acid ratio increases with advancing gestation.[31]

However, there is a large discrepancy in the literature concerning the critical value (from 1.3 to 10.0),[8] which is possibly related to the methodology. Fatty acid analysis is significantly affected by AF contamination with blood or meconium. The method is time-consuming and requires sophisticated equipment. In addition, it was found less predictive of fetal lung maturity than the L/S, particularly in diabetic pregnancies.[31]

Phosphatidic Acid Phosphohydrolase

Recently, phosphatidic acid phosphohydrolase (PAPase), the key enzyme in the pathways for PL biosynthesis, has been detected in human AF.[32] This enzyme catalyzes the hydrolysis of phophatidic acid, a reaction that gives rise to the diglycerides in the synthesis of L and PG. PAPase activity was found to rise with gestational age, precede the surge of disaturated L, and correlate with lung maturity and the incidence of RDS.[33,34] Its usefulness in general clinical practice remains to be determined.

Surfactant Apoproteins

The immunologic assay of human surfactant apoproteins using an antibody against 34,000 M.W. peptide was introduced by King et al [35] who reported that AF concentration of surfactant apoproteins increases with gestation.

Recently, an enzyme-linked immunosorbent assay has been developed for the quantitation of high-M.W. surfactant apoproteins in the human AF.[36] Its concentration was found to correlate well with other parameters of fetal lung maturity, particularly with the presence of PG.[36] This type of assay is relatively simple to perform, but further studies are needed to assess the validity of the method.

BIOPHYSICAL METHODS

These tests have been difficult to standardize and their use in clinical practice has been limited. They are summarized in Table 2.

Surface   Tension Test

After low speed centrifugation, surface tension (γ) of AF is
measured at 37°C in the trough of a Wilhelmy-type surface balance. The sample is allowed to age for 20 min to permit adsorption of surfactants to the interface. The surface is compressed
and decompressed cyclically by a movable barrier between 100%
and 20% of the original area. Cycling is continued until a minimum γ and reproducible isotherms are obtained. The resulting
γ-area diagram is evaluated with respect to (1) maximum γ in
$mN \cdot m^{-1}$ (γ max) at 100% surface area and minimum γ (γmin) at
20% surface area; (2) the area (cm^2) within the loop measured
with a planimeter; and (3) the stability index ($\bar{S}$).

$$\bar{S} = \frac{2 (\gamma \max - \gamma \min)}{\gamma \max + \gamma \min}$$

With advancing gestation there is a progressive decrease of
γ min and an increase in $\bar{S}$ and hysteresis.[37]
The most reliable parameters in predicting lung maturity and
RDS are the γ min and $\bar{S}$. The critical values for fetal lung
maturity vary among reports. In general, a γ min at or below
20 $mN \cdot m^{-1}$ and an $\bar{S}$ of 0.85 or more are indicative of maturity.
This method has been shown to possess a significant correlation
with certain biochemical tests for fetal lung maturity.[3,37,38]
A major disadvantage is that other surface active components
of AF are not excluded from the interfacial film, e.g., from AF
contaminants.[3]

Shake Test and Foam Stability

The shake test is an inexpensive, rapid and simple method for

detecting surfactants in AF. A sample of AF is diluted serially
with 95% ethanol and each sample is shaken. The test evaluates
foam formed from the surfactants of AF.[39] Three or four
dilutions are used in most laboratories (1.0, 0.75, 0.50).
The tubes are shaken for 15 sec, allowed to stand for 15 min
and then inspected. The presence of an unbroken ring of bubbles
at the meniscus in the first three tubes or more (1:2, AF:ethanol
dilution) is considered positive and indicative of fetal lung
maturity. An unstable foam at a 1:1 dilution is classified as
intermediate. No foam at the 1:1 dilution is considered negative and indicative of fetal lung immaturity.

The process of foam formation by surfactants is a complex one
not fully understood. Ethanol acts as an antifoaming agent for
most biological compounds and prevents the formation of stable
bubbles. However, when the surface tension of a mixture of lung
surfactant and ethanol/water ($47.5:52.5, v/v$) is lowered to 29
$mN \cdot m^{-1}$ stable bubbles can be formed. Edwards and Baillie[40]
mixed absolute ethanol with AF so that the volume of ethanol
was 50% (FS_{50}). This modification seems to reduce false nega-
tives significantly. Another modification of the test is the
foam stability index (FSI).[5] FSI is defined as the highest
ethanol volume that permits a stable ring of foam after mixing
with fixed amounts of AF supernatant. The assay differs from
the Clements test in that the latter is positive for amounts
of L greater that 30 mg/l while with FSI they range from 15
to 30 mg/l. A value of 0.48 is analogous to an L/S of 2.0.
The validity of the test also depends upon pH, temperature,
and how vigorously and for how long the tubes are shaken. In
addition the diameter of the tubes (which must be free from

soap, serum or biological fluids) also affects the results. Both modifications practically eliminate false mature results, but increase the false immature values. Whether increasing ethanol concentrations change PL solubility or AF viscosity remains to be defined.

Optical Density

The presence of particles of surfactants suspended in AF increases the turbidity of the specimen. Because pigments such as bilirubin, meconium, and hemolyzed blood interfere at wavelengths around 400 nm, the optical density of centrifuged AF is analyzed at 650 nm. It has been found that the turbidity assessed visually and absorbance at 650 nm increase late in gestation and correlate well with the L/S and fetal lung maturity. [41] The method is simple and rapid but dilutional effects (polyhydramnios), contamination, prolonged refrigeration and high centrifugation speeds affect the results. [42]

Fluorescence Polarization (Microviscosity)

Fluorescence polarization (FP) measures the microviscosity of lipid aggregates in the AF. Microviscosity and γ are interrelated so that changes in FP reflect those of γ . This method uses the degree of rotation of a hydrocarbon probe embedded in a dispersion. The most efficient probe is 1,6-diphenyl 1,3,5-hexatriene (DPH). [43] The FP of L is lower than that of S, depending on the hydrophobic region of lipids. The greater the viscosity the more effectively the lipid dispersion restricts the rotation of the probe. The extent of depolarization of the incident light (to probe rotation) can be measured by a specially custom-designed instrument called FELMA (Fetal Lung Maturity Analizer). It was found that there is a general increase in absorbance as L/S increases and that the OD_{650} reading of 0.15 or greater is indicative of lung maturity.[44] However, the test has high false immature rates and some false mature rates. The presence of PG, PI and other PL other than L alters the microviscosity in a predictable manner. Moreover, AF contains lipoproteins[45] which contribute to FP in an unpredictable manner.[46] The analysis is also affected by surfactant apo-proteins. Contamination with blood or meconium and centrifuga-tion forces alter the results.

Lipid Globule Formation

The lipid globule formation test is based on the determination of γ-lowering properties of AF PL. The AF sample is extracted with chloroform/methanol. Aliquots of the extracted material are added to a layer of distilled water in Petri dishes. γ is measured by a tensiometer as aliquots of the AF lipid extract are added to the water. As γ is being determined, there is a point at which addition of more AF lipid extract causes a lipid globule to appear in the water, which appearance is indicative of lung maturity. Although the method was reported to predict lung maturity reliably in both normal and abnormal pregnancies it has not been studied extensively.[3]

Bubble Clicking

Bubbles produced by shaking the AF specimen with ethanol (95%, 1:1, v/v) are placed as hanging drops of degassed water on a coverglass over a microscope slide containing a well.

Most of the bubbles disappear, but some exhibit a rhytmical
"clicking" movement. This movement is an indication of the
presence of surfactants(18).

Stable Microbubble Rating

A drop of AF is aspirated with a Pasteur pipette from which
the liquid is rapidly expelled in order to produce bubbles.
Most of the bubbles disappear, but some remain for more than
30 sec and can be counted using a microscope graticule.[47] No
systematic studies have been performed with this method.

Capillary Flow Rate

The time taken for a 20 ul sample of untreated AF to drain
from a Pasteur pipette held vertically on Whatman cellulose
filter paper was found to be directly related to the amount of
surfactant PL in AF. The method was found to correlate significantly with both the shake test and L/S.[48]

CLINICAL INTERPRETATION

None of the above methods for predicting fetal lung maturity
has complete reliability: some infants develop RDS in spite of
a normal pulmonary maturity test, whereas others are free from
the disease in spite of an "immature" test. The predictive value
of AF tests for fetal lung maturity that were performed 24-48
hours before delivery is listed in Table 3.

Determination of L/S is by far the most widely used and accepted method. However, there is still controversy regarding (1)
the high incidence of false immature ratios and (2) the increase
in false mature ratios (from 1 to 15%) in complicated preg-

nancies, mainly diabetes mellitus.[22,49] According to several reports, an immature L/S may predict RDS only in about 50% of cases. Attempts to improve predictability by modifying Gluck's original method have not been successful.

TABLE 3

PREDICTIVE VALUE OF AMNIOTIC FLUID TESTS FOR FETAL LUNG MATURITY

	PREDICTIVE VALUE (%)	
	RDS	NO RDS
L/S (8,254 cases)	60-80	98
L, total (575 cases)	67	97.5
Palmitic acid/stearic acid (136 cases)	79	100
PG (244 cases)	74	100
Shake test (1,049 cases)	31-69	98.5
OD_{650} (269 cases)	56	98.5
FP (149 cases)	75	100
Surface tension (82 cases)	25	100
PAPase (233 cases)	53	99.5

From 41 reports (1975-1982) available from authors upon request

The incidence of false immature L/S as well as of other AF tests depends upon patient variability, on the method employed, the treshold value taken for differentiating a normal from an abnormal condition, and on the fact that few authors report their results in terms of sensitivity and specificity.

Furthermore, interpretation and comparison of results is hampered by differences within the same general methodology used. It should also be noted that the predictive value of a test decreases when the interval between AF sampling and delivery increases from 24 to 72 hours.[50] For example, the predictive value for the L/S drops from 85% if performed within 24 hours to 32% if performed within 72 hours. The predictive value for L concentration is better than for any other method within 72 hours of delivery (77%).[8]

Sensitivity, defined as the percentage of sick newborn infants with a true "immature" test result, is almost unaltered for samples taken between 24 and 72 hours of delivery, and it is high with all methods.

Specificity, defined as the percentage of healthy infants with a true "mature" test result, of any test is high if it is performed within 24 hours of delivery but it falls as time to delivery increases. Thus, all methods have more false immature than false mature results.

In general, the larger the difference between a given value and the critical value, the greater the predictability. Boderline values have poor predictability. For L/S values of 1.5-1.9, predictability for RDS is only 21%.[8] Many infants born with L/S in this transitional range do not experience respiratory difficulties. It should be noted also that the shortcomings of L/S less than 2 have been of relatively little practical import because usual obstetric management is to delay delivery whenever possible and/or to accelerate lung maturity by pharmacologic means until "mature" values are obtained.[3] Under these circumstances there may be some delay in the increase in the L/S, although pulmonary surfactant has increased in situ following pharmacologic stimulation.

Several factors may explain the discrepancy between neonatal outcome and results for immature values in AF tests, including: (1) mode of delivery; (2) fetal distress, chronic fetal hypoxia; (3) small-for-dates infants; (4) prolonged rupture of fetal membranes; and (4) preterm delivery and birth asphyxia.[3,5,17]

Another variable is represented by the fact that there are extrapulmonary sources for AF surfactant constituents, although the relative contributions from each are not know precisely and may vary with gestational age.[51]

Finally, certain complications of pregnancy can alter AF analyses. In the presence of Rh-isoimmunization with fetal hydrops, L/S is usually low.[13] A group of disorders, such as gestational diabetes (White's A,B,C), small non-parabiotic twins and chronic nonhypertensive glomerulonephritis has been accociated with delayed lung maturity. On the other hand, other disorders, including severe prolonged hypertension, sickle-cell disease, severe diabetes, maternal infections (chorioamniotis, urinary tract infections), small parabiotic twins and retroplacental bleeding, may serve as stimuli for accelerating lung maturity, possibly by producing chronic fetal distress.[3]

With regard to pregnancies complicated by diabetes mellitus, falsely mature L/S have been reported frequently and some investigators have questioned the predictive value of "mature" results. To the contrary, others have found no difference in the predictability of the results in diabetic or other pregnancies particularly with L/S.[19] Possible explanations for contradictory results include methodologic differences,[23] differences in patient populations (e.g., inclusion of class A diabetes),

and difference in criteria used for the definition of RDS.
Nonetheless, there is general agreement that in diabetic pregnancies, there is continued risk of RDS even with mature L/S.
This risk has been related to fetal hyperinsulinemia. Because
of the controversy over the incidence of RDS associated with a
"mature" surfactant value in these pregnancies, a better predictive test was sought. For the lung profile, an important finding was that the concentration of AF PI in pregnancies complicated by type A diabetes declined later (37-38 weeks) than in
normal pregnancies (35 weeks) and that PG appeared later.[22,25]

CONCLUSION

There are various methods to assess fetal lung maturity.
Their use has undoubtedly helped to reduce perinatal mortality
and morbidity due to RDS. The utilization of these tests is recommended for (1) timing of delivery prior to elective cesarean
section, (2) complicated pregnancies, and (3) institution of
pharmacologic prevention of RDS in utero or at delivery. No
single method has achieved the distinction of reliability and
universal applicability. A mature value in most tests is almost
99% accurate. On the other hand, an immature value has very
low accuracy.

Where laboratory facilities are minimal, it is advisable to
perform the shake test or measure the optical density of AF.
However, when these tests indicate immaturity, additional tests,
such as L/S or determination of the lung profile, must be carried out. An added advantage of measuring PG is its virtual
absence from blood, meconium and vaginal secretions, all of
which contain PL and other components which interfere with

both the determination of L/S and the shake test. The various approaches and extensive literature on the subject have led to much confusion, causing some investigators to opt for new analyses or for more rapid methods. This is a questionable approach. Each laboratory should establish and validate its own analytical methods.

Finally, it should be stressed that no method can predict RDS with accuracy, probably because fetal lung maturity is a complex process that involves more than the ability of the developing lung to synthesize and secrete surfactants.

ACKNOWLEDGEMENT

The authors' research has been supported by the Italian Council of Research, target program on "Perinatal Medicine"

REFERENCES

1. Scarpelli, E.M. (1967) Pediatrics 40,951 and (1968) The Surfactant System of the Lung, Lea & Febiger, Philadelphia.

2. Gluck, L., Kulovich, M.V., Borer, R.C.Jr., Brenner, P.H., Anderson, G.C. and Spellacy, W.N. (1971) Am. J. Obstet. Gynecol., 109,440.

3. Cosmi, E.V. (1981) in: Cosmi E.V. (Ed.) Obstetric Anesthesia and Perinatology, Appleton-Century-Crofts, New York, Chap 7 part. II.

4. Wagstaff, T.I. (1978) in: Fairweather, D.V.I. and Eskes, T.K.A.B. (Eds.) Amniotic Fluid: Research and Clinical Application, 2nd ed, Excerpta Medica, Amsterdam, pp. 341-391.

5. Freer, D.E. and Statland, B.E. (1981) Clin. Chem.,27,1629.

6. Worthington, D. and Smith, B.T. (1978) Obstet. Gynecol., 52,552.

7. Falconer, G.F., Hodge, J.S. and Gadd, R.L. (1973) Br. Med. J., 2,689.

8. Tsao, F.H. and Zachman, R.D. (1982) in: Farrell, P.M. (Ed.) Lung Development: Biological and Clinical Perspectives, Vol. II, Academic Press, New York, pp. 167-203.

9. Strassner, H.T.,Jr., Golde, S.H., Mosley, G.H. and Platt, L.D. (1980) Am. J. Obstet. Gynecol., 138,697.

10. Goldstein, A.S., Mangurten, H.H., Libretti, J.V., and Berman, A.M. (1980) Am. J. Obstet. Gynecol., 138:232.

11. Glick, J.H.,Jr. and Crocker, C.L. (1982) Clin. Chem., 28,1997.

12. Jungalwala, F.B., Evans, J.E. and McCluer, R.H., (1976) Biochem. J., 155, 56.

13. Merritt, T.A., Saunders, B.S. and Gluck, L. (1980) in: Aladjem, S., Brown, A.K., Sureau, C. (Eds.) Clin. Perinatology, the C.V. Mosby Co., St. Louis, pp. 213-224.

14. Condorelli, S., Cosmi, E.V. and Scarpelli, E.M. (1971) Clin. Obstet. Gynecol. (Italian) 73, 228.

15. Jackson, R.W., Anderson, G.D. and Held, B. (1975) Am. J. Obstet. Gynecol., 121,1095.

16. Weller, P.H., Jenkins, P.A., Gupta, J. and Baum, J.D. (1976) Lancet. 1,12.

17. Whitfield, C.R. (1978) in: Fairweather, D.V.I. and Eskes, T.K.A.B. (Eds.) Amniotic luid: Research and Clinical Application, 2nd ed., Excerpta Medica, Amsterdam, pp.393-416.

18. Parkinson, C.E. and Harvey, D. (1981) in: Sandler, M. (Ed.) Amniotic Fluid and its Clinical Significance, Marcel Dekker Inc., New York, pp. 224-252.

19. O'Brien, W.F. and Cefalo, R.C. (1980) Am. J. Obstet. Gynecol. 136, 135.

20. Johnson, L.W. (1977) Am. J. Obstet. Gynecol. 129,190.

21. Kulovich, M.V. and Gluck, L. (1979) Am. J. Obstet. Gynecol. 135,64.

22. Cunningham, M.D., McKean, H.E., Gillispie, D.H. and Greene, J.W.,Jr. (1982) Am. J. Obstet. Gynecol. 142,197.

23. Hallman, M. and Teramo, K. (1981) Br. J. Obstet. Gynaecol. 88,806.

24. Kulovich, M.V., Hallman M.B. and Gluck L. (1979) Am. J. Obstet. Gynecol., 135,57.

25. Feijen, H.W.H., Di Renzo, G.C., Nederstigt, J., Houx, P.C.W. and Eskes, T.K.A.B. (1982) Gynecol. Obstet. Invest. 14,142.

26. Bent, A.E., Gray, J.H., Luther, E.R., Oulton, M. and Peddle, L.J. (1981) Am. J. Obstet. Gynecol. 139,259.

27. Schmidt-Sommerfeld, E., Litmeyer, H. and Penn, D. (1982) Clin. Chim. Acta, 119,243.

28. Muneshige, A., Okazaki, T., Quirk, J.G., MacDonald, P.C., Nozaki, M. and Johnston, J.M. (1983) Am. J. Obstet. Gynecol., in press.

29. Warren, C., Allen, J.T. and Holton, J.B. (1973) Clin. Chim. Acta, 44,457.

30. Moore, R.A., O'Neil, K.T.J., Cooke, R.J. and MacLennan, A.H. (1975) Br. J. Obstet. Gynaecol.,82,194.

31. O'Neil, G.J.,Jr., Davies, I.J. and Siu, J. (1978) Am. J. Obstet. Gynecol., 132,519.

32. Jimenez, J.M., Schultz, F.M. and Johnston, J.M. (1975) Obstet. Gynecol., 46,588.

33. Bleasdale, J.E., Davis, C-S. and Agranoff, B.W. (1978) Biochem. Biophys. Acta, 528,331.

34. Forman, D.T. (1982) Ann. Clin. Lab. Sci. 12,339.

35. King, R.J., Ruch, J., Gikas, E.G., Platzker, A.C.G. and Creasy, R.K. (1975) J. Appl. Physiol. 39,735.

36. Shelley, S.A., Balis, J.U., Paciga, J.E., Knuppel, R.A., Ruffolo, E.H. and Bouis, P.J.,Jr. (1982) Am. J. Obstet. Gynecol. 144,224.

37. Müller-Tyl, E., Lempert, J., Steinbereithner, K. and Benzer, H. (1975) Am. J. Obstet. Gynecol., 122,295.

38. Bichler, A., Daxenbichler, G., Ortner, A., Grill,H., Geir, W. and Dapunt, O. (1979) Respiration 37,114.

39. Clements, J.A., Platzker, A.C.G., Tierney, D.F., Hubel, C.J., Creasy, R.K., Margolis, A.J., Thibeault, D.W., Tooley, W.H. and Oh, W. (1972) N. Engl. J. Med., 286,1077.

40. Edwards, J. and Baillie, P. (1973) S. Afr. Med. J., 47,2070.

41. Sbarra, A.J., Michlewitz, H., Selvaraj, R.J., Mitchell, G.W., Jr., Cetrulo, C.L., Kelley, E.C.,Jr., Kennedy, J.L.,Jr., Herschel, M.J., Paul, B.B. and Louis, F. (1977) Obstet. Gynecol., 50,723.

42. Sbarra, A.J., Blake, G., Cetrulo, C.L., Selvaraj, R.J., Herschel, M.J., Delise, C., Kennedy, J.L. and Mitchell, G.W., Jr. (1981) Am. J. Obstet. Ginecol., 139,214.

43. Cheskin, H.S. and Blumenfeld, T.A. (1981) Clin. Chem. 27,1934

44. Copeland, W., Jr., Stempel, L., Lott, J.A., Copeland, W.,Sr. and Zuspan, F.P. (1978) Am. J. Obstet. Gynecol., 130,225.

45. Di Renzo, G.C., Salati, R., Pasquali-Ronchetti, I., Contin, R., Salvioli, G. (1981) IRCS Med. Sci., 9,1149.

46. Gebhardt, D.O. (1982) Clin. Chem., 28,552.

47. Pattle, R.E., Kratzing, C.C., Parkinson, C.E., Graves, L., Robertson, R.D., Robards, G.J., Currie, J.O., Parsons, J.H. and Sutherland, P.D. (1979) Br. J. Obstet. Gynaecol., 86,615.

48. Sing, E.J. (1980) Am. J. Obstet. Gynecol. 136,228.

49. Mueller-Heubach, E., Caritis, S.N., Edelstone, D.I. and Turner, J.H. (1978) Am. J. Obstet. Gynecol. 130,28.

50. Di Renzo, G.C., Quirk,J.G., Bleadsdale, J.E. (1983) in: Di Renzo, G.C. and Hawkins D.F. (Eds.) Perinatal Medicine: problems and controversies, Raven Press, New York, in press.

51. Condorelli, S., Cosmi, E.V. and Scarpelli, E.M. (1974) Am. J. Obstet. Gynecol., 118,842.

FLUORESCENCE POLARIZATION IN DETERMINING THE PRODUCTION OF FETAL SURFACTANT

MASSIMO LUERTI[1], MARIO SALMONA[2] AND MARIA TERESA CASTIGLIONI[1]

[1]Department of Obstetrics and Gynecology, L.Sacco Hospital, University of Milan

(Italy) and [2]Laboratory for Enzyme Research, M. Negri Institute, Milan (Italy)

Recent studies have indicated that when there is risk of premature birth or when it is intended to induce labor early, it is advisable to determine the degree of pulmonary maturity in the fetus before beginning pharmacological prophylaxis for the respiratory distress syndrome (RDS) (1,2). In fact there is increasing suspicion that prophylaxis with steroids produces both short-term and long-term negative side effects in the neonate (3,4).

So, highly predictive indices for pulmonary maturity are needed, since determination of the L/S ratio, especially in certain types of obstetrical pathology, of which diabetes is the outstanding example, has its limitations (5).

For these reasons, there is a tendency now to use methods that reflect other phospholipids, such as phosphatidylglycerol (PG) and phosphatidylinositol (PI). Among the biochemical methods proposed, Gluck (6) suggests determining a "pulmonary profile" (L/S, saturated lecithin, PG and PI), but this is too complex and expensive for general clinical use. The most promising biophysical method appears to be Shinitzky's for measuring microviscosity (7).

The structure of the surfactant that is secreted by the type II pneumocytes in the form of lamellar bodies is essentially the same as the structure of cell membrane and its physical properties are related to the degree of saturation of the fatty acids in the phospholipids, the concentrations of cholesterol and glycerides and the interaction between lipids and proteins (8-11).

Both the surface tension and the viscosity of the fluids are determined by intermolecular forces, with the first directly related to the second, and the microviscosity is an index of the second (12,13).

This paper was supported by CNR (National Research Council) within the Special Program ("MEDICINA PREVENTIVA E RIABILITATIVA").

Shinitzky has standardized a technique for measuring the microviscosity of lipids by the depolarization of polarized light at 365 nm passing through fluid to which has been added a fluorescent indicator that localizes in the nonpolar hydrophobic region of the lamellar lipid aggregates. The degree of depolarization (P) of the light is proportional to the rotation of the indicator molecules, and this rotational movement becomes greater as the microviscosity of the sample becomes lesser (7). The best indicator available at the moment is 1-6-diphenyl-1,3,5-hexatriene (DPH). Molecules that decrease surface tension are also the most effective in depolarizing DPH fluorescence.

The P value not only indicates the over-all composition of the surface-active substances but is independent of the lipid concentration and not influenced by the dilution of the fluid in which it is measured (7). With the microviscosimeter MV-1 made by Elscint (Haifa, Israel), one can measure P in about 45 minutes with only 0.5 ml of amniotic fluid (7). The coefficient of variation of the measurement is about 2%, much less than the coefficient of variation for measuring the L/S ratio, which varies from 7.5 to 21% (14).

Golde (14) and Elrad (15) have shown there to be a significant correlation between the P values measured by fluorescence and the L/S ratio, and Golde (14) has also shown that there is an even more significant correlation between the P value and the concentration of phosphatidylglycerol. Finally, Stark (16) found a significant correlation between P and gestational age in 116 amniotic fluids collected from 22 pregnancies with iso-immunization.

The ability of P to predict the risk for RDS is good, although there is no total agreement about the exact cut-off point at which risk becomes indicated. The values commonly used for this purpose range from 0.320 to 0.345, with the higher value chosen for greater specificity and greater predictiveness and the lower value for greater sensitivity (17).

The available data that appear to show that this method can be validly used as an alternative to the L/S ratio, both because of its excellent predictive capacity and the rapidity and ease of its determination, induced us to undertake some studies to test its clinical application even under conditions in which it is impossible to obtain uncontaminated amniotic fluid by abdominal puncture.

All the samples we assayed were centrifuged for 10 minutes at 1500 X g, as suggested by Simon (18), and the supernatants stored at -20°C.

Rather frequent in clinical practice are the occasions when transabdominally collected amniotic fluid is not available, such as in premature rupture of membranes or in rapidly advancing labor. In these occasions measurement of surfactant production could be performed in transvaginally collected amniotic fluid or in newborn gastric aspirate, that is essentially amniotic fluid ingested by the fetus before delivery (19). Measurement of the L/S ratio takes too long in these cases and the foam test, which is rapid, is often unreliable.

We have measured the microviscosity of 66 samples of amniotic fluid obtained by transabdominal amniocentesis from women in the 16th to the 40th week of pregnancy and the microviscosity of 56 samples of gastric aspirate taken from the neonates by oral passage of a polyethylene suction catheter immediately after birth during the 31st to the 41st week of gestation.

Gestational age was assigned to all the cases on the basis of the date of the last menstruation and confirmed by ultrasound examination and by a Dubowitz test in the nursery.

No cases in which there had been some type of obstetrical pathology that could modify the maturation of the fetal lungs (diabetes, hypertension, IUGR) were included, nor were any samples assayed that were macroscopically contaminated with blood or meconium.

Linear regression analysis showed there to be a significant correlation ($r = 0.77$; $p < 0.01$) between amniotic fluid P values and gestational age for cases beyond the 28th week. The gastric aspirate samples also showed a significant correlation ($r = 0.50$; $p < 0.01$) between P and gestational age.

The regression lines for amniotic fluid and gastric aspirate were parallel when compared by analysis of covariance ($F = 0.052$; $p = 0.8046$). The heights of the two lines were significantly different ($F = 35.396$; $p < 0.0001$). The mean values for gastric aspirate were lower than those for amniotic fluid. At the 35th week of gestation, the mean P value for amniotic fluid was 0.330 and the mean value for gastric aspirate was 0.280 (Fig. 1).

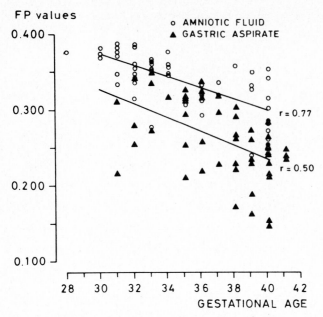

Fig. 1. Correlation between gestational age and amniotic fluid (r = 0.77; p < 0.01) or gastric aspirate (r = 0.50; p < 0.01) FP values. The two regression lines were parallel (F = 0.052; p = 0.8046) and the heights of the two lines were significantly different (F = 35.396; p < 0.0001).

This is probably because of direct ingestion by the neonate of surfactant material in the tracheal and lung fluid.

None of the neonates for whom we had obtained samples by amniocentesis developed RDS. The mean interval between amniocentesis and delivery was 14.11 ± 19.46 days. One infant from whom we took gastric aspirate developed RDS. His P value in the 32nd week was 0.342.

We also evaluated the modifications in microviscosity of amniotic fluid induced by passage through the vagina, for 19 cases. The mean P values for samples collected by membrane puncture, with the liquid allowed to drip through a dry-sterilized amnioscope and for samples collected immediately afterward, after passing through the vagina, were 0.308 ± 0.036 and 0.302 ± 0.035 (p = NS). From four cases we also collected samples of amniotic fluid by transabdominal amniocentesis less than 24 hours before rupture of the membranes and the P values for these samples did not significantly differ from those of the corresponding samples collected by the other two procedures (Tab. 1 and 2).

TABLE 1

FP VALUES

N°	VAGINAL POOL	AMNIOSCOPY	AMNIOCENTESIS	WEEK
1	0.247	0.239		39
2	0.250	0.254		40
3	0.357	0.365	0.342	35
4	0.303	0.333		36
5	0.299	0.303	0.305	41
6	0.345	0.350		39
7	0.318	0.326		40
8	0.284	0.302		40
9	0.239	0.261		40
10	0.339	0.346		41
11	0.295	0.314		41
12	0.353	0.321		40
13	0.307	0.307		40
14	0.278	0.272		41
15	0.304	0.312		40
16	0.293	0.291		40
17	0.333	0.356	0.363	35
18	0.289	0.285		39
19	0.302	0.306	0.318	37

TABLE 2

	VAGINAL POOL	AMNIOSCOPY	AMNIOCENTESIS	p
FP Values Mean ± SD (N)	0.302 ± 0.035 (19)	0.308 ± 0.036 (19)	–	NS
	0.323 ± 0.028 (4)	0.333 ± 0.033 (4)	0.332 ± 0.026 (4)	NS

A very frequent problem in clinical practice is the difficulty of interpreting the values of amniotic indices for samples contaminated with blood or meconium. Buhi (20) showed that contamination with either of these considerably modifies the L/S ratio.

To determine more precisely the effects of contamination on the microviscosity values, we measured P in samples of amniotic fluid to which we added

104

increasing amounts of serum or of a concentrated solution of meconium. The
results showed that addition of serum, even in amounts as small as 10 mcl per
ml of amniotic fluid detectably lowers the microviscosity of immature fluids
and detectably increases the microviscosity of mature fluids, arriving eventually at the P value for serum, which resulted to be 0.330 (Fig. 2).

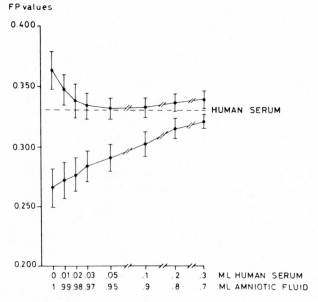

Fig. 2. Modifications of amniotic fluid FP values after contamination with
increasing amounts of human serum.

However, the presence of 25 mcl of whole blood (equivalent to 10 mcl of serum) per ml of amniotic fluid gives a marked color to the sample, a color which
is still visible even at lower concentrations of about 3 mcl of whole blood per
ml. But at levels of contamination lower than 15 mcl per ml the effects on
microviscosity are very much less, especially in mature fluid (Fig. 3). These
determinations at low levels of contamination were carried out after addition
of increasing amounts of whole blood followed by centrifugation of the samples.

Contamination with increasing amounts of a concentrated meconium solution
caused very little change in the microviscosity of immature fluids and an
increase in the microviscosity of mature fluids. This confirms the previous
report of Blumenfeld (22) (Fig. 4).

FP values

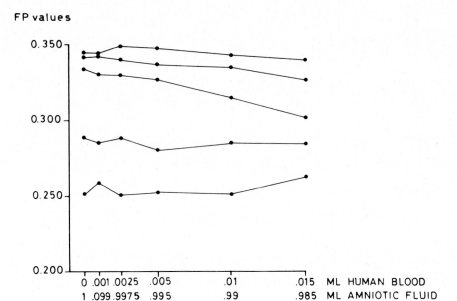

Fig. 3. Modifications of amniotic fluid FP values after contamination with increasing amounts of human blood.

FP values

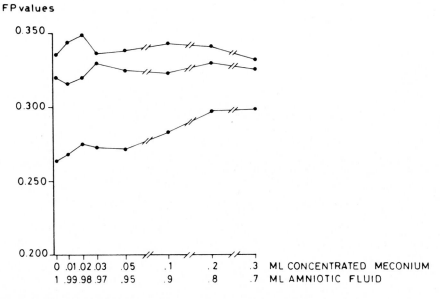

Fig. 4. Modifications of amniotic fluid FP values after contamination with increasing amounts of concentrated meconium.

106

Another problem in clinical management of premature labor are possible adverse effects of antenatal administration of corticosteroids and the limitations of their effectiveness (1-4). The search for alternative substances requires very precise method for the measurement of surfactant production by the fetus.

We proceeded to measure the microviscosity values for 10 women from whom we took amniotic fluid more than once by transabdominal and transvaginal puncture. Two samples were taken from 8 cases and 3 samples from 2 cases. In all, there was a decrease in microviscosity with time, even when the interval between the two collections was only a few days (Fig. 5).

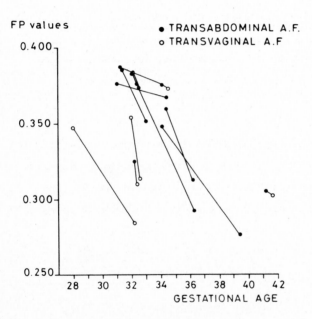

Fig. 5. Modifications of amniotic fluid FP values in serial samples, collected transabdominally and transvaginally.

We then compared the amniotic fluid and gastric aspirate P values of cases treated prophylactically before birth with betamethasone or ambroxol to prevent RDS with those of cases not given any prophylactic treatment. The P values in both fluids were lower in the treated cases than in the untreated cases. The regression lines for the treated and untreated cases intersected at the 37th week of pregnancy, both for amniotic fluid and for gastric aspirate (Fig. 6 and 7).

In conclusion, to be absolutely sure of the validity of this method it will be necessary to obtain more information about its ability to predict RDS and the cut-off value for risk. Perhaps, as suggested by Dohnal and Bowie (21), different fluorimeters might provide different measures of polarization.

Even now the advantages of the method are obvious. Because of the wide range of values (P values from 0 to 0.460), it is very precise and is especially valuable for studying even slight changes in concentrations of surface-active substances. In addition, it is not affected by dilution of the amniotic fluid and is affected less than the L/S ratio by contamination with blood or meconium.

Finally it can be applied to biological fluids other than amniotic fluid taken transabdominally, such as amniotic fluid collected transvaginally or gastric aspirate, extending its possible use to evaluation of pulmonary maturity in almost all cases within a short enough time to undertake intensive treatment of the neonate and, when necessary, have the infant transported to a neonatal intensive care unit.

It is to be hoped that further development of the method will lead to production of an even simpler and less expensive apparatus that could even be used by paramedical personnel.

108

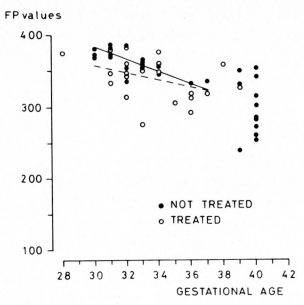

Fig. 6. Amniotic fluid FP values of cases given prophylactically betamethasone or ambroxol for prevention of RDS and of cases not given any prophylactic treatment.

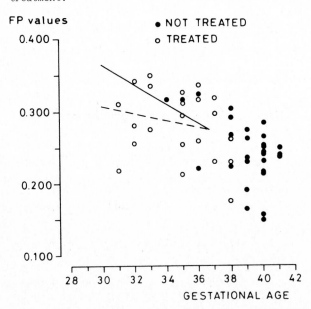

Fig. 7. Gastric aspirate FP values of cases given prophylactically betamethasone or ambroxol for prevention of RDS and of cases not given any prophylactic treatment.

REFERENCES

1. Collaborative group on antenatal steroid therapy (1981) Am. J. Obstet. Gynecol., 141, 276.

2. Garite T.J., Freeman R.K., Linzey E.M., Braly P.S., Dorchester W.L. (1981) Am. J. Obstet. Gynecol., 141, 508.

3. Taeusch H.W. (1975) J. Pediatrics, 87, 617.

4. Taeusch H.W., Frigoletto F., Kitzmiller J., Avery M.E., Mehre A., Fromm B., Lawson E. and Neff R.K. (1979) Pediatrics, 63, 64.

5. Morrison J.C., Whybrew W.D., Bucovaz E.T. et al. (1977) Obstet. Gynecol., 49, 20.

6. Kulovich M.V., Hallman M.B. and Gluck L. (1979) Am. J. Obstet. Gynecol., 135, 57.

7. Shinitzky M., Goldfisher A., Bruck A., Goldmann B., Stern E., Barkai G. et al. (1976) Br. J. Obstet. Gynecol., 83, 838.

8. Gil J. and Reiss O. K. (1973) J. Cell. Biol., 58, 152.

9. Strang L.B. (1977) Ann. Rev. Physiol., 39, 253.

10. Oldfield E. and Chapman D. (1971) Biochem. Biophys. Res. Commun., 43, 610.

11. Schacter D. and Shinitzky M. (1977) J. Clin. Invest., 59, 536.

12. Shinitzky M., Dianoux A.C., Gitler C., Weber G. and Nishida T. (1971) Biochemistry, 10, 4335.

13. Cogan U., Shinitzky M., Weber G. and Nishida T. (1973) Biochemistry, 12, 521.

14. Golde S.H., Vogt J.F., Gabbe S.G. and Cabal L.A. (1979) Obstet. Gynecol., 54, 639.

15. Erald H., Beydoun S.N., Hagen J.H., Cabalum M.T., Aubry R.H. and Smith C. (1978) Am. J. Obstet. Gynecol., 132, 681.

16. Stark R.I., Blumenfeld T.A., George J.D., Vincent B.S., Freda J. and Stanley James L. (1979) Pediatrics, 63, 213.

17. Cheskin H.S. and Blumenfeld T.A. (1981) Clin. Chem., 27, 1934.

18. Simon N.V., Elser R.C., Levisky J.S. and Polk D.T. (1981) Clin. Chem., 27, 930.

19. Cowett R.M., Unsworth E.J., Hakanson D.O., Williams J.R. and William O. (1975) New Engl. J. Med., 293, 413.

20. Buhi W.C. and Spellacy W.N. (1975) Am. J. Obstet. Gynecol., 121, 321.

21. Dohnal J.C. and Bowie L.J. (1981) Clin. Chem., 27, 1834.

22. Blumenfeld T.A., Stark K.I., Stanley James L., George J.D., Dyrenfurthr I., Freda V.J. and Shinitzky M. (1978) Am. J. Obstet. Gynecol., 130, 782.

© 1983, Elsevier Science Publishers B.V.
Pulmonary Surfactant System, E.V. Cosmi
and E.M. Scarpelli eds.

THE ROLE OF β ADRENERGIC AGENTS IN THE CONTROL OF LUNG LIQUID ABSORPTION AND SURFACTANT RELEASE

D. V. WALTERS AND R. E. OLVER

Department of Paediatrics, U.C.L. Medical School, The Rayne
Institute, University Street, London, WCIE 6JJ.

INTRODUCTION

The establishment and maintenance of a stable gas volume in the alveolar space requires that the lung lumen be kept free of liquid and that sufficient pulmonary surfactant be present to prevent alveolar collapse. Abnormalities in the transition of the lungs from their fetal liquid filled state to become the organs of gas exchange demonstrate in a dramatic way some of the underlying physiological mechanisms involved. Deficiency of surfactant in the alveolar lumen is undoubtedly the most important causative factor in hyaline membrane disease (HMD). Delayed absorption of fetal lung liquid may contribute to the genesis of HMD and is implicated in the cause of transient tachypnoea of the newborn.

There is now sufficient evidence to show that β adrenergic stimulation has a crucial role in bringing about the normal adaptive changes in the lung epithelium at birth.

FETAL LUNG LIQUID ABSORPTION

Fetal lung liquid is secreted by a process involving the active movement of chloride ions across the pulmonary epithelium (27). A mature fetal lamb (a much studied preparation) produces liquid at rates of up to 7 ml/hr.kg. body weight so that near term secretion rates approach 500 ml/day.fetus. We have shown (31, 8) that intravenous infusions of physiological amounts of adrenaline (0·1-0·5 μg/min) inhibit secretion of liquid in lamb fetuses of more than 120 days' gestation (term being 147 days). The effect of adrenaline is gestation dependent, increasing with maturity so

that beyond 130 days, absorption of lung liquid is the characteristic response. Given in equimolar amounts, isoprenaline is more
potent than adrenaline, whereas noradrenaline has no effect.
Furthermore the effect of isoprenaline can be blocked with propranolol indicating a mode of action via β adrenergic receptors.
The effect of β adrenergic stimulation can be completely reversed
by amiloride introduced into the fetal lung lumen (7) - strong
evidence that the mechanism of absorption is dependent on active
sodium transport. An example of such an experiment is given in
figure 1.

Amiloride probably acts by blocking sodium entry at the apical
surface of the epithelial cells and thus prevents sodium ions
from gaining access to the site of active sodium movement on the
baso lateral surface of the cells.

The physiological significance of β adrenergic stimulation on
fetal lung liquid secretion is seen during delivery at which time
we have observed spontaneous absorption of lung liquid in the
latter stages of labour (7, 8). An example is shown in figure 2.

The pooled data of several such observations, with the corresponding fetal plasma adrenaline concentrations, is given in
table 1.

TABLE 1

J_v is the rate of fetal lung liquid secretion (positive) or
absorption (negative) at various times during labour. [A] is
adrenaline concentration in fetal carotid arterial plasma measured by a radio-enzymatic method. Means $\pm$ standard errors are
given.

	Time before delivery (minutes)			Time after (minutes)
	900-150	150-50	50-0	0-50
J_v (ml/hr)	+7.06(+1·5) n = 4	-2·2(+5·0) n = 6	-15·2(+5·9) n = 7	-28·7(+2·6) n = 4
[A] (ng/ml)	0·087(+0·04) n = 3	0·525(+0·25) n = 5	6·86(+4·3) n = 6	7·17(+3·35) n = 4

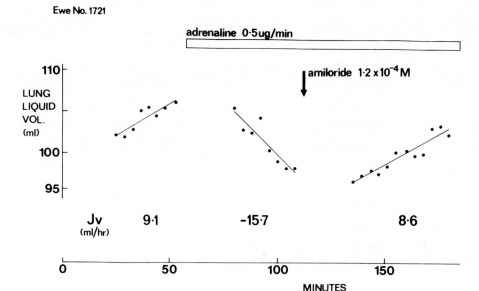

Fig. 1. An experiment performed in a chronically catheterized fetal lamb set up as described previously (31). Accumulated lung liquid volume is calculated from the dilution of an impermeant tracer mixed into the fetal lung liquid at time zero. Each point is derived from one sample. The slopes of the regression lines give J_v, the secretion rate (positive values) or absorption rate (negative values). Adrenaline was infused intravenously for the period shown by the bar and caused absorption of lung liquid across the pulmonary epithelium at a rate of 15·7 ml/hour. Amiloride, mixed into the lung liquid at the time indicated by the arrow, blocked the absorption and caused secretion to return to a rate similar to the initial control value. In other experiments in which adrenaline was administered for the same duration, in the absence of amiloride, absorption of lung liquid continued throughout the infusion.

The slowing of secretion and subsequent absorption of liquid can be completely accounted for by the rise in fetal plasma concentrations of adrenaline resulting from endogenous catecholamine secretion in response to the stress of labour. The relationship between lung liquid secretion or absorption rate

114

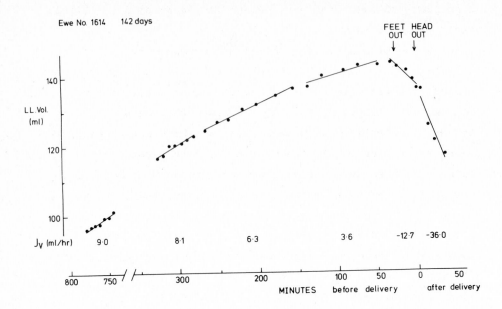

Fig. 2. The effect of labour on lung liquid secretion in the fetal lamb. For experimental details see legend of figure 1 and reference (31). Secretion of fetal lung liquid continued, albeit at a reducing rate, until quite late in labour. Observations were made after delivery with the non-breathing lamb at the vaginal outlet and its umbilical circulation intact.

and plasma adrenaline concentration is the same irrespective of whether the adrenaline is exogenously administered by infusion or endogenously released during labour. That labour is a very potent stimulus for catecholamine release, even in the absence of fetal distress (pH > 7.25) is well demonstrated by the studies of Lagercrantz and co-workers (22). In human fetal scalp blood samples adrenaline rises to levels of 0·37 ng/ml as early as 3-5 cm dilatation of the cervix and by 9-10 cm dilatation adrenaline concentrations of 1·0 ng/ml are reached. Extrapolating from the lamb data, we may conclude that these concentrations are more than enough to produce lung liquid absorption, in which case

absorption of lung liquid in humans may begin at a relatively
early stage of labour.

The absorption of fetal lung liquid produced by β adrenergic
stimulation explains the mechanism underlying the reports that
various β adrenergic agonists decrease lung water content in fetal
and neonatal lungs (3, 13, 15). Fetuses that have undergone
labour have 'drier' lungs than those who have not, regardless of
whether delivery is via the vagina or by hysterotomy (4). This
effect is presumably mediated by endogenous fetal adrenaline
released in response to the stress of labour and obviously cannot
be attributed to mechanical squeezing in the birth canal.

Near term the sensitivity of the fetal lamb lung to adrenaline
increases fifteen fold over the last 10 days of gestation (8). In
fetuses within a few days of term a plasma adrenaline concentration of $0 \cdot 029$ ng/ml ($0 \cdot 16$ nmoles/L) is sufficient to inhibit
secretion completely, (i.e. produce neither secretion nor absorption of lung liquid). This concentration of adrenaline is lower
than that found in chronically catheterised sleeping adults of
several species (rat, cat, rabbit, dog, man and cow) in whom
plasma adrenaline concentrations range from $0 \cdot 31$ nM to $1 \cdot 11$ nM
(9). Thus, it is at least a possibility that the lung epithelium
retains its secretory potential postnatally but that it is constantly inhibited by circulating plasma adrenaline. It is con-
ceivable that this system may provide the means for control of
the volume and ionic composition of the liquid subphase lining
the pulmonary epithelium. It is noteworthy that amiloride sensitive movement of sodium from mucosa to serosa has been described
in vitro and in vivo in bronchial airways of adult monkeys and
man (25).

SURFACTANT RELEASE

β adrenergic stimulation has been shown to cause release of
surfactant in various situations.

Fetal rabbits 2-5 days before term, injected with β agonists, appear to secrete increased amounts of surfactant as measured by increased stability of whole lungs on deflation (3, 20, 32), lower minimum surface tensions in lung washes (3), higher L/S ratios in lung washes (15, 20) and a decreased number of lamellar bodies in their type II epithelial cells (15). [Studies using increased lung compliance or improved deflation stability of whole lungs as the sole criteria for surfactant release should be interpreted with caution. Alterations in total lung water content and/or distribution, as are produced by β agonists, will obviously affect total gas volumes, tissue compliance and perhaps airway resistance]. Release of surfactant in response to adrenaline (albeit large doses, 3·3 μg/min) has been described in the fetal lamb, and the amount of surfactant released increased with gestation (24).

The effect of labour on surfactant secretion has been investigated by Marino and Rooney (26) using slices of fetal rabbit lung from which release of labelled phosphatidyl choline was measured under different conditions. They concluded that labour stimulated release of surfactant by a process involving β agonists and prostaglandins since the effect of labour could be blocked with propranolol and indomethacin. Atropine had no effect.

In newborn rabbits 1 to 3 days old, Abdellatif and Hollingsworth (1) showed that adrenaline caused an increase in the amount of phosphatidyl choline in lung washes within 30 minutes of administration and that the effect was blocked by propranolol. Oxotremorine, a muscarinic agonist, also produced surfactant release. Although this effect could be blocked by atropine, it was argued that the action of oxotremorine was indirect because it was also blocked by propranolol and prior adrenalectomy.

TABLE 2

Phosphatidyl choline (PC) secretion in neonatal rabbits. From Abdellatif and Hollingsworth (1), [figures rounded up].

b	n	PC content (mg/g dry lung wt)	
		Lung wash	Lung residue
Saline	5	26 + 2	73 + 6
Oxotremorine	7	51 + 3	72 + 7
Adrenaline	5	78 + 15	76 + 13
Oxotremorine) dl-propranolol)	5	20 + 2	85 + 8
Oxotremorine) Adrenelectomy)	4	27 + 5	74 + 1

Dose and timing prior to lung excision: adrenaline 50 μg/kg (30 min), Oxotremorine 0·2 mg/kg (30 min), dl-propranolol 1 mg/kg (40 min), adrenelectomy (45 min).

This is an important observation because it explains other reports implicating muscarinic agonists in causing surfactant release (12, 13).

In neonates and adult animals, distension of the lungs increases the amount of surfactant in the lung lumen (23, 29, 30). This effect is blocked by atropine and the β antagonists, propranolol and sotalol. However, blocking with atropine does not prove local stimulation of acetycholine receptors in the lung but only that acetycholine is required somewhere in the in-vivo reflex initiated by lung distension (13). In isolated lungs (1) and in cultured alveolar type II cells (14) cholinergic agents are without effect whereas β agonists cause surfactant release in both of these in vitro preparations.

CLINICAL STUDIES

The contention that β adrenergic agents are important in the perinatal period in adapting the lungs to air breathing is supported by several clinical observations. Tidal volume, minute ventilation and dynamic lung compliance are lower in babies born by elective Caesarean section compared with those born vaginally (6, 16). Furthermore, in the vaginally delivered babies dynamic compliance measured at 2 hours of age correlates with the total catecholamine concentration in umbilical cord blood (16). There is no such relationship in babies born by Caesarean section. Although adrenaline concentrations in cord blood following elective Caesarean section (i.e. non labouring mothers) are high (22) the effect is likely to be small since the babies are exposed to raised adrenaline concentrations for only a very short time (unlike babies who undergo labour and who subsequently are born by emergency Caesarean section or the vaginal route). Other studies on crying vital capacity (11), total thoracic gas volume (6) and incidence of hyaline membrane disease (17) in new born babies support the hypothesis that it is the exposure to labour which is the critical beneficial factor to the lungs at birth, not the type of delivery. A more direct measure, in humans, of the effect of labour on surfactant release is the finding that the L/S ratio in amniotic liquid is greater after the onset of labour than before (10).

It has been claimed that the incidence of hyaline membrane disease might be reduced by pre-partum treatment of mothers with β agonists (2, 5, 19, 21). However, this view is not universally accepted and there is evidence from animals that a single dose of β agonist given to a fetus 24 hours before premature delivery may be harmful (18) perhaps by exhausting stored surfactant at a time when synthesis is inadequate.

CONCLUSION

There is substantial evidence that adrenaline is a key factor in lung adaptation at birth, as a stimulus both for fetal lung liquid absorption and release of surfactant. In the adult, β receptors mediate the response to certain stimuli for surfactant release. In addition, they may serve to maintain an inhibitory influence on alveolar fluid secretion.

REFERENCES

1. Abdellatif, N.M. and Hollingsowrth, M. (1980) Effect of oxotremorine and epinephrine on lung surfactant secretion in neonatal rabbits. Ped. Res. 14: 916-920.

2. Bergman, B. and Hedner, T. (1978) Antepartum administration of terbutaline and the incidence of hyaline membrane disease in preterm infants. Acta Obstet. Gynecol.Scand. 57: 217-221.

3. Bergman, B., Hedner, T. and Lundborg, P. (1980) Pressure-volume relationship and fluid content in fetal rabbit lung after beta-receptor stimulating drugs. Ped. Res. 14: 1067-1070.

4. Bland, R.D., McMillan, D.D. and Bressack, M.A. (1979) Labor decreases lung water content of newborn rabbits. Am. J. Obstet. Gynecol. 134: 364-367.

5. Boog, G., Ben Brahym, M. and Gandar, R. (1975) Beta-minetic drugs and possible prevention of respiratory distress syndrome. Br. J. Obstet. Gynecol. 82: 285-288.

6. Boon, A.W., Milner, A.D. and Hopkins, I.E. (1981) Lung volumes and lung mechanics in babies born vaginally and by elective and emergency lower segmental Caesarean section. J. Peds. 98: 812-815.

7. Brown, M.J., Olver, R.E., Ramsden, C.A., Strang, L.B. and Walters, D.V. (1980) Effects of adrenaline infusion and of spontaneous labour on lung liquid secretion and absorption in the fetal lamb. J. Physiol. 313: 13-14P.

8. Brown, M.J., Olver, R.E., Ramsden, C.A., Strang, L.B. and Walters, D.V. (in press) Effects of adrenaline and of spontaneous labour on the secretion and absorption of lung liquid in the fetal lamb. J. Physiol.

9. Buhler, H.V., Da Prada, M., Haefely, W. and Picotti, G.B. (1978) Plasma adrenaline, noradrenaline and dopamine in man and different animal species. J. Physiol. 276: 311-320.

10. Cabero, L., Roses, A., Viscasillas, P., Quiley, M., Giralt,E. and Duran-Sanchez, P. (1976) Influence of labour on the lecithin, lecithin sphingomyelin (L/S) ratio, and palmitic acid values in the amniotic fluid. Br. J. Obstet. Gynecol. 83: 452-453.

11. Chiswick, M.L. and Milner, R.D.H. (1976) Crying vital capacity. Measurement of neonatal lung function. Arch. Dis. Childh. 51: 22-27.

12. Corbet, A.J.S., Flax, P. and Rudolph, A.J. (1976) Reduced surface tension in lungs of fetal rabbits injected with pilocarpine. J. Appl. Physiol. 41: 7-14.

13. Corbet, A.J.S., Flax, P. and Rudolph, A.J. (1977) Role of autonomic nervous system controlling surface tension in fetal rabbit lungs. J. Appl. Physiol. 43: 1039-1045.

14. Dobbs, L.G. and Mason, R.J. (1979) Pulmonary alveolar type II cells isolated from rats. Release of phosphatidyl choline in response to β adrenergic stimulation. J. Clin. Invest. 63: 378-387.

15. Enhorning, G., Chamberlain, D., Contreras, C., Burgoyne, R. and Robertson, B. (1977) Isoxuprine-induced release of pulmonary surfactant in the rabbit fetus. Am. J. Obstet. Gynecol. 129: 197-202.

16. Faxelius, G., Hagnevik, K., Lagercrantz, H. Lundell, B. and Irestedt, L. (in press) Lung function after vaginal delivery versus Caesarean section in general or epidural anaesthesia - possible relation to catecholamine surge. Arch. Dis. Childh.

17. Fredrick, J. and Butler, N.R. (1972) Hyaline membrane disease. (letter) The Lancet, 2: 768-769.

18. Hallman, M., Teramo, K., Sipiner, S. and Raivio, K.O. (manuscript in preparation). Effects of betamethasone and ritodrine on the phospholipids of the lung lavage fluid in premature rabbits.

19. Hastwell, G. (1977) Salbutamol and respiratory distress syndrome. Lancet, 2: 354.

20. Kanjanapone, V., Hartig-Beecken, I. and Epstein, M.F. (1980) Effect of isoxuprine on fetal lung surfactant in rabbits. Ped. Res. 14: 278-281.

21. Kero, P., Hirvonen Tand Valimaki, I. (1973) Prenatal and postnatal isoxuprine and respiratory distress syndrome (letter). Lancet, 2: 198.

22. Lagercrantz, H., Bistoletti, P. and Nylund, L. (1981) Sympathoadrenal activity in the foetus during delivery and at birth. In: Intensive care of the newborn. 1-12. Eds: Stern, L., Salle, B., Friis-Hansen, Mason Press, N.Y.

23. Lawson, E.E., Birdwell, R.L., Huang, P.S. and Taeusch, H.W. (1977) Augmentation of pulmonary surfactant secretion by lung expansion at birth. Ped. Res. 13: 611-614.

24. Lawson, E.E., Brown, E.R., Torday, J.S., Madansky, D.L. and Taeusch, H.W. (1978) The effect of epinephrine on tracheal fluid flow and surfactant efflux in fetal sheep. Am. Rev. Resp. Dis. 118: 1023-1026.

25. Legris, G.J., Will, P.C. and Hopfer, V. (1982) Human and baboon bronchial sodium absorption: implications for airway fluid movement and the mucociliary clearance mechanism. Chest, 81 (Suppl). 9S-11S.

26. Marino, P.A. and Rooney, S.A. (1981) The effect of labor on surfactant secretion in newborn rabbit lung slices. Biochim. Biophys. Acta. 664: 389-396.

27. Olver, R.E. and Strang, L.B. (1974) Ion fluxes across the pulmonary epithelium and the secretion of lung liquid in the foetal lamb. J. Physiol. 241: 327-357.

28. Olver, R.E , Ramsden, C.A. and Strang, L.B. (1981) Adrenaline-induced changes in net lung liquid volume flow across the pulmonary epithelium of the fetal lamb: evidence for active sodium transport. J. Physiol. 319: 38-39P.

29. Oyarzun, M.J. and Clements, J.A. (1977) Ventilatory and cholinergic control of pulmonary surfactant in the rabbit. J. Appl. Physiol. 43: 39-45.

30. Oyarzun, M.J. and Clements, J.A. (1978) Control of lung surfactant by ventilation, adrenergic mediators and prostaglandins in the rabbit. Am. Rev. Resp. Dis. 117: 879-891.

31. Walters, D.V. and Olver, R.E. (1978) The role of catecholamines in lung liquid absorption at birth. Ped. Res. 12: 239-242.

32. Wyszogrodski, I., Taeusch, H.W. and Avery, M.E. (1974) Isoxuprine induced alterations of pulmonary pressure-volume relationships in premature rabbits. Am. J. Obstet. Gynecol. 119: 1107-1111.

© 1983, Elsevier Science Publishers B.V.
Pulmonary Surfactant System, E.V. Cosmi
and E.M. Scarpelli eds.

EPIDEMIOLOGY AND ETIOLOGY OF RESPIRATORY DISTRESS SYNDROME/HYALINE
MEMBRANE DISEASE (RDS/HMD) OF THE NEWBORN

GIOVANNI BUCCI AND MODESTO MENDICINI

Institute of Pediatrics, La Sapienza University Medical School, Rome (Italy)

RDS/HMD is still a major cause of neonatal morbidity, and perhaps
the main cause of neonatal death in most developed countries (1).

EPIDEMIOLOGY

Incidence. It is difficult to define the incidence of RDS/HMD in large,
unselected populations of liveborn infants, and to compare available
data, mostly because of the difficulty in establishing a clear cut and
consistent separation with other, usually less severe, respiratory disorders.
The diagnosis is expecially difficult in the tiny baby, who may present
with clinical and X-ray findings due to extreme lung prematurity, and
where at autopsy pulmonary hyaline membranes are not unfrequently
absent. With these reservations in mind, it is pertinent to report that
in recent studies the incidence of RDS/HMD has ranged from 0.3% of
live births in Scandinavian countries (2, 3), to 0.8% in Switzerland
(4) and to 1% in U.S.A. (5).

Risk factors. The incidence of RDS/HMD is inversely related to gestational age (GA) and, in a recent study, it decreased from 30% in neonates
with GA < 30 weeks to 0.01% in full term infants (2).

Males are more frequently affected than females and, in recent studies,
the M/F ratio ranged between 1.5 and 2 (2, 6). This difference is presumably related to the hormonal factors involved in sex differentiation.
The antioestrogenic effect of testosteron might play a role, since in
animal experiments a stimulating effect of oestrogen administration on
the maturation of surfactant in the fetal lung has been documented (7).
This hypothesis is substanciated by the observation of a slower lung
biochemical maturation in male as compared to female fetal rabbit (8).

At variance with previous beliefs, no clear cut evidence of racial influences could be demonstrated in a recent study, when other risk factor were taken into account (6). On the other hand, a familial pre-disposition is likely, as suggested by a study showing an incidence of RDS/HMD of 90% in low birth weight deliveries when the previous low birth weight baby was also affected, and only of 5% when the pre-vious son was not affected (9).

Perinatal asphyxia represents an highly significant risk factor in the full term neonate, less so in the premature one (10), and it is the most likely cause of the greater risk in the second twin (11). Another well documented risk factor is represented by Cesarean section performed before the onset of labour (10, 12). It has been suggested that this might be due to the lack of increased catecholamine incretion (mostly epinephrin) which occurs at the onset of labour, and which might play a key role by inhibiting the production and by enhancing the reabsorp tion of the alveolar fluid, and in the dismission of surfactant into the alveoli (13, 14, 15).

The association of RDS/HMD with maternal diabetes is still apparent even when other frequently associated risk factors (such as prematurity and Cesarean section) are taken into account (16). This is currently attributed to fetal hyperinsulinism, possibly through its antagonistic action to the maturational effect of cortisol (17). Interestingly, in a recent study on fetal lambs chronic hyperglycemia reduced the flux of surface material in tracheal fluid (18).

Protective factors. RDS/HMD is observed more seldom following pro-longed rupture of fetal membranes, most markedly when rupture occurs before the onset of labour (19). However, in one report, no differences were found when comparing rupture lasting 24 to 72 hours or more than 72 hours (20). In the same study it was shown that the benefit associa ted with prolonged rupture of membranes was limited to the infants with birth weight of 1,500-2,500 g and/or with GA of 33-36 weeks, whereas no effect was evidenced in smaller subjects. Similarly, a protective effect was found in association with factors able to induce chronic fetal

stress and growth retardation, such as maternal hypertension and toxemia (20).

Preterm infants of heroin-addicted mothers are less predisposed to
HMD/RDS (22), suggesting a maturational effect of the drug on lung
surfactant. According to most controlled trials (23) the administration
to the mother of corticosteroids at least 24 hours before the preterm
delivery is followed by a decrease in the incidence of RDS/HMD. However
in a recent, nation-wide epidemiological study in Sweden this incidence
was similar in units with or without a maternal corticosteroid program
(2). In another report (24), a significant protection following antenatal betamethasone administration was evidenced only in females.

Mortality data. In the last 10 to 15 years studies from leading ICU's
consistently reported a marked improvement in the neonatal outcome,
with a survival rate in one Center close to 100% in infants with birth
weight above 1,500 g, and as high as 75% in smaller patients (25).
Unfortunately, nation wide statistics, allowing to evaluate the impact
of advanced neonatal care on a broad scale, are remarkably limited.
In a recent, regional prospective study from Sweden the case fatality
rate was of 24% (with no deaths occurring in infants with GA > 34 weeks
or with birth weight > 2,500 g), and the rate of deaths attributable to
RDS/HMD was 0.77 per 1,000 live births (2). In U.S.A. in the period
1968-1978 the death rate due to the disease decreased from 2.36 to only
1.66 per 1,000 live births, and the percentage of total neonatal deaths
due to RDS/HMD increased from 14.7% in 1968 to a maximum of 21.3%
in 1974, before declining to 17.5% in 1978 (1). These death patterns
reflected, at least in part, the relatively faster decrease in mortality
due to perinatal asphyxia. It has been suggested that the relatively
stable death rate due to RDS/HMD might be attributed to some extent
to the increased number of deliveries of liveborn tiny or severely asphy-
xiated fetuses (previously dying before or shortly after birth), thereby
increasing the population of candidates to the most severe forms of the
disease. The steady rate of premature births may also contribute to

this pattern.

ETIOLOGY

The deficiency of surface active material in the alveolar lining layer
at the peack of the disease has been well documented (26), and most
likely it is the primary factor precipitating RDS/HMD. Since its first
proposal (27), amniotic fluid analysis of surfactant has become the method of choice in the evaluation of fetal lung maturity. At present,
the lecithin/sphingomyelin (L/S) ratio is the most widely and, perhaps,
the most accurate single index used in the evaluation of lung maturity,
but the occurrence of false mature or of false immature L/S ratios has
prompted the search for a more accurate biochemical characterization
of the surfactant complex (23). Perhaps the most interesting phospholipid component is phosphatidylglycerol (PG), which has been found consistently absent in lung effluent of infants with RDS/HMD (28, 29). In
neonates without RDS/HMD, PG can be detected in increasing amounts
in the lung effluent after 25-26 weeks of gestation; in the meantime
phosphatidylinositol (PI), another important phospholipid fraction, decreases (23, 28). Available evidence suggests that PG improves the performance of the whole surfactant system, perhaps by enhancing the
spreading of surfactant on the alveolar lining layer (30). The six-carbon
sugar myoinositol enhances the biosynthesis of PI and blocks the synthesis
of PG, thus regulating the sequential appearance of PI and PG in the
fetal lung: in fact, plasma myoinositol levels are high in immature foe-
tuses and decrease during maturation (31). The above observations suggests
that, in the immature lung, surfactant is deficient qualitatively as well
as quantitatively, and provide a biochemical explaination of the key
role of prematurity in the etiology of RDS/HMD.

However prematurity alone cannot explain the etiology of the disease,
and other contributing factors (partly mentionned in the discussion on
epidemiology) may play a role in the occurrence of RDS/HMD. These
factors may conceivably act by modifying the velocity of biochemical

maturation during pregnancy, by affecting the physiological mechanisms regulating the production and release of surfactant at the moment of birth, or by influencing the production and inactivation of surfactant after birth.

Several hormons may play a significant role in the regulation of lung maturation (17). The enhancement of maturation by glucocorticoids, particularly of cortisol, has been well documented. It appears that cortisol contributes to the induction of enzymes involved in surfactant synthesis by acting on specific receptors of fetal pneumocytes and of fibroblasts (32, 33). The action of thyroid hormons apeears to be similar (34) and to be potentiated by glucocorticoids (35). Other hormons that may enhance maturation are catecholamines (17), estrogens (7), and prolactin (36), whereas insulin and testosteron may delay maturation (16, 17, 18). It is also interesting to remind that in infants with RDS/HMD low levels of cortisol (37), thyroid hormons (38), estrogens (39), and prolactin (40) have been observed at birth, although the significance of these findings is not entirely clear. In any case, it is likely that changes of the normal hormonal set up may explain individual cases with markedly accelerated or delayed surfactant maturation for GA, and may play more than an occasional role in the occurrence of RDS/HMD.

The possible role of catecholamines in the production and dismission of surfactant at the moment of birth has been previously mentionned (13, 14, 15). It appears that air inflation represents the main stimulus for the postnatal release of surfactant (41). The latter is inhibited by the presence of alveolar fluid, and in this way contributes to the continuing physiological turnover of the surfactant system components (42). Clearly, in abnormal circumstances a vicious circle may ensue, and it may be maintained by conditions likely to produce lung edema, such as the abnormal lymphatic drainage of lung fluid observed in asphyxia (43) and pulmonary hyperperfusion. The latter frequently occurs in the tiny neonate, due to the poorly developed pulmonary muscular arteries, with decreased pulmonary vascular responses to hypoxia and sympathetic stimulation (44), and often associated with a widely patent Ductus Arteriosus (45, 46). In the latter condition left heart failure frequently occurs, furtherly contributing to the development of lung edema (46).

Whereas lung edema presumably plays a relevant role in the tiny baby, asphyxia seems an important causal factor in the few infants developing RDS/HMD beyond 36 weeks of gestation (2), suggesting that at full term the etiologic role of other factors is very limited. Asphyxia might act in several ways, i.e. by direct damage of type II cells and of other bronchoalveolar structures, by increasing capillary permeability and intraalveolar plasma transudation, by impairing drainage of lung fluid and, finally, by inducing pulmonary ischemia (47, 48). Hyatrogenic damage of the surfactant system may also occur, the most important examples being represented by oxygen toxicity due to high oxygen breathing (49) and by the barotrauma associated with mechanical ventilation (50).

Plasma transudation in the bronchiolar and alveolar lumen may develop in many of the above mentionned circumstances and deserves some additional comment. The plasma transudate not only inactivates surfactant, but also may produce lung wall damage (51), possibly starting a vicious circle which may lead to plasma transudation. The administration of surfactant is able to decrease the large bidirectional flow of plasma albumin through the alveolar wall of preterm lambs with RDS (52). This situation may be worsened by the exhaustion of plasma fibrinolytic activity, reportedly present in infants with RDS/HMD (53).

Besides the fibrinolytic system, other cascade systems may be involved in the disease process. Evidence indicating the activation of the kallicrein-kinin system in neonates with RDS/HMD has been recently reported (54), a finding in keeping with previous studies showing decreased plasma levels of α-1 antitripsin, a powerful kallicrein antagonist (55). On the other hand the kallicrein-kinin system is interlocked with the arachidonic acid cascade, leading to prostaglandin (PGD_2) and to prostacyclin (PGI_2)

formation, and in a recent study (56) findings suggesting an increased PGI_2 generation have been reported. These abnormalities may be involved in the pathogenesis of hypotension, edema, and other changes observed in the course of the disease (57, 58, 59), but it cannot be presently excluded that they may play a more causal role in some cases.

In conclusion, there is no doubt that severe surfactant deficiency plays a key role in the etiology of neonatal RDS/HMD, but the role of other factors in the whole spectrum of the disease is still poorly defined (23). In preterm infants the origin of surfactant deficiency is presumably to a great extent developmental, and the role of other factors in precipitating the surfactant deficiency to the degree needed for the full development of the disease seems to be relatively minor and inversely related to the degree of the lung developmental immaturity. In contrast, in full term infants the role of developmental immaturity seems less relevant, and other precipitating factors, such as perinatal asphyxia, apparently play a major role. Little is known on the role of quantitative and/or qualitative surfactant deficiency in atypical forms of RDS, or in other neonatal respiratory disorders. The tiny baby with GA below 29 weeks may present with severe respiratory distress, which by no means is distinguishable from RDS/HMD, or with a more chronic picture of moderate RDS associated with relatively minor chest X-ray changes resembling Chronic Pulmonary Insufficiency of Prematurity (60) and with PDA, but in several cases a clear cut separation between these two entities is difficult and the criteria for the differential diagnosis may be controversial. As another example, in septic neonates RDS might be due to endotoxemia and shock lung, or to the coexistence of HMD (61). Further studies on lung effluent phospholipid will most likely be of great value for a better understanding of neonatal respiratory disorders.

REFERENCES

1. Perelman, R.H. and Farrell, P.M. (1982) Analysis of causes of neo-natal death in the United States with specific emphasis on fatal Hya-line Membrane Disease. Pediatrics, 70, 570.

2. Hjalmarson, O. (1981) Epidemiology and classification of acute neonatal respiratory disorders. Acta Paediatr Scand, 70, 773.

3. Reed, D.M., Bakketeig, L.S. and Nugent, R.P. (1978) The epidemiology of respiratory distress syndrome in Norway. Am J Epidemiol, 107, 299.

4. Fanconi, A., Stoll, W., Duc, G. et al. (1976) Das atemnosyndrom des neugeboren in der Schweiz. Schweiz Med Wochenschr, 106, 1426.

5. Avery, M.E. and Fletcher, W. (1981) The lung and its disorders in the newborn infant. Saunders, Philadelphia, p. 225.

6. Ross, S. and Naeye, R.L. (1981) Racial and environmental influences on fetal lung maturation. Pediatrics, 68, 790.

7. Khosla, S.S. and Rooney S.A. (1979) Stimulation of fetal lung surfactant production by administration of 17 β estradiol to the maternal rabbit. Am J Obstet Gynecol, 133, 213.

8. Nielsen, H.C. and Torday, J.S. (1981) Sex differences in fetal rabbit pulmonary surfactant production. Pediatr Res, 15, 1245.

9. Graven, S.N. and Misenheimer, H.R. (1965) Respiratory distress syn-drome and the high risk mother. Am J Dis Child, 109, 489.

10. Hjalmarson, O., Krantz, M.E., Jacobsson, B. and Sörensen, S.E. (1982) The importance of neonatal asphyxia and caesarian section as risk factors for neonatal respiratory disorders in an unselected population. Acta Paediatr Scand, 71, 403.

11. Rokos, J., Vaeusorn, O., Nachman, R. and Avery, M.E. (1968) Hyaline Membrane Disease in twins. Pediatrics, 42, 204.

12. Fredrik, J. and Butler, N.R. (1972) Hyaline Membrane Disease (Letter). Lancet II, 768.

13. Olver, R.E. (1981) Of labour and the lung. Arch Dis Child, 56, 659.

14. Bland, R.D., Mc Millan, D.D., Bressack, M.A. and Dong, L. (1980) Clearence of liquid from lungs of newborn rabbits. J Appl Physiol, 49, 171.

15. Boon, A.W., Hopkin, I.E. and Milner, A.D. (1981) Lung volumes and lung mechanics in babies born vaginally and by elective and emer-gency lower segmental cesarean section. J Pediatr, 98, 812.

16. Robert, M.F., Neff, R.K., Hubbell, J.P. et al (1976) Association between maternal diabetes and the respiratory distress syndrome in the newborn. New Eng J Med, 294, 357.

17. Gross., I (1979) The hormonal regulation of lung maturation. Clin Perinatol, 6, 377.

18. Warburton, D. (1982) Chronic hyperglicemia reduces surface active material flux in tracheal fluid of fetal lambs. Pediatr Res, 16, 118A.

19. Bauer, C.R., Stern, L. and Colle, E. (1974) Prolonged rupture of membranes associated with a decreased incidence of respiratory distress syndrome. Pediatrics, 53, 7.

20. Lee, K., Eidelman, A.I., Tseng, P. et al (1976) Respiratory distress syndrome of the newborn and complications of pregnancy. Pediatrics, 58, 675.

21. Tanswell, A.K. and Smith, B.T. (1978) The relationship of amniotic membrane 11-oxidoreductase activity to lung maturation in the human fetus. Pediatr Res, 12, 957.

22. Glass, L., Rajegowda, B.K. and Evans, H.E. (1971) Absence of respi ratory distress syndrome in premature infants of heroin-addicted mothers. Lancet II, 685.

23. Hallman, M. and Gluck, L. (1982) Respiratory distress syndrome-Update 1982. Pediat Clin North Am, 29, 1057.

24. Papageorgiou, A.N., Colle, E., Farri-Kostopoulos, E. and Gelfand, M.M. (1981) Incidence of respiratory distress syndrome following antenatal betamethasone: role of sex, type of delivery and prolonged rupture of membranes. Pediatrics, 67, 614.

25. Tooley, W.H. (1979) Epidemiology of bronchopulmonary dysplasia. J Pediatr, 95, 851.

26. Adams, F.H., Fujiwara, T., Emmanouilides, G.C. and Rahia, N. (1970) Lung phospholipids of human fetuses and infants with and without Hyaline Membrane Disease. J Pediatr, 77, 833.

27. Gluck, L., Kulovich, M.V., Borer, R.C. et al (1971) Diagnosis of respiratory distress syndrome by amniocentesis. Am J Obstet Gynecol, 109, 440.

28. Hallman, M., Feldman, B.H. and Kirkpatrick, E. (1977) Absence of phosphatidylglycerol (PG) in respiratory distress syndrome in the newborn. Pediatr Res, 11, 714.

29. Kankaanpää, K. and Hallman, M. (1982) Respiratory distress syndrome in very low birth weight infants with occasionally normal surfactant phospholipids. Eur J Pediatr, 139, 31.

30. Bangham, A.D., Morley, C.G. and Phillips, M.C. (1979) The physical properties of an effective lung surfactant. Biochim Biophys Acta, 573, 552.

31. Hallman, M. and Epstein, B.L. (1980) Role of myoinositol in the synthesis of phosphatidylglycerol and phosphatidylinositol in the lung. Biochim Biophys Res Commun, 92, 1151.

32. Giannopoulos, G., Mulay, S. and Solomon, S. (1972) Cortisol receptors in rabbit fetal lung. Biochem Biophys Res Commun, 47, 411.

33. Smith, B.T. (1979) Lung maturation in the fetal rat. Acceleration by injection of fibroblast pneumocyte factor. Science, 204, 1094.

34. Wu, B., Kikkawa, Y., Orzalesi, M. et al (1973) The effect of thyroxin on the maturation of fetal rabbit lungs. Biol Neonat, 22, 161.

35. Hitchcock, K.R. (1979) Hormones and the lung. I. Thyroid hormones and glucocorticoids in lung development. Anat Rec, 194, 15.

36. Hanort, M. (1977) The effect of prolactin on the lecithin content of fetal rabbit lung. J Clin Invest, 59, 1002.

37. Murphy, B.E.P. (1974) Cortisol and cortisone levels in the cord blood at delivery of infants with and without the respiratory distress syndrome. Am J Obstet Gynecol, 119, 1112.

38. Cuestas, R.A., Lindall, A. and Engell, R.R. (1976) Law thyroid hormones and respiratory distress syndrome. Studies on cord blood. New Eng J Med, 295, 297.

39. Conly, P.W., Le Marie, W.J., Monkus, E.F. and Cleveland, W.W. (1973) Plasma estriol concentration in infants with respiratory distress syndrome. J Pediatr, 83, 851.

40. Gluckman, P.D., Ballard, P.L., Kaplan, S.L. et al (1978) Prolactin in umbilical cord blood and the respiratory distress syndrome. J Pediatr, 93, 1011.

41. Hildebran, J.N., Goerke, S. and Clements, J.A. (1981) Surfactant release in excised rat lung is stimulated by air inflation. J Appl Physiol, 51, 905.

42. Hills, B.A. (1981) What is the true role of surfactant in the lung? Thorax, 36, 1.

43. Strang, L.B. (1979). Heterogenicity of pathogenetic mechanisms in Hyaline Membrane Disease. In: The surfactant System and the neonatal lung. Mead Johnson Symp. on Perinatal and Develop. Medicine. Mead Johnson & Co., Evansville, n. 14, p. 53.

44. Lewis, A.B., Heimann, H.A. and Rudolph, A.M. (1976) Gestational changes in pulmonary vascular responses in fetal lambs in utero. Circ Res, 39, 536.

45. Staub, N.C. (1980) Pulmonary edema–hypoxia and overperfusion. N Engl J Med, 302, 1085.

46. Jacob, J., Gluck, L., Di Sessa, T.G. et al (1980) The contribution of PDA in the neonate with severe RDS. J Pediatr, 96, 79.

47. Rudolph, A.M. and Yuan, S. (1966) Response of the pulmonary vasculature to hypoxia and H ion concentration changes. J Clin Invest, 45, 399.

48. Chu, J., Clements, S.A., Cotton, E.K. et al (1967) Neonatal pulmonary ischemia. Pediatrics (suppl), 40, 709.

49. Frank, L. and Massaro, D. (1980) Oxygen toxicity. Am J Med, 69, 117.

50. Nilsson, R., Grossman, G. and Robertson, B. (1978) Lung surfactant and patogenesis of neonatal bronchiolar lesions induced by artificial ventilation. Pediatr Res, 12, 249.

51. Sundell, H., Brigham, K., Green, R. et al (1981) Lung water and vascular permeability. Surface area in lambs with Hyaline Membrane Disease (HMD). Pediatr Res, 15, 731.

52. Jobe, A.H., Ikegami, M., Jacobs, H.C. and Jones, S.J. (1982) The effect of natural surfactant therapy on alveolar permeability in preterm lambs with RDS. Pediatr Res, 16, 352A.

53. Ambrus, C.M., Weintraub, D.H., Dunphy, D. et al (1963) Studies on hyaline membrane disease. I. The fibrinolysin system in patogenesis and therapy. Pediatrics, 32, 10.

54. Sangstad, O.D., Harvie, A. and Langslet, A. (1982) Activation of the kallikrein-kinin system in premature infants with respiratory distress syndrome (RDS). Acta Paediatr Scand, 71, 965.

55. Singer, A.D., Thibeault, D.W., Hobel, C.J. and Heiner, D.C. (1976) Alpha 1 antitrypsyn in amniotic fluid and cord blood of premature infants with the respiratory distress syndrome. J Pediatr, 88, 87.

56. Kääpä, P., Kovisto, M., Viinikka, L. and Yukorkala, O. (1982) Increased plasma immunoreactive 6-keto-prostaglandin $F_{1\alpha}$ levels in newborn with idiopathic respiratory distress syndrome. Pediatr Res, 16, 827.

57. Engle, W.D., Arant, B.S., Wiriyathian, S. and Resenfeld, C.R. (1982) Diuresis and respiratory distress syndrome (RDS): A role of prostacyclin (PGI_2)? Pediatr Res, 16, 286A.

58. Langman, C.B., Engle, W.D., Baumgart, S. et al (1981) The diuretic phase of respiratory distress syndrome and its relationship to oxygenation. J Pediatr, 98, 462.

59. Heaf, D.P., Belik, J., Spitzer, A.R. et al (1982) Changes in pulmonary function during the diuretic phase of respiratory distress syndrome. J Pediatr, 101, 103.

60. Krauss, A.N., Klein, D.B. and Auld, P.A.M. (1975) Chronic pulmonary insufficiency of prematurity (CPIP). J Pediatr, 55, 55.

61. Jacob, J., Edwards, D. and Gluck, L. (1980) Early onset sepsis and pneumonia observed as respiratory distress syndrome. Assessment of lung maturity. Am J Dis Child, 134, 766.

© 1983, Elsevier Science Publishers B.V.
Pulmonary Surfactant System, E.V. Cosmi
and E.M. Scarpelli eds.

RESPIRATORY MUSCLE FATIGUE AND ITS IMPLICATIONS IN RDS

JOSEPH MILIC-EMILI

Meakins-Christie Laboratories and Department of Physiology,
McGill University, 3775 University Street, Montreal, P.Q.
H3A 2B4 (Canada)

It is well recognized that respiratory muscle fatigue can
cause respiratory failure (1). Recently, Bellemare and Grassino
(2,3) made an elegant analysis of diaphragmatic fatigability in
humans. They have shown that in normal adults there is a fatigue
threshold which is reached when the so-called tension-time index
of the diaphragm (TTdi) exceeds 0.15. TTdi is the product of
T_I/T_{TOT} and $\overline{Pdi}$/Pdi max, where T_I/T_{TOT} is the diaphragmatic
duty cycle, i.e. the time during which the diaphragm is contracted
(T_I) as a fraction of total respiratory period (T_{TOT}), $\overline{Pdi}$ is the
mean pressure developed by the diaphragm during inspiration, and
Pdi max is the pressure developed by the diaphragm during a
maximum static inspiratory effort performed at FRC.

As shown in Fig.1, a plot of T_I/T_{TOT} vs. $\overline{Pdi}$/Pdi max allows to
define the range of fatiguing and non-fatiguing breathing patterns.
All patterns which fall above the fatigue threshold will in time
lead to respiratory failure due to diaphragmatic fatigue. On the
other hand, patterns falling below the fatigue threshold can be
sustained indefinitely without the development of diaphragmatic
fatigue. Also shown in Fig.1 is the average breathing pattern for
normal young adults breathing room air at rest, T_I/T_{TOT} amounting
to about 0.38 and $\overline{Pdi}$/Pdi max to 0.07. Since this point lies far
from the fatigue threshold, it is evident that normal adults have
a large respiratory reserve in terms of fatigability of the diaphragm. For newborns, only T_I/T_{TOT} data is available. This
according to Fisher et al (4) amounts to 0.47 ± 0.03(SD)in normal
babies a few days after birth. Pdi max which in normal young
adults amounts to about 100 cmH_2O is most probably much lower in
babies. In 7-8 year-old boys and girls, the maximum inspiratory
static pressure at FRC amount to 60-70% of the corresponding
adult values (5). As a tentative approximation, I will assume
that in newborns Pdi max amounts to 50 cmH_2O (Table 1). This

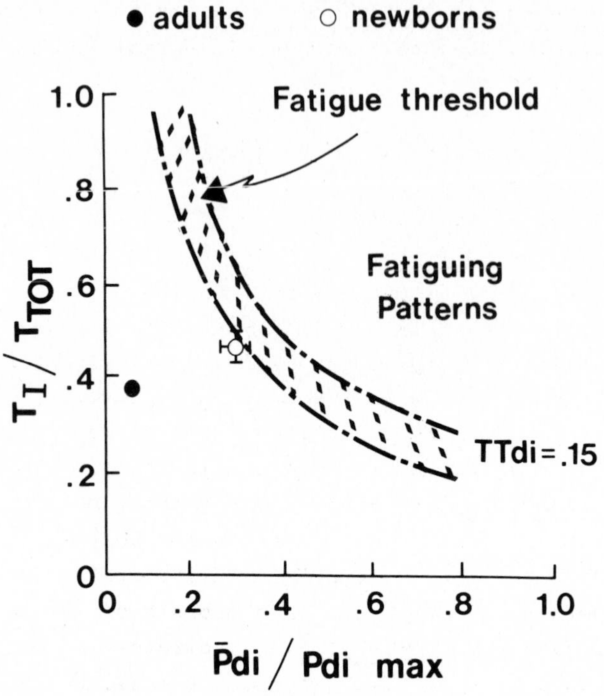

Fig.1. Relationship between T_I/T_{TOT} and $\bar{P}di/Pdi$ max. The hatched area defines the diaphragmatic fatigue threshold, and corresponds to TTdi = 0.15. Filled circle: average value for normal young adults during resting breathing. Open circle: average value for babies (1-5 days old). Bars indicate ± 1SD. After Bellemare and Grassino (2,3).

TABLE 1

	Ref.	T_I/T_{TOT}	$\bar{P}di$ (cmH$_2$0)	Pdi max (cmH$_2$0)	$\bar{P}di/Pdi$ max	TTdi
Newborns (1-5 days old)	4	0.47	(14)	(50)	(0.28)	(0.13)
Adults	2	0.38	7	100	0.07	0.03

Values in parentheses indicate estimates.

is consistent with the maximum negative swings in esophageal pressure recorded by Karlberg et al (6) in normal babies immediately after birth.

To my knowledge, $\bar{P}di$ data for newborns are not available. Since the minute ventilation per kg of body weight ($\dot{V}_E$/BW) is about four times greater in newborns than in adults (410 vs. 110 ml/min/kg) (7), it is also likely that $\bar{P}di$ is substantially greater in the newborns. In fact, $\bar{P}di$ of newborns can be estimated on the basis of the mechanics and breathing pattern data for newborns recently provided by Mortola and co-workers (4,7). These are shown in Table 2 together with the corresponding adult values. The compliance of the total respiratory system (Crs) normalized for body weight, is slightly greater in adults, while the time constant of the total respiratory system (τrs) is about the same in adults as in newborns. Tidal volume (V_T), corrected for body weight, is also similar in adults and newborns, while inspiratory duration (T_I) is much shorter in newborns. On the basis of the mechanics data in Table 2, and assuming that the inspiratory driving pressure (P) increases linearly with time (T), i.e. P = aT, where a is the rate of rise of pressure (cmH_2O/s), it is possible to predict the time-course of volume during inspiration (8). Fig.2 illustrates such predicted inspirograms for newborns and adults. In this prediction it was assumed that the rate of rise of inspiratory

TABLE 2

	Crs/BW ($ml/cmH_2O/kg$)	τ rs (sec)	V_T/BW (ml/kg)	T_I (sec)
Newborns* (1-5 days old)	1.08	0.208	7.2	0.49
Adults	1.29	0.216	7.2	1.50

*From Mortola et al (7).

driving pressure was the same in newborns as in adults. It can be seen that, for equal inspiratory driving pressure, the volume inspired at any time (per kg of BW) was smaller in the newborns, reflecting lower specific compliance (Crs/BW). Furthermore, as a

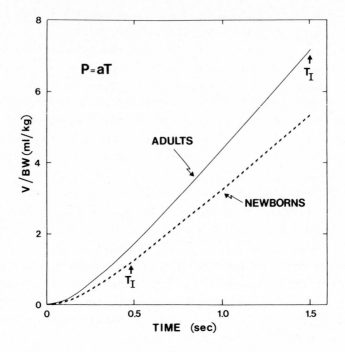

Fig.2. Inspiratory volume-time profiles for newborns and adults, predicted according to Siafakas et al (8) using the Crs/BW and $\dot{V}$rs data in Table 2. Inspiratory driving pressure is assumed to be the same for newborns and adults. Arrows indicate actual durations of inspiration (T_I). For further explanation see text.

result of shorter T_I, in the newborns the tidal volume would amount only to 1.2 ml/kg as compared to 7.2 ml/kg in adults. On the basis of this analysis, it is evident that in order to achieve a tidal volume of 7.2 ml/kg (Table 2) at a T_I of 0.49s, the rate of rise of inspiratory driving pressure must be much greater in newborns than in adults. Indeed, on the basis of model calculations, it can be shown that in order to achieve a tidal volume of 7.2 ml/kg the rate of rise of inspiratory pressure should in newborns be about 6-times greater than in adults. This is consistent with measurements of the mouth occlusion pressure ($P_{0.1}$) which, according to Mortola et al (7), in newborns amounts to 4 cmH_2O ± 1 (SD), as compared to 1 cmH_2O ±0.5 (SD) in adults. On this basis,

and taking T_I into account, $\bar{P}di$ in newborns should amount to
14 cmH$_2$0 (Table 1) (For calculations see APPENDIX). Thus, during
resting breathing in newborns $\bar{P}di/Pdi$ max should be of the order
of 0.28 as compared to 0.07 in adults. By multiplying these
$\bar{P}di/Pdi$ max values by the corresponding T_I/T_{TOT} data, TTdi is obtained. This amounts to 0.03 in adults and 0.13 in newborns.
Thus, during quiet breathing newborns should be close to the
fatigue threshold (TTdi = 0.15), as indicated by the open circle
in Fig.1. This is consistent with the studies of Bryan and his
co-workers (9,10). On the basis of spectral analysis of the diaphragmatic EMG and measurements of rib cage and abdominal motion,
they found evidence of diaphragmatic fatigue in healthy infants
under "normal" conditions. While these studies as well as my
predictions concerning diaphragmatic fatigability in the newborn
require further confirmation, it seems safe to state that newborns
are much closer to the fatigue threshold than adults. Accordingly,
in the face of abnormalities of respiratory mechanics due to chest
disease, newborns should be more prone to ventilatory failure due
to respiratory muscle fatigue than adults.

In RDS, the pulmonary compliance is greatly reduced and furthermore, ventilation increases due to greater wasted ventilation
(increased V_D/V_T ratio caused both by increased physiologic dead
space and decreased tidal volume)(11). As a result, the inspiratory efforts are greatly increased (12). This increased burden to
breathe should promote diaphragmatic fatigue. In this connection
it should be stressed that rapid and shallow breathing is deleterious not only because it increases wasted (dead space) ventilation, but also because when T_I is low relative to τrs a large
fraction of the inspiratory effort is wasted in terms of generation of tidal volume (13). Consequently, minute ventilation is
small in relation to the intensity of the inspiratory efforts.

In conclusion, in newborns the respiratory reserve in terms of
diaphragmatic fatigue is reduced because (a) their T_I/T_{TOT} is
increased, (b) diaphragmatic strength (Pdi max) is low, and (c)
$\bar{P}di$ is high as a result of relatively high minute ventilation. In
addition, the low compliance of their rib cage promotes its para-
doxing during inspiration, rendering the contraction of the

diaphragm less effective in terms of generation of negative intra-thoracic pressure.

APPENDIX

If the pressure developed by the diaphragm (Pdi) is assumed to increase linearly during inspiration (Pdi = aT, where a is rate of rise of the pressure and T is time), it follows that the mean Pdi ($\bar{\text{Pdi}}$)developed during inspiration (T_I) is equal to Pdi = 0.5a T_I. Since in newborns the rate of rise of inspiratory pressure is about 6-times greater than in adults (see text), and T_I is shorter (0.49s vs. 1.5s), it follows that $\bar{\text{Pdi}}$ in newborns is about 2-times greater than in adults (0.5 x 6a x 0.49/0.5 x a x 1.5 = 1.96).

REFERENCES

1. Roussos, C.S., and Macklem, P.T. (1977) Diaphragmatic fatigue in man. J. Appl.Physiol.: Respirat.Environ.Exercise Physiol., 43,189.

2. Bellemare, F. and Grassino, A.(1982) Effect of pressure and timing of contraction on human diaphragm fatigue. J. Appl. Physiol.: Respirat. Environ.Exercise Physiol.,53, 1190.

3. Bellemare,F. and Grassino,A.(1982) Evaluation of human dia-phragm fatigue. J.Appl.Physiol.: Respirat.Environ.Exercise Physiol.,53,1196.

4. Fisher, J.T.,Mortola, J.P.,Smith,J.B.,Fox,G.S. and Weeks,S. (1982) Respiration in newborns. Am. Rev. Resp. Dis.,125, 650.

5. Gaultier, C., Perret, L.,Boule,M.,Buvry,A. and Girard,F.(1981) Occlusion pressure and breathing pattern in healthy children. Respir.Physiol.,46,71.

6. Karlberg,P.(1962) The adaptive changes in the immediate post-natal period with particular reference to respiration. J. Pediat.,56,121.

7. Mortola,J.F.,Fisher,J.T.,Smith,B.,Fox,G.and Weeks,S.(1982) Dynamics of breathing in infants. J. Appl.Physiol.:Respirat. Environ.Exercise Physiol.,52, 1209.

8. Siafakas,N.M.,Peslin,R.,Bonora,M.,Gautier,H.,Duron,B. and Milic-Emili, J.(1981) Phrenic activity, respiratory pressures, and volume changes in cats. J.Appl.Physiol.: Respirat.Environ. Exercise Physiol.,51, 109.

9. Muller,N.,Gulston,G.,Cade,D.,Whitton,J.,Froese,A.B.,Bryan,M.H. and Bryan,A.C.(1979) Diaphragmatic muscle fatigue in the new-born. J.Appl.Physiol.:Respirat.Environ.Exercise Physiol., 46,688.

10. Lopes, J.M., Muller,N.L.,Bryan,M.H.,and Bryan,A.C.(1981) Synergistic behavior of inspiratory muscles after diaphragmatic fatigue in the newborn. J. Appl. Physiol.: Respirat. Environ.Exercise Physiol.,51,547.

11. Chu,J.,Clements,J.A.,Cotton,E.K.,Klous, M.H.,Sweet,A.Y. and Tooley,W.H.(1967) Neonatal pulmonary ischemia. Pediatrics, Springfield,40,709.

12. Cook,C.D.,Sutherland,J.M.,Segal,S.,Cherry,R.B.,Mead,J., McIlroy,M.B.,and Smith,C.A.(1957 Studies of respiratory physiology in the newborn infant.III. Measurements of the mechanics of respiration. J.Clin.Invest.,36,440.

13. Milic-Emili, J. and Zin,W.A.(1983) Mechanical aspects of ventilatory control. Bull.europ.Physiopath.resp.(In Press).

© 1983, Elsevier Science Publishers B.V.
Pulmonary Surfactant System, E.V. Cosmi
and E.M. Scarpelli eds.

HIGH FREQUENCY VENTILATION AND OSCILLATORY TECHNIQUES IN THE
TREATMENT OF RESPIRATORY DISTRESS SYNDROME.

A. Charles Bryan, Respiratory Physiology, Hospital for Sick
Children, Toronto, Ontario, Canada.

INTRODUCTION

In recent years there has been a substantial drop in mortality
in the infant respiratory distress syndrome (RDS). Despite this,
mechanical ventilation of infants is still a dangerous practice.
Large volumes and hence large pressures, are being applied to a
structurally immature lung with a non-uniform distribution of
compliances. Acute complications, such as pneumothoraces are not
uncommon and often appear to precipitate intraventricular
hemorrhages (1). The incidence of bronchopulmonary dysplasia
(BPD) is still quite high and carries a significant morbidity and
mortality. Although the etiology of BPD is still controversial,
high ventilator pressures are certainly implicated.

High frequency ventilation (HFV) at least in theory, might
resolve some of these problems. HFV has been shown to be very
effective in removing CO_2 from the lungs using tidal volumes less
than the volume of the anatomical dead space (2,3). The use of
small volumes implies low pressures and distensions that may
reduce parenchymal damage.

Definitions of HFV

The term high frequency ventilation has been introduced as
though it had a universal definition. It is about as vague as
the word 'pasta' - it does not determine ingredient, shape or
sauce. Physiologically its origins go back to Yandall-Henderson
et al (4) who appreciated that the dead space depended on flow
regime and later on some elegant work by Briscoe et al confirming
this in man (5). Meanwhile Sjostrand and his colleagues (6)
started using a high frequency jet device which used small tidal
volumes at frequencies of about 1-2 Hz. The emphasis on these
devices was that the small tidal volume was possible because there
was a low compressible system volume. At about the same time,
Lunkenheimer et al (7), while examining another problem, observed
that he could maintain normocarbia in apneic dogs using a loud-

speaker driven up to 40 Hz. This extraordinary experiment did not get the attention it deserved because all the dogs developed severe metabolic acidosis. Bohn et al (2) subsequently showed that excellent gas exchange could be achieved with a normal pH if the mean airway pressure was not too high.

Since that time there has been an explosive growth in the literature on HFV, divided roughly into two classes:
(1) relatively low frequency, 1-3 Hz jet ventilation applied in a variety of configurations which comprise the bulk of the adult clinical literature.
(2) higher frequency ventilation - 10 Hz and up, generally utilizing oscillatory wave forms and subsequently smaller volumes. The relative merits of these two approaches has not been systematically studied and all the work in this paper has been done at 15 Hz with a tidal volume of about 1-2 ml/kilo.

Mechanism of High Frequency Ventilation

The mechanism for CO_2 removal when the tidal volume is less than the dead space is still conjectural. Certainly more than one mechanism is involved. Taylor dispersion appears to play a major role (8,9). The superimposition of a convective flow on diffusion can substantially enhance the diffusive process. The effective diffusivity (Deff) depends on velocity (u) and a characteristic diameter (d) and L the Wormsley number in oscillatory flow in the general form (3).

$$Deff = Dmol + k_1 u^2 d^2 \qquad \text{Laminar flow}$$
$$Deff = Dmol + k_2 u\, d \qquad \text{Turbulent flow}$$
$$Deff = Dmol + k_3 u^2 d^2 / L^7 \qquad \text{Oscillatory}$$

A second process was observed by Lehr et al (10) who showed that there were gross phase lags in inflation and deflation between adjacent units. This pendeluft may play an important role in intra-regional mixing.

Finally the path lengths to alveoli vary and some units with short path lengths may receive direct alveolar ventilation.

Probably the dominant mechanism depends on the particular system and frequency involved. Most of the physiological studies have been carried out at very high frequency where gas exchange varies with volume (V) and frequency (f) from Vf to $V^2 f$ depending on flow regime.

High Frequency Ventilation Strategy

There is now ample evidence that HFV is highly effective in "shaking" CO_2 out of normal and abnormal lungs. The same is true for "shaking" O_2 into normal lungs and into some types of lung disease. But in diseases such as RDS characterized by extensive atelectasis, no amount of shaking will open up a shut lung. For this an entirely different strategy is required.

In an atelectic lung pressure is required to open closed units. There are likely to be a range of opening pressures. Similarly, when pressures are reduced, units will close and there will be a range of closing pressures (figure 1). On the standard ventilator at end expiration, there will be extensive closure. With the ventilator stroke there will be no volume change until the pressure exceeds opening pressure, after which there will be rapid alveolar recruitment. During expiration, as soon as closing pressure is reached, there will be substantial de-recruitment back to the original atelectatic state. Effective gas exchange will only occur during late inspiration and early expiration. Furthermore, there is a potential of parenchymal damage from the constant opening and closing of units.

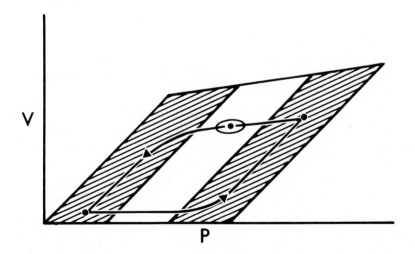

Figure 1:   Schematic P-V curve on conventional ventilation bounded by bands of opening and closing pressure. Oval represents the optimum position for HFV.

An entirely different strategy is used with HFV. The pressure has to be increased to above the closing pressure. But this is on the inflation limb of the PV curve and not much volume is recruited. Further, as the peak pressure on HFV is small, it is unlikely to exceed opening pressure. Volume has to be recruited by slowly inflating the lung to about 30 cmH_2O and then letting it return to the original pressure on the deflation limb of the PV curve. As this pressure is above closing pressure, there should be no de-recruitment of lung volume unless the system is disconnected, e.g. for suctioning. Thus, a single sigh is theoretically capable of recruiting substantial lung volume and maintaining that recruitment.

Experimental Work on High Frequency Ventilation

Although this strategy is schematic, it has proved very effective in models of the respiratory distress syndrome. Adult rabbits anesthetized, intubated and paralyzed, had their lungs repeatedly lavaged with normal saline until they had an arterial oxygen tension of about 100 torr on $F_IO_2 = 1$ (11). One group was put on a standard ventilator, with pressures of 25/5 and a mean pressure of 15 cmH_2O - the other group was put on HFV (1-2 ml/kg at 15 Hz) with a mean pressure of 15 cmH_2O. Both groups were then slowly inflated to 30 cmH_2O pressure and then returned to their initial pressure setting at an F_IO_2 of 1. This resulted in an immediate improvement in PaO_2 on the HFV animals, but had no sustained effect on the standard ventilated animals. At the end of 4 hours, the blood gases showed:

	PaO_2 torr	$PaCO_2$ torr	pH units	
CMV	56 ± 4	56 ± 5	7.15 ± 0.07	$\bar{m}$ ± SE
HFV	403 ± 26	37 ± 3	7.29 ± 0.11	

These experiments have been carried out to 20 hours in the HFV group and the good blood gases were maintained throughout. In contrast, none of the animals on the conventional ventilator lasted beyond 16 hours, dying either with a progressive metabolic acidosis, or as a result of pneumothoraces. At autopsy all the rabbits on standard ventilation had extensive hyaline membranes throughout all sections, in contrast, the HFV group were almost entirely free from any hyaline membrane formation. When alveoli were atelectatic, the large ventilator pressures cause over distension of respiratory bronchioles in alveolar ducts. This causes distraction of the epithelium with an eventual necrosis and shedding, the shed epithelial debris forms these hyaline membranes.

The absence of hyaline membranes on HFV probably has two causes. First, alveoli have been recruited so that there is a substantial lung volume and secondly, the small volume distensions do not cause epithelial distraction. Oscillation of even a small volume in the lung in which alveolar recruitment had not occurred might be as damaging, or more damaging than conventional ventilation. These pathological changes are mirrored physiologically, by changes in pressure volume curve. On conventional ventilation there is a progressive decrease in the compliance of the lung throughout the period of ventilation. In contrast, on HFV there is almost no change in the PV curve throughout the four hour period of ventilation.

Unfortunately we cannot usually achieve such dramatic results in treating infants with RDS. The problem is largely geographical, we are a referral hospital and all the babies we receive have been ventilated for at least 4 hours before we see them. As a result we are not dealing with a simple surfactant deficiency, but a lung with extensive hyaline membrane formation and a substantial protein leak into the alveoli. The lung has become stiff and the hysteresis illustrated on Figure 1 has largely been lost, therefore it is much more difficult to recruit volume. Furthermore, in the damaged lung there is probably considerable overlap of opening and closing pressures. Despite this we have embarked on a Controlled Clinical Trial, comparing conventional mechanical ventilation with high frequency ventilation in the management of RDS. Once the infant has been diagnosed as RDS, they are randomised by minimization (12) and assigned to either control or high frequency ventilation. Randomization by minimization is a powerful technique for keeping the groups balanced for age, sex, weight and severity of disease during the course of the study. The study is still in its early stages, but it is quite clear that dramatic results, such as were achieved in the lavaged rabbits, are only rarely being achieved, presumably because all the infants that we have studied have been pre-treated for many hours with mechanical ventilation.

Respiratory Control on High Frequency Ventilation

One interesting aspect of this study is that the infants are apneic throughout most of the period of HFV. They appear much more comfortable than infants on conventional ventilators who are often 'fighting' the ventilator. We have observed this apnea previously in animals (2,13) and it is not simply that the requirement to breathe has been removed because HFV is achieving the gas exchange. It is an active apnea, the result of inhibition of respiration by stimulation, presumably of the slowly adapting stretch receptors in the upper airways and also an inhibition from the chest wall muscle spindles. The apnea is not absolute, if the child is aroused it will breathe normally, also when the infant enters rapid eye movement sleep, breathing is present. This is of some interest as the Hering Breuer reflex is markedly diminished in REM sleep (14) and the muscle spindles are disabled (15). The only other time that the infant breathes are when there is something mechanically wrong and the high frequency ventilation is not achieving adequate gas exchange. Therefore, in the absence of REM sleep breathing becomes a useful indicator of malfunction.

REFERENCES
1. Dykes, F.D., Lazzara, A., Ahmann, P., Blumenstein, B., Schwartz J. and Brann, A.W. (1980). Pediatrics, 66:42.

2. Bohn, D.J., Miyasaka, K. Marchak, B.E., Thompson, W.K., Froese A.B. and Bryan A.C. (1980) J. Appl. Physiol:Respirat Environ Exercise Physiol. 48:710-716.

3. Slutsky A.S., Drazen, J.M., Ingram, R.H., Kamm R.D., Shapiro, A.H., Fredberg, J.J., Loring E.H. and Lehr J. (1980) Science 209:608-611.

4. Henderson, Y., Chillingworth, F.P., Whitney, J.L. (1915) Am. J. Physiol. 38:1.

5. Briscoe, W.A., Forster, R.E., and Comroe J.H. (1954) J. Appl. Physiol:7:27-30.

6. Jonzon, A., Oberg, P.A., Sedin, G., and Sjöstrand, U. (1971). Acta. Anaesthesiol. Scand. (Suppl)43:1

7. Lunkenheimer, P.P., Frank, I., Ising, H., Keller, H. and Dickhut, H.H. (1972). Drukwechsel Anaesthetist, 22:232.

8. Taylor G. (1953) Proc. Roy. Soc. A219, 186-203.

9. Taylor G. (1954) Proc. Roy. Soc. A223, 446-468.

10. Lehr,J. (1980) Fed. Proc. 39:676A.

11. Hamilton P., Onayemi, B., Gillan,J., Smyth, J., and Bryan, A.C. (1982) Fed. Proc. 41:1747.

12. Taves, D.R.   (1974) Clin. Pharmacol. & Therap. 15:443-453.

13. Thompson, W.K., Marchak, B.E., Bryan, A.C., and Froese, A.B.
    (1981). J. Appl. Physiol:Respirat Environ. Exercise Physiol.
    51:1484-1487.

14. Phillipson, E.A.   (1978). Annual Rev. Physiol. 40:133-155.

15. Gassel, M.M., and Pompeiano, O.   (1965). Arch. Ital. Biol.
    103:347-368.

© 1983, Elsevier Science Publishers B.V.
Pulmonary Surfactant System, E.V. Cosmi
and E.M. Scarpelli eds.

HIGH FREQUENCY VENTILATION IN RABBITS WITH EXPERIMENTALLY IN-
DUCED RDS

G. PAGANI[1], R. REZZONICO[1], A. MARINI[1], G. AGUGGINI[2]

[1]Newborn Unit, Department of Obstetrics and Gynecology, University of Milan, Via Commenda,12 - 20122 Milan (Italy) and [2]Institute
of Veterinary Physiology and Biochemistry, University of Milan,
Via Celoria,10 - 20133 Milan (Italy)

INTRODUCTION

It has been suggested that High Frequency Jet Ventilation (HFJV)
compared to conventional ventilation (IPPV) can improve gas exchanges, especially oxygenation, in acute respiratory failure
(1,2,3,4). Afterwards, controlled studies comparing HFJV to
IPPV in clinical or experimental setting failed to confirm these
observations for similar FiO_2 and airways pressures (5,6). Further experimental studies and technological advances are needed
to give better clinical indications.

We previously studied in healthy animals (rabbits) the comparative effects of HFJV, of IPPV and of High Frequency Positive
Pressure Ventilation (HFPPV). Similar values of PaO_2 and PCO_2
were observed with each technique, but MAP were significantly
lower with HFJV when inspiratory time was strictly controlled;
haemodynamic involvment was also reduced. Similar results were
obtained on animals with infectious respiratory diseases, and
the improvement in metabolic and haemodynamic parameters was
even more pronounced in this case.

We now report the effects of HFJV versus IPPV in rabbits previously treated with oleic acid to produce experimental Respiratory Distress Syndrome (RDS) with reduced compliance caused by
haemorragic pulmonary oedema. Rabbits were recently selected by
several Authors as animals for studies on respiratory physiopathology (8,9). This model seem fit for purposes of research oriented on the neonate.

METHODS

Eighteen rabbits weighing 2.8 - 3.4 Kg were used to study the response to HFJV versus IPPV in RDS. Anesthesia was induced with ethylurethane 25%, and respiratory paralysis with pancuronium bromide (0.05 mg/Kg repeated as needed). Oleic acid was infused in the right atrium over 5 minutes at a dose of 0.050 ml/Kg to produce RDS. The following parameters were monitored: sistolic Blood Pressure (sBP), diastolic Blood Pressure (dBP), Central Venous Pressure (CVP), Heart Rate (HR), arterial blood gases and pH, Alveolar - arterial Difference in O_2 tension (A-aDO$_2$) and Mean Airways Pressure (MAP). Arterial blood samples were analyzed for gases and acid-base status with Emogasanalizer IL 213; haemodynamic parameters were evaluated with electromagnetic transducers and recorded on a multichannel Grass 7B with integration of the pressure waveform signal to allow accurate determination of MAP at high frequencies. IPPV with PEEP was obtained by a conventional continuous flow ventilator (BAMP 06, Bertocchi - Cremona Italy) adjusted to obtain a moderate degree of hyperventilation. HFJV was delivered by a ventilator with flow interrupted by a solenoid valve. The flow was forced through an injector of 0.8mm diameter which ended in a metal device connected to the external side of an endotracheal tube (Rusch, diameter 3 mm). The ventilator rate was about 5-6 Hz and the inspiratory rate was controlled and lasted 1/3 - 1/4 of each cycle. The ventilator was connected to a high pressure gas source and the flow (air) regulated at about 0.8 1/Kg/minute. Slight modifications of the flow were introduced, when needed, in order to obtain optimal arterial blood gases. In the espiratory phase gas from airways was allowed to be released freely. The following protocol was adopted: after initial preparation (cannulation of femoral artery and external jugular vein, orotracheal blind intubation) rabbits were allowed to stabilize for 2 hours, maintaining normal temperature, in supine position. Then oleic acid was administered. 1 hour after 6 rabbits were left unassisted, 6 were ventilated on IPPV and 6 on HFJV. Ventilation was continued for 3 and a half hours on IPPV, and 3 hours and 50 minutes on HFJV. Results are reported as mean values $\pm$ SE. Variations were analyzed by Student's t-test for paired data.

RESULTS

The results are illustrated in the graphs 1 and 2.

One hour after oleic acid administration (t_1) a non significant decrease in pH, sistolic and diastolic BP and HR was observed in all groups of rabbits. PaO_2 decreased from 65 $\pm$ 12 torr to 50.8 $\pm$ 10 torr in control group, from 65 $\pm$ 11 to 55 $\pm$ 19 torr in IPPV group and 68.8 $\pm$ 8 to 63 $\pm$ 16 torr in HFJV group. All animals were finally in distress but a variability in the time of appearance was observed; this justifies the slight differences in PaO_2 at T_1. Afterwards there was progressive derangement in all parameters considered in the control group, and two animals died. In the group ventilated with HFJV, the pressure wave in the airways was monitored and efforts were made to obtain always a square form; when sinusoidal shape was produced all parameters proved unsatisfactory. At the end of the observation (t_2) in ventilated rabbits there was further decrease in pH, more pronounced in IPPV group (7.183 $\pm$ 0.05) than in HFJV group (7.244 $\pm$ 0.11) but the difference was not significant ($p < 0.1$). PCO_2 decreased in both groups (27 $\pm$ 5 torr in IPPV, 28 $\pm$ 8 in in HFJV) in a similar fashion. PaO_2 increased reaching identical levels (88 $\pm$ 28 torr in IPPV and 88 $\pm$ 16 in HFJV) and $A-aDO_2$ decreased from 55 $\pm$ 22 torr to 28 $\pm$ 16 torr in IPPV and from 48 $\pm$ 11 torr to 25.5 $\pm$ 15 torr in HFJV group. These results were obtained with a MAP of 6 $\pm$ 0.9 torr on IPPV and 3.5 $\pm$ 0.5 torr on HFJV; the difference is highly significant ($p < 0.001$).

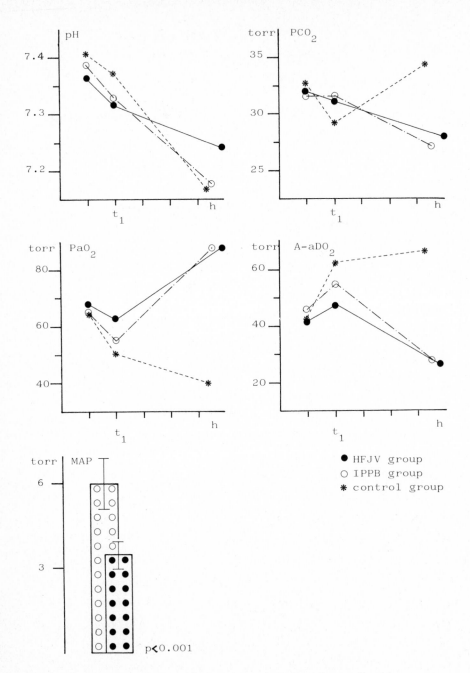

Fig.1.Variation of respiratory parameters (mean)

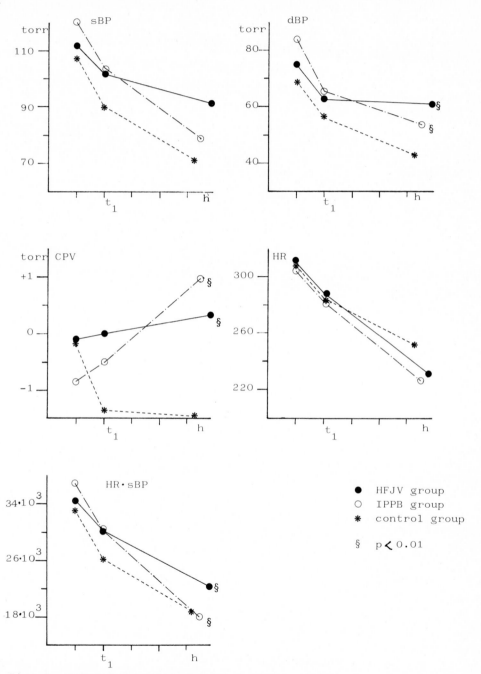

Fig. 2. Variation of hemodynamic parameters (mean)

We measured identical values of MAP in HFJV at any distance from the injector to the carena. Probably, as a consequence of low MAP, we observed no modification in CPV with HFJV (from -0.1 ± 1 to $+0.3 \pm 1$ torr) whereas with IPPV there was a rise from -0.83 ± 1 to $+ 1 \pm 0.7$ torr; the difference between the two groups is significant (p 0.01). The BP decreased from $104 \pm 19/66 \pm IO$ torr in IPPV and from $102 \pm 24/62 \pm 17$ in HFJV to $79 \pm 22/54 \pm 15$ and to $92 \pm 30/61 \pm 21$ respectively ($p < 0.01$).

An indirect index of cardiac output also revealed a minor derangement in HFJV: the product of HR and sBP passed from 30065 ± 9400 to 22229 ± 11000 (from 30387 ± 6600 to 17945 ± 5272 with IPPV - $p < 0.01$).

DISCUSSION

The first aim of this work was to obtain the same values of blood gases both with HFJV and IPPV in order to compare ventilation induced changes on metabolic and haemodynamic parameters. As expected, the moderate hyperventilation obtained by IPPV caused metabolic acidosis, slight hypotension, and rise in CVP, in correlation with sustained MAP. Similar results in respiratory parameters were obtained on HFJV with a lower MAP, along with minor decrease of pH and BP. CVP was not modified compared to control values when HFJV was adopted. Therefore this kind of ventilation, as obtained in our experiences, could afford good oxygenation: 1) by enhancement of alveolar gas exchange; 2) by reducing the intrapulmonary right to left shunt; 3) by raising the O_2 content in venous blood as expected through preserving a good cardiac output in relation to metabolic demands. This hypothesis might be supported by the maintenance of good values of the product of the HR and sBP ($HR \cdot sBP$) observed on HFJV.

I has been suggested that the high velocity of the gas flow generated in the airways by high frequency ventilation enhances the gas transport through an increase of axial molecular diffusivity (10). The turbulence produced by HFJV (with corresponding high Reynolds numbers calculated in this setting) moreover modifies axial velocity profiles of the flow in the inspiratory and expiratory phase which depends on geometric and aereodynamic characteristics of bronchial tree and its bifurcations (11).

Both convection and diffusivity of gases could be enhanced in airways on high frequency ventilation (12), but the theory of gas exchanges in HFJV is not fully explained. From these and our previous results we can draw some empiric considerations: 1) satisfactory gas exchanges with low airways pressure can only be attained by generating square pressure waves; 2) the best frequencies are similar to those measured in the heart during exercise, in a given experimental model; 3) an I:E ratio of 1:3 - 1:4 seems the more suitable way to obtain a compromise between molecular acceleration (enhanced molecular diffusivity) and other properties of the ventilatory pattern i.e. high enough pressure (but lower than in IPPV) to prevent alveolar collapse. However, when it will be not possible to obtain a square pressure wave with above mentioned ratios, we would prefer to increase inspiratory time in order to generate a square wave. This is in agreement with Hammeroff (13). In previous studies with healthy rabbits ventilated on HFJV we demonstrated (14) lower generation of Prostacyclin by pulmonary circulation than on IPPV. This could mean that lesser barotrauma is created to the airways, in accordance with Gryglewsky (15). Preliminary data in rabbits treated with oleic acid suggest that this hypothesis is correct, but more data are needed.

In conclusion rabbits with experimentally induced RDS through an infusion of oleic acid seem to be a good model for evaluating different kinds of ventilatory support. HFJV is a promising technique in order to obtain the reduction of haemodynamic derangement and risk of barotrauma, air leaks and Bronchopulmonary Dysplasia in the treatment of patients with RDS, but many more experimental studies are needed to fully understand how this model works and before to be translated in the clinical field.

REFERENCES

1) CARLON G.C., KAHN R.C., HOWLAND W.S., RAY C.Jr. and TURNBULL A.D. (1981) Clinical experience with high frequency jet ventilation. Crit. Care Med. 9, pp1-6.

2) SCHUSTER D.P., SNYDER J.V., KLAIN M., et al (1981) High frequency jet ventilation during the treatment of acute fulminant pulmonary edema: A case study. Chest 80, p 682.

3) DERDERIAN S.S., RAJAGOPAL K.R., ABBRECHT P.H., BENNETT L.L. DOBLAR D.D. and HUNT K.K. (1982) High frequency positive pressure jet ventilation in bilateral bronchopleural fistulae. Crit. Care Med. 10, pp 119-121.

4) POKORA T.J., BING D.R. and BOROS S.J. (1982) Neonatal High Frequency Jet Ventilation (Abstract) Pediat. Res. 16, p 359A.

5) MAMMEL M.C., GORDON M.J. and BOROS S.J. (1982) A comparison of High Frequency Jet Ventilation (HFJV) and conventional mechanical ventilation (CMV) In experimentally induced meconium aspiration. (Abstract) Pediatr. Res. 16, p 355A.

6) SCHUSTER D.P., KLAIN M. and SNYDER J.V. (1982) Comparison of high frequency jet ventilation to conventional ventilation during severe acute respiratory failure in humans. Crit. Care Med. 10, pp 625-630.

7) PAGANI G., MARZANI M., MARINI A. and AGUGGINI G. Rilievi sperimentali su alcune tecniche di ventilazione ad alta frequenza. Submitted for publication to Giornale Ital. Mal. Torace.

8) RAJU T., BRAVERMAN B., KIM W.D., NADKARNY U. and VIDYASAGAR D. (1982) Some difficulties with High frequency Oscillator (HFO) and Interruptor (HFI). (Abstract) Pediatr. Res. 16, p 360A.

9) LACHMANN B., JONSON B., LINDROTH M. and ROBERTSON B.(1982) Modes of artificial ventilation in severe respiratory distress syndrome. Lung function and morphology in rabbits after washout of alveolar surfactant. Crit. Care Med 10, pp 724 - 732.

10) FREDBERG J.J. (1980) Augmented diffusion in the airways can support pulmonary gas exchange. J. Appl. Physiol.: Respirat. Environ Exercise PHysiol. 49, pp 232 -238.

11) SCHERER P.W. and HASELTON F.R. (1982) Convective exchange in oscillatory flow through bronchial-tree models. J. Appl. Physiol.: Respirat. Environ. Exercise PhysioL 53, pp 1023-1033.

12) GALLAGHER T.J., KLAIN M.M. and CARLON G.C. (1982) Present status of high frequency ventilation. Crit. Care Med. 10, p 613 - 617.

13) HAMMEROFF S.R., CALKINS J.M., WATERSON C.K. et al (1981) Cardiac-pulmonary interactions in high frequency jet ventilation. Crit. Care Med. 9,p160.

14) PAGANI G., MARINI A., AGUGGINI G and MARZANI M.(1982) Effects of two different kinds of respiratory assistence on 6-Keto-PGF_1 levels in adult rabbits (Intermittent Positive Pressure Ventilation - IPPV and Very High Frequency Jet Ventilation _ VHFJV). Fifth International Conference Prostaglandins Florence (Italy)- May 18-21, 1982, p 331.

15) GRYGLEWSKY R.J., KORBUT R. and OLETKIEWICZ A.C. (1978) Generation of Prostacyclin by lungs in vivo and its release into arterial circulation. Nature 273, p 765.

SURFACTANT REPLACEMENT IN THE TREATMENT OF THE NEONATAL RESPIRATORY DISTRESS SYNDROME (RDS)

BENGT ROBERTSON

Department of Pathology, St Göran's Hospital, S-112 81 Stockholm (Sweden)

INTRODUCTION

Replacing the missing surfactant would seem a logical therapeutic regimen in neonatal RDS. The first experimental evidence suggesting the efficacy of this type of treatment was provided by Rüfer (1) who showed that the pressure-volume characteristics of lungs from infants dying with RDS could be improved by "rinsing" the airspaces with natural surfactant. Similar studies were later performed by Enhörning & Robertson (2) on lung preparations from fetal rabbits; these animal experiments were the first to show that the mechanical properties of a surfactant-deficient immature lung can be converted into those of a mature lung simply by adding crude natural surfactant to the fetal pulmonary fluid. The results suggested to the authors that "tracheal deposition of surfactant might be adopted as a prophylactic measure against the idiopathic respiratory distress syndrome" (2). Today, surfactant replacement has been tested in many units not only prophylactically, but also as treatment for severe RDS. This paper will give a brief review of these clinical trials, with special emphasis on some basic problems related to the production of artificial surfactant for clinical use.

ENRICHED NATURAL SURFACTANT

The composition of surfactant material recovered from lung tissue by extraction procedures or bronchial lavage does not necessarily reflect that of the alveolar lining of the same lungs. The obvious reason for this discrepancy is that the "purification" procedures available do not clearly discriminate between alveolar phospholipids, and similar molecules from cell membranes or from the lining layer of conducting airways. Furthermore, since only few biochemical studies in this field have been based on material directly sampled from the alveolar surface (3-5), our knowledge of the composition of lung surfactant in situ is still incomplete. Paradoxically, many investigators have been "purifying" surfactant without knowing the exact composition of the material to be purified.

TABLE 1
The composition of "Fuji-surf" (7); data from Fujiwara & Adams (8).

Total lipid phosphorus	19 µmol/ml
DPPC	56 %
Unsaturated phosphatidylcholines	21 %
PG	10 %
Other phospholipids	6 %
Neutral lipids	5 %
Protein	2 %

Fujiwara et al (6) have described a method for production of "artificial surfactant" based on phospholipids and proteins extracted from bovine lungs. The phospholipid composition of this material, shown in Table 1, is different from natural surfactant, as the material is enriched with the synthetic phospholipids dipalmitoylphosphatidylcholine (DPPC) and unsaturated phosphatidylglycerol (PG). The reason for this modification is that the extracted natural surfactant failed to reduce surface tension to very low values on surface compression, when spread on a hypophase of saline at 37°C. However, when DPPC and PG were added up to the relative concentrations given in Table 1, the surfactant film had a significantly lower compressibility and a surface tension of 10.3 ± 1.5 mN/m ($\bar{X} \pm SD$) was recorded already at 50 % surface compression (6).

After having documented the physiological activity of this preparation in experiments on immature newborn rabbits (9,10), Fujiwara et al (11) successfully applied their semi-synthetic surfactant in a clinical trial on 10 babies with severe RDS. All these patients were on artificial ventilation and the material was given at a mean age of 12 h. They received a comparatively large dose of surfactant lipids (ca 100 mg/kg) via the tracheal cannula and were then reconnected to the ventilator system. The response was impressive: shortly after instillation

of surfactant there was a striking improvement of blood gases
and the insufflation pressure and oxygen dose could therefore
be significantly reduced. Radiological changes in the lungs
disappeared within 6 h after surfactant replacement.

Fujiwara (12) has now extended this clinical trial to include
38 patients, and the conclusion remains the same. Treatment
with this type of surfactant has a dramatic immediate effect
on blood gases even in severe RDS, but some patients remain
dependent on ventilator treatment for several days. Problems
related to left-to-right shunting via a patent ductus arteriosus
may appear after surfactant replacement and necessitate surgical
closure of the ductus.

OTHER PREPARATIONS BASED ON NATURAL HETEROLOGOUS SURFACTANT

Fujiwara's first study of surfactant replacement in RDS was
a major break-through, which attracted world-wide, justified
attention (7,13-15). Clinical trials, based on alternative preparations of natural surfactant soon followed.

One of the materials currently tested is based on porcine
surfactant, suspended with $CaCl_2$ (16). The rationale of this
formula is that bivalent cations preferentially form bridges
between the polar heads of saturated phospholipid molecules
in an air-liquid interface, further reducing the compressibility
of the surface film (17). Kobayashi et al (18) and Ohta et al
(19) have tested this type of surfactant preparation, "Surfactant
CK" in newborn infants with RDS. The first two cases were reported
in some detail. In one patient (18) surfactant replacement at
the age of 6 h, resulted in a permanent improvement of blood
gases, similar to that usually observed in Fujiwara's trial
(11,12). The other patient, treated at the age of 36 h showed
only a transient response and died, in spite of additional instil-
lations of surfactant, 22 h later (19). Possible explanations
to this latter failure are that the treatment was given too
late and that the dose of surfactant lipids, ca 25 mg/kg, might
have been insufficient.

It has been claimed that the "apoproteins" of the pulmonary surfactant system might accelerate the surface adsorption of the phospholipid fraction (20,21). However, recent data from in-vitro studies (22), animal experiments (23-25) and a limited clinical trial (26) suggest that natural surfactant administered via the airways is physiologically active also after removal of most of its protein components. The patients receiving protein-depleted material, prepared by repeated chloroform-methanol extraction of natural surfactant (22), showed the same immediate therapeutic response as reported in other clinical trials of surfactant replacement (26). These new experimental and clinical data are somewhat obscured, however, by the fact that the surfactant preparations were not entirely protein-free (27), nor was it clearly stated whether remaining traces of protein were related to the surfactant apoproteins or not.

AMNIOTIC-FLUID SURFACTANT

Fetal lung liquid is periodically expelled into the amniotic cavity (28). Towards the end of gestation the lung liquid, and therefore also the amniotic fluid, contains mature pulmonary surfactant. The human fetus is thus "a potential surfactant donor" (29).

Hallman et al (29) have succeeded in "purifying" surfactant from human amniotic fluid by a combination of sucrose-gradient centrifugation and nylon mesh filtration. They have documented the physiological activity of this preparation in experiments on immature newborn rabbits (30) and then proceeded with a clinical trial, so far reported only in abstracts (31,32). Available data clearly indicate that this amniotic-fluid surfactant is as effective as the abovementioned preparations based on various animal sources. The major problem with this low-yield method for production of surfactant is to obtain sufficient quantities of uncontaminated amniotic fluid for extraction.

SYNTHETIC "DRY" SURFACTANT

DPPC has a solid-to-liquid-crystal transition temperature of 41.5°C (33) and therefore does not spread in an air-liquid interface at normal body temperature. It has to be mixed with,

for example, unsaturated phosphatidylcholines or other phospholipids in appropriate proportions to be able to exert its vital
functions in the alveolar lining layer.

Bangham et al (34) have suggested that a physiologically active,
entirely artificial lung surfactant can be prepared from DPPC
and unsaturated PG, mixed in proportions 7:3; they furthermore
claim that this type of surfactant is particularly active in
dry form, i.e., when administered into the airways as a powder.
At 37°C, such a powder adsorbs instantaneously to an air-liquid
interface, generating a mixed phospholipid film with an equilibrium surface tension of about 30 mN/m (35). If the film is
compressed, the unsaturated PG-molecules are squeezed out, leaving
the DPPC-molecules more closely packed in the air-liquid interface. At a certain stage of film compression, the "refined"
film solidifies and the contractile force of the film is thereby
reduced to very low values, close to 0 mN/m. Such a phase transition might also occur in the alveolar lining at forced end-expiration, explaining why lung surfactant can annihilate the destabi-
lizing effect of surface tension in a system of alveoli of different size (34,36).

Morley et al (37) reported that administration of dry artificial
surfactant into the airways of immature newborn rabbits resulted
in a statistically significant improvement of lung-thorax compliance. However, the effect was inferior to that obtained with
natural surfactant, especially as the synthetic powder did not
seem to arrest the development of bronchiolar epithelial lesions
during artificial ventilation. In a recent clinical trial, dry
artificial surfactant was administered in a series of "very
premature babies", who for one reason or another required intubation at birth. Surfactant was here given prophylactically, and
the main parameters evaluated were the number of patients requiring artificial ventilation, the insufflation pressure levels
that had to be applied during ventilation, and survival. Babies
receiving surfactant had improved lung compliance (i.e., required
a lower insufflation pressure) and a higher survival rate than
had a parallel series of control infants (35). This study has
been the target of criticism, particularly because the trial
was not strictly randomized (38-40). A recent, double-blind

clinical evaluation of surfactant prophylaxis failed to show any beneficial effect of dry artificial surfactant among preterm infants (41).

Today the odds are against dry surfactant, in spite of the fact that this material exhibits admirable surface properties under in-vitro conditions. A major practical problem is that the powder is highly hygroscopic, which means that it is difficult to handle. Dry surfactant swells on the moist surface of the central bronchi and may block the entrances of smaller airways. Another more serious objection is that this material has virtually no respreadability. Surface balance recordings indicate that PG-molecules, squeezed out of the surface film, are irreversibly lost to the hypophase and that a low surface tension is obtained only as long as a particle of dry material is available at the surface. This is different from a system based on natural surfactant, in which the surface-active molecules seem to be able to enter the film from "below", i.e., from the liquid-crystalline phase. Natural surfactant is characterized by both rapid surface adsorption and good respreadability.

CRITERIA FOR AN OPTIMAL SURFACTANT PREPARATION

To avoid disappointing clinical trials, strict criteria should be applied in the experimental evaluation of potential surfactant substitutes. If excess material is applied as a droplet on a hypophase of water, an optimal lung surfactant spreads within a second to form a film with an equilibrium surface tension of 25-30 mN/m. This film should have a low compressibility, but it may not be necessary that a surface tension of 0 mN/m is achieved on surface compression (20). When administered into the airways of immature newborn experimental animals, an optimal surfactant should improve lung compliance and gas exchange (42-46). It should also enhance the air expansion of the alveolar compartment as evaluated in histological sections (42,43,47), prevent the development of epithelial lesions in bronchioles and alveoli during artificial ventilation (42,47), and reduce the leak of proteins into the alveolar spaces (48). In brief, the surfactant substitute should be able to prevent the development of hyaline membrane disease in the experimental animals

(49). Only then can it be expected to offer an effective prophylaxis or treatment of respiratory insufficiency in surfactant-
deficient newborn babies.

CONCLUDING REMARKS

Although several clinical trials have now documented the efficacy of surfactant replacement in RDS, certain important problems
remain unsolved. It is not clear which lipid components, except
DPPC, are truly essential for the physiological properties of
pulmonary surfactant, nor do we know whether the in-vivo activity
of a protein-depleted exogenous surfactant depends on interaction
with specific proteins already present in the alveolar lining.
On the other hand, proteins leaking from damaged epithelial
surfaces can be deleterious to the surfactant system. This has
been documented recently by Ikegami et al, who were able to
identify a very potent "surfactant inhibitor" in the airspaces
of immature lambs with severe respiratory insufficiency
(48,50,51), and in tracheal effluents from babies with RDS (52).
Future experimental studies on artificial surfactants will have
to consider not only their phospholipid composition, physical
properties, and physiological effects in immature animals. They
also have to analyse to what extent such preparations are vulne-
rable to surfactant inhibitors that under certain conditions
might compromise the result of replacement therapy.

ACKNOWLEDGEMENTS

This work was supported by The Swedish Medical Research Council
(Project No. 3351), The Swedish National Association against
Heart and Chest Diseases, The "Expressen" Prenatal Research
Foundation, Karolinska Institutets Fonder, Stiftelsen Samariten,
and Stiftelsen Allmänna BB:s Minnesfond.

REFERENCES

1. Rüfer, R. (1968) The influence of surface active substances
    on alveolar mechanics in the respiratory distress syndrome.
    Respiration 25: 441-457.

2. Enhörning, G. and Robertson, B. (1972) Lung expansion in
    the premature rabbit fetus after tracheal deposition of
    surfactant. Pediatrics 50: 58-66.

3. Reifenrath, R. and Zimmermann, I. (1973) Blood plasma cont-
    amination of the lung alveolar surfactant obtained by various
    sampling techniques. Respir. Physiol. 18: 238-248.

4. Reifenrath, R. (1973) Chemical analysis of the lung alveolar
    surfactant obtained by alveolar micropuncture. Respir.
    Physiol. 19: 35-46.

5. Reifenrath, R. and Zimmermann, I. (1973) Surface tension
    properties of lung alveolar surfactant obtained by alveolar
    micropuncture. Respir. Physiol. 19: 369-393.

6. Fujiwara, T., Tanaka, Y. and Takei, T. (1979) Surface proper-
    ties of artificial surfactant in comparison with natural
    and synthetic surfactant lipids. IRCS Med. Sci. 7: 311.

7. Avery, M.E. (1980) On replacing the surfactant. Pediatrics
    65: 1176-1177.

8. Fujiwara, T. and Adams, F.H. (1980) Surfactant for hyaline
    membrane disease. Pediatrics 66: 795-798.

9. Fujiwara, T., Maeta, H., Chida, S. and Morita, T. (1979)
    Improved pulmonary pressure-volume characteristics in pre-
    mature newborn rabbits after tracheal instillation of arti-
    ficial surfactant. IRCS Med. Sci. 7: 312.

10. Fujiwara, T., Maeta, H., Chida, S. and Morita, T. (1979)
    Improved lung-thorax compliance and prevention of neonatal
    pulmonary lesion in prematurely delivered rabbit neonates
    subjected to IPPV after tracheal instillation of artificial
    surfactant. IRCS Med. Sci. 7: 313.

11. Fujiwara, T., Maeta, H., Chida, S., Morita, T., Watabe,
    Y. and Abe, T. (1980) Artificial surfactant therapy in hya-
    line-membrane disease. Lancet 1: 55-59.

12. Fujiwara, T. (1982) Artificial surfactant therapy in respira-
    tory distress syndrome (RDS). Paper presented at Mackinac
    Workshop on Artificial Surfactants.

13. Editorial (1979) Cow-lung surfactant saves hyaline-membrane
    babies. Medical World News, 14 May: 10-16.

14. Editorial (1980) The cow-lung concoction. It may save "pree-
    mies" from early death. Time Magazine, 25 February: 50.

15. Enhörning, G. (1980) Artificial surfactant to prevent and
    treat neonatal respiratory distress syndrome. Pediatrics
    66: 799-800.

16. Kobayashi, T. and Kishizuchi, S. (1980) Effect of electro-
    lytes especially $CaCl_2$ on surface activity of extracted
    lipids from lung washings. J. Jap. Med. Soc. Biol. Interface
    11: 1-7.

17. Kobayahsi, T. and Robertson, B. (1983) Surface adsorption of pulmonary surfactant in relation to bulk-phase concentration and presence of $CaCl_2$. Respiration 44:63-70.

18. Kobayashi, T., Kataoka, H., Murakami, S. and Haruki, S. (1981) A case of idiopathic respiratory distress syndrome treated by newly developed surfactant (Surfactant CK). J. Jap. Med. Soc. Biol. Interface 12: 1-6.

19. Ohta, A., Muramatsu, K. and Oda, T. (1981) A case of respiratory distress syndrome (RDS) treated with Surfactant CK. J. Jap. Med. Soc. Biol. Interface 12: 33-39.

20. King, R.J. and Clements, J.A. (1972) Surface active materials from dog lung. II. Composition and physiological correlations. Am. J. Physiol. 223: 715-726.

21. King, R.J. and Macbeth, M.C. (1979) Physiological properties of dipalmitoyl phosphatidylcholine after interaction with an apolipoprotein of pulmonary surfactant. Biochim. Biophys. Acta 19: 86-101.

22. Metcalfe, I.L., Enhörning. G, and Possmayer, F. (1980) Pulmonary surfactant-associated proteins: their role in the expression of surface activity. J. Appl. Physiol.: Respirat. Environ. Exercise Physiol. 49: 34-41.

23. Berggren, P., Grossmann, G., Nilsson, R., Tollbom, Ö., Thunell, S. and Robertson, B. (1981) A protein-free physiologically active preparation of natural lung surfactant. IRCS Med. Sci. 9: 283-284.

24. Egan, E.A., Notter, R.H. and Shapiro, D.L. (1982) Natural and artificial surfactant replacement in premature lambs. Pediatr. Res. 16: 348 A.

25. Metcalfe, I.L., Burgoyne, R. and Enhörning, G. (1982) Surfactant supplementation in the preterm rabbit: effects of applied volume on compliance and survival. Pediatr. Res. 16: 834-839.

26. Smyth, J.A., Metcalfe, I.L., Duffty, P., Enhörning, G.E., Possmayer, F., Olley, P.M. and Bryan, M.H. (1981) Surfactant therapy in hyaline membrane disease (HMD). Pediatr. Res. 15: 681.

27. Possmayer, F., Yu, S.F., Weber, M. and Harding, P.G.R. (1982) Characterization of bovine pulmonary surfactant. Paper presented at Mackinac Workshop on Artificial Surfactants.

28. Adams, F.H., Desilets, D.T. and Towers, B. (1967) Control of flow of fetal lung fluid at the laryngeal outlet. Respir. Physiol. 2: 302-309.

29. Hallman, M., Schneider, H. and Gluck, L. (1981) Human fetus, a potential surfactant donor: isolation of lung surfactant from amniotic fluid. Pediatr Res. 15: 663.

30. Schneider, H.A., Hallman, M., Benirschke, K. and Gluck, L. (1982). Human surfactant: a therapeutic trial in premature rabbits. J. Pediat. 100: 619-622.

31. Hallman, M., Schneider, H., Merritt, T.A. and Gluck, L. (1982) Human surfactant (HS) substitution in a case of RDS Pediatr. Res. 16: 290 A.

32. Hallman, M., Schneider, H., Merritt, T.A. and Gluck, L. (1982) Human surfactant substitution. Pediatr. Res. 16: 691.

33. Albon, N. and Sturtevant, J.M. (1978) Nature of the gel to liquid crystal transition of synthetic phosphatidylcholines. Proc. Natl. Acad. Sci. USA 75: 2258-2260.

34. Bangham, A.D., Morley, C.J. and Phillips, M.C. (1979) The physical properties of an effective lung surfactant. Biochim. Biophys. Acta 573: 552-556.

35. Morley, C.J., Bangham, A.D., Miller, N. and Davis, J.A. (1981) Dry artificial lung surfactant and its effect on very premature babies. Lancet 1: 64-68.

36. Clements, J.A. (1977) Functions of the alveolar lining. Am. Rev. Resp. Dis. 115 (Suppl. June): 67-71.

37. Morley, C.J., Robertson, B., Lachmann, B., Nilsson, R., Bangham, A., Grossmann, G. and Miller, N. (1980) Artificial surfactant and natural surfactant. Comparative study of the effects on premature rabbit lungs. Arch. Dis. Child. 55: 758-765.

38. Ikegami, M. (1981) Artificial lung surfactant and prematurity. Lancet 1: 379-380.

39. James, D. and Harkes, A. (1981) Dry artificial surfactant in prematurity. Lancet 1: 555.

40. Phelps, D.L. (1981) Dry artificial surfactant in prematurity. Lancet 1: 556.

41. Wilkinson, A.R., Jeffery, J.A., and Jenkins, P.A. (1982) Controlled trials of dry surfactant in preterm infants. Arch. Dis. Child. 57: 802.

42. Nilsson, R., Grossmann, G. and Robertson, B. (1978) Lung surfactant and the pathogenesis of neonatal bronchiolar lesions induced by artificial ventilation. Pediatr. Res. 12: 249-255.

43. Adams, F.H., Towers, B., Osher, A.B., Ikegami, M., Fujiwara, T. and Nozaki, M. (1978) Effects of tracheal instillation of natural surfactant in premature lambs. I. Clinical and autopsy findings. Pediatr. Res. 12: 841-848.

44. Enhörning, G., Hill, D., Sherwood, G., Cutz, E., Robertson, B. and Bryan, C. (1978) Improved ventilation of prematurely-delivered primates following tracheal deposition of surfactant. Am. J. Obstet. Gynecol. 132: 529-536.

45. Ikegami, M., Adams, F.H., Towers, B. and Osher, A.B. (1980) The quantity of natural surfactant necessary to prevent the respiratory distress syndrome in premature lambs. Pediatr. Res. 14: 1082-1085.

46. Jobe, A., Ikegami, M, Glatz, T., Yoshida, Y., Diakomanolis, E. and Padbury, J. (1981) Duration and characteristics of treatment of premature lambs with natural surfactant. J. Clin. Invest. 67: 370-375.

47. Cutz, E., Enhörning G., Robertson, B., Sherwood, W.G. and Hill, D.E. (1978) Hyaline membrane disease. Effect of surfactant prophylaxis on lung morphology in premature primates. Am. J. Pathol. 92: 581-594.

48. Jobe, A., Ikegami, M., Jacobs, H., Jones, S. and Conaway, D. (1983) Permeability of premature lamb lungs to protein and the effect of surfactant on that premeability. J. Appl. Physiol.: Resp. Environ. Exercise Physiol. (in press).

49. Robertson, B. (1983) Lung surfactant for replacement therapy. Clin. Physiol. (1983).

50. Ikegami, M., Jobe, A. and Glatz, T. (1981) Surface activity following natural surfactant treatment in premature lambs. J. Appl. Physiol.: Respirat. Environ. Exercise Physiol. 51: 306-312.

51. Ikegami, M., Jobe, A., Jacobs, H. and Jones, S.J. (1981) Sequential treatments of premature lambs with an artificial surfactant and natural surfactant. J. Clin. Invest. 68: 491-496.

52. Ikegami, M., Jacobs, H.C. and Jobe, A.H. (1982) Inhibition of surfactant function in the respiratory distress syndrome (RDS). Pediatr. Res. 16: 292A.

© 1983, Elsevier Science Publishers B.V.
Pulmonary Surfactant System, E.V. Cosmi
and E.M. Scarpelli eds.

MEDICAL TREATMENT OF NEONATAL HYALINE MEMBRANE DISEASE USING
BROMHEXINE, AMBROXOL AND CDP-CHOLINE

ROLAND R.WAUER
Charité, Humboldt-Universität, Kinderklinik Schumannstr. 2o/21
DDR-104 Berlin, GDR

INTRODUCTION

For 1979 we have calculated that about 20% of the total infant
mortality of the GDR is caused by the mortality due to Hyaline
Membrane Disease (HMD). The general introduction of the prenatal prophylaxis of HMD using glucocorticoids or ambroxol could
reduce HMD mortality only by the half, therefore, the quest of
more effective methods for the treatment of HMD remains of further major importance.

The principal causes of the surfactant deficiency in neonatal
HMD are 1. an insufficient content or biosynthesis of surfactant
due to lung immaturity, 2. a reduced rate of surfactant biosynthesis caused by hypoxia, acidosis and/or deficiency of the metabolic precursors mainly of these of the dipalmitoil-lecithin,
3. an inactivation of existing surfactant in the alveola, 4. an
increased clearance of the surfactant from the alveolar surface.
Therefore, the possipilities of the causal treatment of HMD con-
sist in an increase of the surface-active material in the alveolar space by 1. direct application of surfactant into the bronchial tree, 2. release of the surfactant stored in the alveolar
type II cells, 3. acceleration of the surfactant biosynthesis
and 4. reduction of the surfactant clearance.

In animal studies bromhexine[1] and ambroxol[1] have stimulating
effects on the fetal lung maturation provided that large doses
are given. CDP-choline[2] stimulates the production of lung phospholipids and improves the neonatal lung mechanic (7). Antenatal
application of ambroxol reduces the risk of neonatal HMD in premature infants (11). Medical treatment of HMD with CDP-choline
and a low doses of ambroxol in human newborns indicated only

[1]Manufacturer: Dr. Karl Thomae GmbH, Biberach an der Riss, GFR
[2]Manufacturer: Werft-Chemie, Wien, Austria

moderate or inconclusive effects (2,5). Therefore, we have started a controlled clinical study to test the influence of CDP-
choline and high doses of ambroxol and bromhexine in premature
newborns with HMD.to assess the efficiency of these substances on
the course of this disease. For this purpose we have used in addition to the clinical and chest X-ray findings breathing mechanic parameters, too. Since the compliance of the neonatal lung
is determined mainly by the surface forces of the lung (8) it

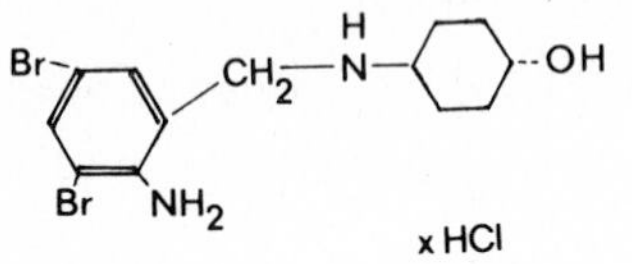

Fig. 1. Ambroxol (metabolite VIII,
NA 872). The substance is one of the
metabolites formed by the biotransfor-
mation of bromhexine in the organism.

can serve as a direct criterion for the evidence of a moderate
activity of the surfactant system. Own experiences have shown
that the dynamic compliance C_{dyn} and the ratio maximal esophageal pressure to tidal volume $P_{e\ max}/\ V_t$ are most suitable to
control the course of a neonatal pulmonary illness and to exa-
mine the efficiency of the postnatal medical treatment (10).

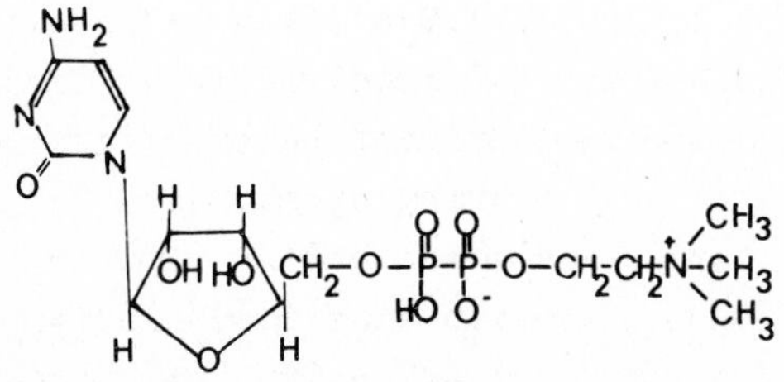

Fig. 2. CDP-choline (citidin-
diphosphat-choline, citicho-
line, nicholin)

MATERIAL AND METHODS
Material. 47 spontaneously breathing newborns with HMD delivered in our perinatal centre were involved in the prospective
clinical study. No one had received a prenatal treatment to prevent HMD. The criteria for the diagnosis of HMD are indicated in
Table 1. All clinical criteria had to be given to confirm the

diagnosis of HMD.

The gestational age was determined by maternal menstrual dates and by physic and neurologic criteria of the newborn according to (4). In the delivery room, the condition of the newborn was assessed by Apgar score at 1 and 5 min., by pH measured in blood taken from the umbilical cord artery, and by the Silverman score.

TABLE 1

CRITERIA FOR THE DIAGNOSIS OF HMD

- Respiratory rate > 60/min for more than 24 hours
- Silverman score > 2 for more than 24 hours
- Cyanosis in air-breathing
- Autopsy findings of hyaline membranes
- Chest X-ray HMD-stages I - IV

Stage	I :	reticulo-granular patterns of the lung
Stage	II :	Stage I and air-bronchogramm outside the heart shadow
Stage	III :	Stage II and impossibility to distinguish the border of the heart
Stage	IV :	Stage III and impossibility to distinguish the border of the diaphragm and the thymus up to the air-less, so called, "white" lung

Therapeutical management. All newborns were treated in incubators with CPAP using the face chamber FC 100 of Siemens-Elema(1) or nasal tubes. Infants with indication of respirator treatment during the first 12 hours of life were excluded because the analysis of ventilation was possible only during spontaneous breathing. All newborns were fed both by infusion and by duodenal application of human milk to achieve a step-wise increase from an initial quantity of 210 - 250 kJ/kg to 420 - 500 kJ/kg body weight during the first week of life. On the first day the newborns received 70 ml/kg of a 10% glucose solution combined with 1 molar solution of $NaHCO_3$ in case there was a metabolic acidosis. On the third day and further on we gave 120 ml/kg of a glucose-amino acid electrolite mixture according to the metabolic needs of the infant.

Infections were treated with Ampicillin, Gentamicin or colistin alone or in combination according to the microbial resistogramm.

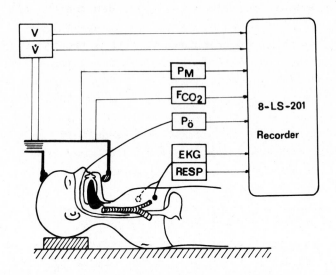

Fig. 3. Schematic representation of measurement device of the investigation of the basic parameters esophageal pressure,$P_ö$, flow,$\dot{V}$, tidal volume,V_t (is obtained by electrical integration of $\dot{V}$),for calculation of the breathing mechanic parameters. P_M = pressure in the face chamber, F_{CO2} = CO_2-fraction in the face chamber.

During the examinations some newborns who initially breathed spontaneously had to be ventilated due to repeated apnoic spells with bradycardia and cyanosis, permanent hypercarbia (>9 kPa pCO_2) and/or hypoxia ($p_aO_2 < 7$ kPa) inspite of high FIO_2. The used respirators were the Bourns BP 200 and in some cases the Loosco-infant-ventilator MK 1 or 2. We started the artificial ventilation with following parameters: inspiratory pressure 2,0 - 2,5 kPa, PEEP 0,3 - 0,6 kPa, I:E ratio 1:1, FIO_2 0,6, frequency of respiration 35/min.

Diagnostic management. Generally, the first chest X-ray was taken between the 6th and 12th hour of life and the followings on the 3rd, 5th and 7th day if there was not a clinical indication for an earlier chest X-ray. Table 1 shows the criteria for the determination of the roentgenological stages.

The blood gases were controlled 2-3 times daily. The mode of breathing mechanic investigation and the measurement device is demonstrated in Figure 3 and described in detail in (10). The analysis was done at the first day (between the 6th and 12th hour), on the 2nd, 3rd, 4th, 5th and 7th day of life.

Procedure. The study was carried out with 3 treatment groups and one control group. The following treatment regimes were applied: A-group 20 mg/kg/day ambroxol i.v. for 7 days, B-group 50 mg/kg and day bromhexine i.v. for 3 days and N-group 10 mg/kg/day Nicholin (CDP-choline) i.v. for 7 days.

After the admission in our intensive-care-unit it was decided by randomisation to which group a newborn with respiratory distress will belong. Thereafter, the treatment was initiated. 24 hours later all diagnostic procedures were done and after analysing the results the diagnosis of the respiratory distress was fixed. Only newborns with HMD were involved into the study.

The criteria for the estimation of the medical action of the drugs were as follows: 1. FIO_2, p_aO_2, the ratio p_aO_2/FIO_2, 2.CPAP and its duration, 3. duration of the respirator treatment,4.chest X-ray HMD-stages, 5. the breathing mechanic parameters dynamic compliance, C_{dyn}, and the ratio maximal esophageal pressure to tidal volume,$P_{e\ max}/V_t$.

Statistical analysis. The X^2-test(Yate's modification) was used for qualitative data. The t-test was applied for the comparison of the mean values and for the statistical analysis of the correlation coefficients and the differences of the regression coefficients.

RESULTS

The clinical data of the four HMD treatment groups are shown in Table 2. There was no statistically significant difference between the groups in the mean value of gestational age, birth weight, pH of the umbilical cord, 1 and 5 min. Apgar score. Also the initial severity of HMD indicates more or less the same distribution in all groups if one takes into consideration the mean value of chest X-ray-stage, of the ratio p_aO_2/FIO_2, C_{dyn} and $P_{e\ max}/V_t$ of the first day (Table 2, Fig.7, 8 and 10).

About 50% of the HMD newborns of each group needed respirator

TABLE 2
CLINICAL DATA

		CONTROL N=17	AMBROXOL N=13	BROMHEXINE N=8	CDP-CHOLINE N=9
Gestational age	x̄	32,6 ± 2,53	31,4 ± 2,47	32,0 ± 2,9	32,2 ± 3,38
(weeks)	range	30 - 39	30 - 34	29 - 36	30 - 38
Birth-weight	x̄	1,89 ± 0,49	1,54 ± 0,59	1,79 ± 0,49	1,85 ± 0,68
(kg)	range	1,05 - 2,56	0,7 - 2,12	1,08 - 2,4	1,05 - 3,25
pH of umbili-cal cord	x̄	7,23 ± 0,09	7,26 ± 0,09	7,23 ± 0,08	7,22 ± 0,07
Apgar 1 min	x̄	5,6 ± 2,8	5,3 ± 3,2	5,4 ± 2,4	5,7 ± 2,8
Apgar 5 min	x̄	6,1 ± 1,5	6,1 ± 2,1	6,7 ± 1,8	6,7 ± 2,0
chest X-ray HMD-stages I-IV	1. day	2,5 ± 1,1	2,7 ± 0,9	2,6 ± 0,8	2,4 ± 1,3
	3. day	2,0 ± 1,4	1,7 ± 0,9	1,9 ± 0,7	2,0 ± 1,7
	5. day	1,2 ± 1,1	0,6 ± 0,9	0,7 ± 0,9	0,6 ± 1,3

treatment, its necessary duration was significantly lower in the
A and B groups than in the control group (p< 0.01, Fig. 4) whereas the difference between the control and N groups was not considerable. The essential continuous positive airway pressure decreased significantly faster in the A and B groups than in the
control and N groups (p< 0,05, Fig. 5).

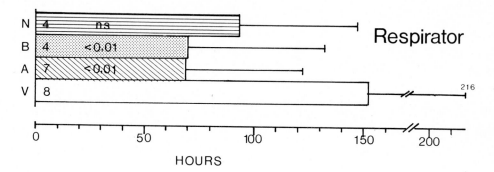

Fig. 4. The duration ($\bar{x}$ + SD) of ventilator treatment of the four
HMD groups. The letters indicate the following treatment groups:
N = CDP-choline, B = bromhexine, A = ambroxol, V = controls. The
numbers in the columns represent the number of newborns. The difference between the duration of the respirator treatment of the
A and B groups on one side and the controls on the other side is
statistically significant (p< 0,01), n.s. = not significant.

In the A and B groups the value of essential FIO_2 could be constantly reduced during the first week of life whereas the required FIO_2 of the N and control groups must remain high. The descent differences of the regression lines of the ambroxol and
bromhexine-treated newborns on one side and the controls on the
other side were significant.(p< 0.05, Fig. 6).
After the 3rd day the ratio p_aO_2/FIO_2 shows a remarkably faster
improvement in the A and B groups in comparison to the control
group (Fig. 7). There is no difference between the N and control groups.
The mean value of the chest X-ray HMD-stages improved quicklier
but not significantly in the A and B groups compared to the N and
V groups. (Table 2).
Figure 8 indicates the results of dynamic compliance during the

180

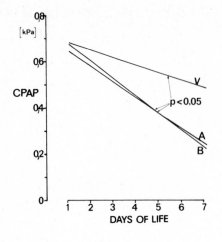

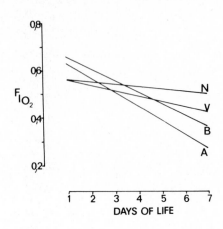

Fig. 5. Regression lines of the essential CPAP during the first week for newborns treated with ambroxol (A), bromhexine (B) and for the controls (V). For a better clearness we did not draw the regression line of the CDP-choline treated group(N). The descents of A and B differ significantly from the descent of V (p < 0,05). The regression lines are defined by
A=0,67-0,065x, B=0,65-0,059x
N=0,69-0,049x, V=0,69-0,03x

Fig. 6. The regression lines for the essential FIO2 of the 4 HMD groups. For the explanation of symbols see Fig. 5. The descents of A and B differ statistically significant from V (p < 0,05). The regression lines are defined by
A=0,63-0,05x, B=0,66-0,04x,
N=0,56-0,01x, V=0,56-0,02x

first week. On the first day the HMD newborns of all groups had characteristically low C_{dyn} values which showed - starting from the 3rd day - a faster improvement in the A and B groups. Thereafter the differences between the values of these newborns and the controls became statistically significant. The results of the N group do not differ from the controls, therefore, they are not demonstrated in Figures 8. and 9. There was a statistically considerable higher ascent of C_{dyn} in the ambroxol and bromhexine treated newborns compared with the controls (p<0,001,Fig.9)

On the first day the ratios P_{emax}/V_t of the 4 HMD groups showed high, partly extreme values (Fig.10). During the second and third day, the ratios of A and B newborns decrease faster than these of the controls. On the 5th and 7th day the differen-

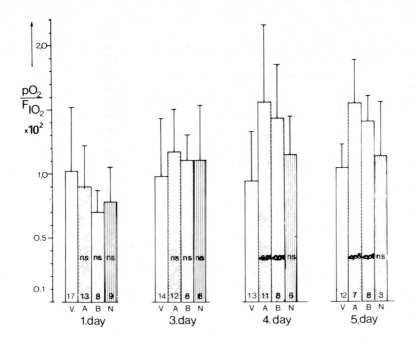

Fig. 7. The ratio p_aO_2/FIO_2 ($\bar{x}\pm SD$) of the 4 treatment groups during the first, 3rd, 4th, 5th day of life. The numbers in the columns represent the number of examined infants. On the 4th and 5th day there was a statistically significant difference between the A and B groups on one side and the V group on the other side. For explanation of the symbols see Fig. 4.

Table 3 and 4 demonstrate the neonatal mortality and the causes of death. Although the 28 day mortality does not show a statistically significant difference compared to the N and V groups there is a tendency of a lower early neonatal mortality in the A and B groups especially if one takes into account the lower birth weight of the infants of these groups who died (Table 4). The mortality rate due to HMD was higher among the controls and the CDP-choline treated infants.

There was no patient with broncho-pulmonary dysplasia among the A and B group newborns. 6 infants developed symptoms of persistent ductus arteriosus, all were treated with indomethazine, all died and showed a persistent ductus arteriosus in autopsy.

TABLE 3

THE MORTALITY OF THE FOUR HMD TREATMENT GROUPS

Group	≤ 28th day	≤7th day	HMD
control N = 17	5 (29,4%)	4 (23,5%)	4
ambroxol N = 13	3 (23,1%)	2 (15,8%)	1
bromhexine N = 8	2 (25%)	0	0
CDP-choline N = 9	4 (44,4%)	3 (33,3%)	3

TABLE 4

CAUSES OF DEATH, DAY OF DEATH AND INCIDENCE OF PDA

Group	cause of death	birth-weight	day of death	PDA
control N = 17	h.M.,CB	1050 g	8	+
	h.M.,CB	1100 g	7	+
	h.M.,CB	1650 g	3	−
	h.M.,CB	1800 g	6	−
	h.M., septicemia	2100 g	4	−
ambroxol N = 13	h.M.,CB	1010 g	3	+
	CB	700 g	3	+
	septicemia	1100 g	8	−
bromhexine N = 8	septicemia	1080 g	12	+
	septicemia	1280 g	8	−
CDP-choline N = 9	h.M.,CB	1050 g	3	+
	h.M.,CB	1350 g	3	−
	h.M., meningitis	1220 g	4	−
	septicemia	2200 g	10	−

PDA = persistent ductus arteriosus
h.M.= hyaline membranes
CB = cerebral bleeding

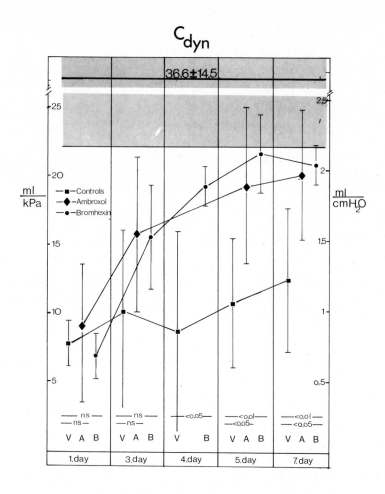

Fig. 8. Dynamic compliance C_{dyn} ($\bar{x} \pm$ SD) during the first
week of life in HMD newborns with different medical treatment
regimes. The dark field in the upper part of the diagramm indicates the normal range of C_{dyn} in mature healthy newborns.
V = controls, A = ambroxol, B = bromhexine, n.s.= not significant.

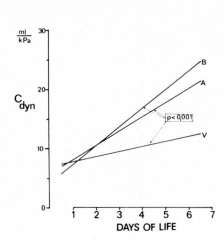

Fig. 9. The regression lines of the dynamic compliance C_{dyn} during the first week of life for differently treated HMD newborns. The descents of A and B differ significantly from V (p < 0,001). A= ambroxol, B= bromhexine, V= control. For a better clearness we did not draw the regression line for the N (CDP-choline) group. The regression lines are defined by A=7,0+2,1x, B=5,8+2,7x, N=9,1+1,8x, V=7,5+0,7x

DISCUSSION

To prove the influence of drugs on the course of HMD in a clinical study some suppositions must be given: 1. reliability of the diagnose HMD, 2. comparability of the treatment groups, 3. standardized nursing, 4. proof of pharmacological action with clinical and, in particular, such paraclinical methods which can give direct information about the altered surface tension in the alveola as for instance the C_{dyn}.

All 47 newborns fulfilled the criteria of neonatal HMD. The clinical data demonstrate the comparability of the 4 groups, because the essential clinical factors with relation to the etiology of HMD (immaturity, birth weight, perinatal asphyxia) and the degree of the initial HMD-severity do not differ from one group to the other. During the study the nursing and therapeutical conditions of our intensive-care-unit remained the same.

Therefore, we can conclude that in comparison to the controls the faster improvement of HMD after ambroxol and bromhexine treatment indicate a pharmacological action of these substances. CDP-choline does not have any effect.

There were no statistically significant differences in the mortality rates because predominantly immature newborns with cerebral bleeding and persistent ductus arteriosus (PDA) died. A cerebral haemorrhage is caused mainly by intranatal hypoxia or

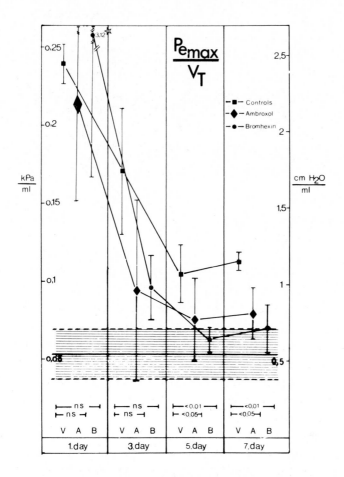

Fig. 10. The ratio of maximal esophageal pressure to tidal volume $P_{e\ max}/V_t$ ($\bar{x}\pm SD$) during the first week of life in HMD newborns with different medical treatment regimes. The dark field in the lower part of the diagramm indicates the normal range in mature healthy newborns.
A = ambroxol, B = bromhexine, V = control, n.s.=not significant.

hypoxia during the first 48 hours of life. This and a PDA could
not be influenced by a postnatal induction of surfactant.

Using ambroxol for medical treatment of HMD with a dosage of
2 - 3 mg/kg/day for 6 days in a clinical double blind study
Renovanz & Keuth (5) could show an effect on the course of HMD
only in newborns with a gestational age of more than 37 weeks
and a birth weight of more than 2300 g respectively. It is possible that the applied dose was to small to get an effect in
preterm infants. Finilä et al. (2) also have proved the action
of a slightly higher dose of ambroxol (8mg/kg/day for 6 days)
in preterms with HMD in a randomized clinical study and they
found a faster normalisation of the Silverman score and the
chest X-ray within the first week of life compared with controls.
Furthermore, the number of intubations was smaller and the duration of CPAP was shorter in the ambroxol than in the control
group.

In connection with the results of animal experiments (7) and of
the prenatal prophylaxis of HMD using ambroxol (11) we can inter-
prete that in our study the pharmacological action of both substances is probably caused by an increase of surfactant in the
lung. This conclusion is mainly confirmed by the faster improvement of C_{dyn} in the A and B groups since the lung compliance of
newborns is determined in 80% by the surface tension(8). It is
not clear whether ambroxol and bromhexine act by an increase of
the surfactant metabolism or by a release of intracellularly
stored surfactant (9). The fact that the clinical and paraclinical findings improved at the earliest 72 hours after the start
of medication suggest a stimulating effect on the metabolism.

The shortening of HMD duration diminish the time of harmful
therapeutic managements, for instance the respirator treatment
which causes epithelial lesion by "barotrauma" and shearing forces (3), and the increased FIO_2. Both factors may cause the
broncho-pulmonary dysplasia (3,7).

Apart from these adventages of ambroxol mentioned above there
are other pharmacological properties being helpful for the respiratory intensive care. Ambroxol increases the antibiotic level in the lung (12) and improves the secretolysis, probably by
an influence on the bronchial phospholipid content (6).

SUMMARY

In order to assess the effect of the postnatal i.v. application
of bromhexine (B) 50 mg/kg/day for 3 days, ambroxol(A) 20 mg/kg
and day for 7 days and CDP-choline (N) 10 mg/kg/day for 7 days
on the course of the hyaline membrane disease (HMD) a randomized
clinical study was carried out in 47 newborns with HMD without
prenatal stimulation of surfactant maturation. There were no significant differences between the control (N=17), A-group(N=13),
B-group(N=8) and CDP-choline group (N=9) in the gestational age
birth weight, in the values of the umbilical arterial blood pH
and the 1 and 5 min Apgar. As compared to the controls the newborns of the A and B groups showed a shorter duration of the respirator and oxygen therapy, an earlier reduction of the essential CPAP and an earlier improvement of the breathing mechanic
parameters as the dynamic compliance and the relation of maximal
esophageal pressure to tidal volume. No effect could observed
under CDP-choline treatment. The relative improvement of HMD and
of the breathing parameters under the application of A and B
suggest that the claimed maturing effect of the drugs is mediated by an increase of surfactant in the sick lung.

REFERENCES

1. Ahlström,H.,Jonson,B. and Svenningsen,N.W. (1976) Continuous
   positive airway pressure treatment by a face chamber in idiopathic respiratory distress syndrome . Arch.Dis.Childh. 51:
   13 - 21

2. Finilä, M.J., Österlind,K. and Lethi,H. (1978) Die Behandlung
   des idiopathischen Atemnotsyndroms mit Ambroxol. Atemwegs-
   und Lungenkr. 4: 62 - 67

3. Nilsson,R., Grossmann,G. and Robertson,B. (1978) Lung surfactant and the pathogenesis of neonatal bronchiolar lesions induced by artificial ventilation. Pediat.Res. 12:249 - 255

4. Rautenbach,M. and Hoepfner,W. (1974) Vorschläge für ein stan-
   dardisiertes Programm zur Klassifizierung Neugeborener mit
   niedrigem Geburtsgewicht. Pädiatrie und Grenzgebiete 13:
   219 - 227

5. Renovanz,H.D. and Keuth,U. (1978) Respiratory distress syndrom
   und Ambroxoltherapie - Teamstudien an Kinderkliniken. Atem-
   wegs- und Lungenkr. 4: 50 - 61

188

6. Rensch,H. (1980) Möglichkeiten der Ambroxolwirkung bei ge-
störten Sekrettransport in: Rensch,H. (Ed.), Mukustransport,
Dustri-Verlag, Dr.Karl Feistle, München-Deisenhofen pp.82 -90

7. Robertson,B. (1981) Neonatal Pulmonary Mechanics and Morphology after Experimental Therapeutic Regimes in: Scarpelli,
E.M. and Cosmi,E.V. (Ed.), Reviews in Perinatal Medicine vol.
4, Raven Press New York pp. 337 - 379

8. Rüfer,R. (1981) Mechanical development of fetal lung. in:
v.Wichert,P. (Ed.), Clinical importance of surfactant defects,
Karger, Basel pp. 41 - 48

9. v.Seefeld,H. and Renovanz,H.D. (1978) Das oberflächenaktive
System der Lunge - eine Übersicht. Atemwegs- und Lungenkr.
4 : 1 - 14

10. Wauer,R.R.(1982) Ergebnisse klinischer, biochemischer und atem
mechanischer Untersuchungen zur medikamentösen pränatalen Pro-
phylaxe und postnatalen Therapie der Hyaline-Membranen-Krank-
heit, Dissertation Humboldt-Universität, Berlin

11. Wauer,R.R., Schmalisch,G. et al. (1982) The antenatal use of
ambroxol to prevent hyaline membrane disease : A controlled
double blind study, Int.J.Biolog.Res.Pregn. 3: 84 - 91

12. Wiemeyer,J.C.M. (1981) Influence of ambroxol on the broncho-
pulmonary level of antibiotics, Arzneim.-Forsch./Drug Res.
31/I : 974 - 976

© 1983, Elsevier Science Publishers B.V.
Pulmonary Surfactant System, E.V. Cosmi
and E.M. Scarpelli eds.

THE EFFECTIVENESS OF AMBROXOL VERSUS BETAMETHASONE FOR PREVENTION OF RESPIRATORY DISTRESS SYNDROME (RDS). A MULTICENTRIC PROSPECTIVE CONTROLLED STUDY.

MASSIMO LUERTI[1], ANTONIO TOMASSINI[2], CONCETTO DE NIGRIS[2], CESARE PASQUINUCCI[3], ENZO CORBELLA[1], GUIDO ZAVATTINI[1], MARIO VIGNALI[1]

[1]Department of Obstetrics and Gynecology and Pediatrics L. Sacco Hospital, University of Milan. [2]Department of Obstetrics and Gynecology Del Ponte Hospital, Varese and [3]S. Carlo Borromeo, Milan (Italy)

SUMMARY

Ambroxol has been found effective in comparison with placebo, but it has not yet been assessed in comparison with betamethasone. We designed a prospective randomized study for which pregnant women at an estimated gestational age 27 to 34 completed weeks were eligible.

Consenting patients received 6 mg of betamethasone acetate and 6 mg phosphate i.m., two doses, 24 hours apart, ambroxol 1 g i.v. every day for 5 days (SCHEDULE A), or ambroxol 1 g every 12 hours for four times (SCHEDULE B). The choice between the two drugs was made at random and the ambroxol regimen was selected on the basis of estimated retardation of labor, 43 infants in the betamethasone group and 31 infants in the ambroxol group were born before 36 weeks of gestation.

The incidence of RDS appeared lower in the ambroxol group (9.7%) than in the betamethasone group (20.9%) but the difference was not significant. The efficacy of ambroxol did not result lower before 32nd week. Schedule B resulted less effective than schedule A, but at least as beneficial as beta-methasone.

INTRODUCTION

Antenatal administration of corticosteroids is known to reduce both the incidence and mortality of respiratory distress syndrome

(RDS) (1), even though some recent studies have failed to demonstrate a significantly lower rate of RDS in treated preterm infants than in untreated infants (2-4).

Some limitations of their effectiveness have been described, such as gestational age, treatment to delivery interval, sex and race of the newborn and rupture of membranes (3,4). Furthermore several potential adverse effects are suspected (5) and an increased rate of maternal and neonatal infections after prophylaxis with steroids has been shown (6).

So, alternative drugs, such as aminophylline (7) , thyroxine (8) and ambroxol (9,10) have been evaluated for antenatal prevention of RDS. Ambroxol has been shown to reduce significantly the incidence of RDS compared to placebo and not to produce important adverse effects either in mothers or infants (9,10).

In September 1981 we began a multicentric prospective controlled study to compare the effectiveness of antenatal administration of ambroxol or betamethasone in the prevention of RDS. We now are able to give the preliminary results.

MATERIALS AND METHODS

Pregnant women admitted to the hospitals taking part in the study at the 27th to the 34th week of gestation for threatened premature delivery or planned premature delivery were eligible. Consenting patients were randomly given betamethasone or ambroxol. Patients in the betamethasone group received 6 mg betamethasone acetate and 6 mg betamethasone sodium phosphate i.m., repeated 24 hours later.

Patients in ambroxol group received 1 g in 500 ml saline every day for 5 days (schedule A) or 1 g in 500 ml saline every 12 hours for four times (schedule B) i.v. The choice between the two regimens of ambroxol was made on the basis of when labor was expected to start.

Every patient received only one course of therapy whatever

the treatment to delivery interval.

Gestational age was assigned on the basis of the date of the last menstruation and confirmed by ultrasound examination and by a Dubowitz test in the nursery (11).

Patients with more than 2 weeks disagreement in assessing gestational age, with delivery expected within 24 hours, with severe hypertension or diabetes and those treated in pregnancy with corticosteroids, heroin, aminophyllin, thyroxine or estrogens were excluded.

Betamimetics were used in most cases to delay labor. RDS was diagnosed with clinical and radiological criteria (Tab. 1).

The non-parametric chi square test and the Student t test were used for statistical analysis.

The critical level of significance was 5%.

RESULTS

Between September 1981 and December 1982, 104 patients were admitted to the study. 55 of them were given betamethasone and 49 ambroxol. A total of 114 infants were born alive (18 twins) and there were 2 stillbirths. 74 of these 114 infants were born at ≤36 weeks of gestation. The mothers of 43 of these 74 infants had received betamethasone and the mothers of the remaining 31 had received ambroxol (Tab. 2).

Our discussion deals only with these 74 infants. The two groups of patients were well matched for maternal age, gestational age at entry, duration of ROM, treatment to delivery interval, percentage of cesarean section, use of betamimetics, planned delivery and presence of pathology other than diabetes or hypertension (Tab. 3).

The two groups of infants were well matched for percentage of male and twins and Apgar score, whereas gestational age at birth and birth weight were significantly lower ($p < 0.05$) in the betamethasone (224.3 ± 15.2 days and 1800 ± 430 g) than in the ambroxol group (231.9 ± 13.4 days and 2040 ± 540 g) (Tab. 4).

The incidence of RDS was 20.9% in the betamethasone group and 9.7% in the ambroxol group. The incidence of RDS was higher in the betamethasone group than in the ambroxol group both those born before 32 weeks and those born between 33 and 36 weeks of gestation (Tab. 5).

No RDS was observed after antenatal treatment with ambroxol by schedule A, that was used only in 9 cases. All 3 cases of RDS after ambroxol followed treatment with schedule B, that was used in 22 cases (incidence of RDS 13.6%). Mean treatment to delivery time was 15.9 ± 15.6 after ambroxol schedule A and 8.4 ± 11.6 after ambroxol schedule B (Tab. 6): in 5 of 22 cases treated with schedule B this time was longer than 5 days.

The incidence of non-fatal RDS was 11.6% in the betamethasone group and 3.2% in the ambroxol group, the incidence of fatal RDS was 9.3% in the betamethasone group and 6.4% in the ambroxol group.

Morbidity for other causes was 16.3% in the betamethasone group and 12.9% in the ambroxol group, mortality for other causes was 11.6% in the betamethasone group and 16.1% in the ambroxol group (Tab. 7).

All causes of early neonatal mortality, other than RDS, are reported in Tab. 8. No differences in Tab. 5,6 and 7 were statistically significant. The incidence of RDS in each week of gestation in shown in Fig. 1.

The comparison of mean birth weight, gestational age at birth, ROM to delivery time, treatment to delivery time, Apgar score, percentage of male, twins and use of beta-mimetics in cases with and without RDS of both groups showed that birth weight, gestational age at birth, treatment to delivery time, Apgar score at 1' and mean Apgar score between 1' and 5' were significantly lower in infants who developed RDS (Tab. 9).

Standard laboratory tests of 33 mothers treated with betamethasone and 28 mothers treated with ambroxol, on the day

before treatment and one week later, showed a significant
increase of gamma GT (p < 0.05) after betamethasone treatment and
a significant decrease of urinary specific gravity (P < 0.05)
after ambroxol treatment (Tab. 10/a and 10/b).

TABLE 1

CRITERIA FOR DIGNOSIS OF RDS

RDS was defined by the presence of:

	• Respiratory rate 60/min
	• Intracostal retraction
CLINICAL CRITERIA	• Flaring of the alae nasi
	• Grunting on expiration
	• Cyanosis in room air with falling in PaO_2
RADIOLOGICAL CRITERIA	• Thoracic roentgenogram showing reticulogranular pattern and/or air bronchograms

TABLE 2

STUDY POPULATION

	BETAMETHASONE Group	AMBROXOL Group	TOTAL
• Patients randomized	55	49	104
• Liveborn infants at > 36 weeks	18	22	40
• Liveborn infants at ≤ 36 weeks	43	31	74
• Twins	14	4	18
• Stillbirths	1	1	2

TABLE 3

COMPARISON OF CHARACTERISTICS OF PATIENTS IN BETAMETHASONE AND
AMBROXOL GROUPS

CHARACTERISTICS	BETAMETHASONE Group	AMBROXOL Group
• MATERNAL AGE mean ± S.D. (years)	29.62 ± 6.40	27.06 ± 5.58
• GESTATIONAL AGE AT ENTRY mean ± S.D. (days)	215.70 ± 13.03	221.24 ± 15.09
• CESAREAN SECTION (%)	43.2	33.3
• USE OF BETA-MIMETICS (%)	89.2	90.0
• ROM TO DELIVERY TIME mean ± S.D. (h)	66.65 ± 120.04	70.66 ± 166.82
• TREATMENT TO DELIVERY TIME mean ± S.D. (days)	8.64 ± 10.89	10.72 ± 13.13
• PLANNED DELIVERY (%)	27.0	26.6
• PATHOLOGY OTHER THAN DIABETES AND HYPERTENSION (%)	43.2	40.0

TABLE 4

COMPARISON OF CHARACTERISTICS OF LIVEBORNS IN BETAMETHASONE AND
AMBROXOL GROUPS

CHARACTERISTICS	BETAMETHASONE Group	AMBROXOL Group
• GESTATIONAL AGE mean ± S.D. (days)	224.35 ± 15.21	231.96 ± 13.44*
• BIRTH WEIGHT mean ± S.D. (gr)	1800 ± 430	2040 ± 540*
• MALE (%)	60	37
• TWINS (%)	18.9	9.5
• APGAR (mean ± S.D.) 1' 5' $\frac{1' + 5'}{2}$	5.21 ± 2.80 7.02 ± 2.18 6.11 ± 2.42	6.19 ± 2.53 7.34 ± 2.26 6.75 ± 2.31

* $P < 0.05$

TABLE 5

INCIDENCE OF RDS IN LIVEBORN INFANTS OF ≤ 36 WEEKS GESTATION AT
BIRTH IN BETAMETHASONE AND AMBROXOL GROUPS

GESTATIONAL AGE AT BIRTH (wks)	BETAMETHASONE Group	AMBROXOL Group
≤ 32	6/17 (35.0%)	2/ 8 (25.0%)
33-36	3/26 (11.5%)	1/23 (4.3%)
T O T A L	9/43 (20.9%)	3/31 (9.7%)

TABLE 6

INCIDENCE OF RDS IN LIVEBORN INFANTS ≤ 36 WEEKS GESTATION TREATED
WITH AMBROXOL SCHEME A AND B

	AMBROXOL schedule A	AMBROXOL schedule B
• RDS	0/9 (0%)	3/22 (13.6%)
• TREATMENT TO DELIVERY TIME (mean ± S.D. days)	15.88 ± 15.61	8.4 ± 11.55

TABLE 7

NEONATAL OUTCOME IN LIVEBORN INFANTS OF ≤ 36 WEEKS GESTATIONS IN
BETAMETHASONE AND AMBROXOL GROUPS

OUTCOME	BETAMETHASONE Group	AMBROXOL Group
• MORBIDITY FOR RDS	5/43 (11.6%)	1/31 (3.2%)
• MORTALITY FOR RDS	4/43 (9.3%)	2/31 (6.4%)
• MORBIDITY FOR OTHER CAUSES	7/43 (16.3%)	4/31 (12/9%)
• MORTALITY FOR OTHER CAUSES	5/43 (11.6%)	5/31 (16.1%)
T O T A L	21/43 (48.8%)	12/31 (37.0%)

TABLE 8

MORBIDITY AND MORTALITY FOR OTHER CAUSES IN LIVEBORN INFANTS OF AMBROXOL
AND BETAMETHASONE GROUPS

BETAMETHASONE

Case N°	MORBIDITY	Case N°	MORTALITY
13	. Severe hyperbilirubinemia	47	. Potter's Syndrome Renal agenesis
32	. Spontaneous pneumothorax	73	. Severe hypoxia
46	. Staphilococcal infection	90	. I – Multiple lung abscesses
77	. Hypoxia and fetal distress	90	. II– Multiple lung abscesses
81	. Bronchopulmonary dysplasia	93	. Multiple malformations
89	. Severe hyperbilirubinemia		
91	. Severe hyperbilirubinemia		

AMBROXOL

Case N°	MORBIDITY	Case N°	MORTALITY
19	. Severe hyperbilirubinemia	43	. Fetal distress Severe hypoxia
23	. Severe fetal distress	48	. Rh–Isoimmunization Severe hyperbilirubinemia
69	. Group B–Streptococcal infection	68	. Multiple malformations
87	. Severe hyperbilirubinemia	76	. Patency of Ductus Arteriosus
		96	. Fetal hydrops

TABLE 9

FACTORS INFLUENCING DEVELOPMENT OF RDS, INDEPENDENTLY FROM
TREATMENT

FACTORS	RDS	NO RDS
• BIRTH WEIGHT mean $\pm$ S.D. (gr)	1480.00 $\pm$ 350.00	1980.00 $\pm$ 480.00**
• GESTATIONAL AGE AT BIRTH mean $\pm$ S.D. (days)	211.90 $\pm$ 16.19	230.51 $\pm$ 13.49**
• ROM TO DELIVERY TIME mean $\pm$ S.D. (days)	63.83 $\pm$ 108.02	50.50 $\pm$ 107.30
• TREATMENT TO DELIVERY TIME mean $\pm$ S.D. (days)	2.81 $\pm$ 1.25	11.18 $\pm$ 13.24*
• APGAR 1' (mean $\pm$ S.D.)	4.00 $\pm$ 2.19	6.05 $\pm$ 2.64*
• APGAR 5' (mean $\pm$ S.D.)	6.10 $\pm$ 1.79	7.45 $\pm$ 2.16
• APGAR $\frac{1' + 5'}{2}$ (mean $\pm$ S.D.)	4.95 $\pm$ 1.90	6.76 $\pm$ 2.30*
• MALE (%)	67%	49%
• USE OF BETA-MIMETICS (%)	85%	88%
• TWINS (%)	31%	21%

* P < 0.05

** P < 0.01

TABLE 10/A

MATERNAL BIOCHEMICAL PARAMETERS BEFORE AND AFTER TREATMENT WITH BETAMETHASONE

| | B E T A M E T H A S O N E | |
PARAMETERS (mean $\pm$ S.D.)	BEFORE	AFTER
RED CELLS (million/cu mm)	3.66 $\pm$ 0.4	3.60 $\pm$ 0.4
WHITE CELLS (1000/cu mm)	10.48 $\pm$ 2.4	11.03 $\pm$ 3.4
HB (g/100 ml)	11.38 $\pm$ 1.2	11.23 $\pm$ 1.5
ALKALINE PHOSPHATASE (U/100 ml)	72.36 $\pm$ 47.3	75.12 $\pm$ 47.8
γ GT	19.00 $\pm$ 10.8	24.13 $\pm$ 15.1*
DIR. BILIRUBIN (mg/100 ml)	0.18 $\pm$ 0.2	0.18 $\pm$ 0.2
IND. BILIRUBIN (mg/100 ml)	0.28 $\pm$ 0.1	0.30 $\pm$ 0.2
SGOT (U/ml/min)	21.18 $\pm$ 9.5	29.81 $\pm$ 31.1
SGPT (U/ml/min)	23.59 $\pm$ 18.2	33.40 $\pm$ 52.5
TOTAL LIPIDS (mg/100 ml)	809.94 $\pm$ 306.5	1247.58 $\pm$ 1408.8
CHOLESTEROL (mg/100 ml)	216.20 $\pm$ 47.8	215.84 $\pm$ 43.9
TRIGLICERYD (mg/100 ml)	182.18 $\pm$ 74.6	192.27 $\pm$ 75.0
AZOT (mg/100 ml)	19.00 $\pm$ 17.2	18.26 $\pm$ 5.4
URINE S.P.	1018.62 $\pm$ 5.5	1017.33 $\pm$ 5.8

* $P < 0.05$

TABLE 10/B

MATERNAL BIOCHEMICAL PARAMETERS BEFORE AND AFTER TREATMENT WITH AMBROXOL

	AMBROXOL	
PARAMETERS (mean $\pm$ S.D.)	BEFORE	AFTER
RED CELLS (million/cu mm)	3.73 $\pm$ 0.4	3.86 $\pm$ 0.4
WHITE CELLS (1000/cu mm)	10.09 $\pm$ 2.8	10.51 $\pm$ 3.1
HB (g/100 ml)	11.43 $\pm$ 1.4	11.81 $\pm$ 1.2
ALKALINE PHOSPHATASE (U/100 ml)	80.60 $\pm$ 69.4	85.04 $\pm$ 65.4
γ GT	19.73 $\pm$ 14.3	21.47 $\pm$ 6.5
DIR. BILIRUBIN (mg/100 ml)	0.30 $\pm$ 0.3	0.28 $\pm$ 0.2
IND. BILIRUBIN (mg/100 ml)	0.30 $\pm$ 0.2	0.32 $\pm$ 0.1
SGOT (U/ml/min)	41.12 $\pm$ 74.9	47.33 $\pm$ 102.4
SGPT (U/ml/min)	57.54 $\pm$ 141.8	73.00 $\pm$ 195.8
TOTAL LIPIDS (mg/100 ml)	896.27 $\pm$ 353.1	913.36 $\pm$ 339.7
CHOLESTEROL (mg/100 ml)	236.38 $\pm$ 45.5	231.28 $\pm$ 44.7
TRIGLICERYD (mg/100 ml)	227.80 $\pm$ 115.34	208.25 $\pm$ 96.9
AZOT (mg/100 ml)	19.81 $\pm$ 13.2	19.74 $\pm$ 6.9
URINE S.P.	1020.65 $\pm$ 6.4	1018.00 $\pm$ 6.3*

* $P < 0.05$

GESTATIONAL AGE AT BIRTH (weeks)	BETAMETHASONE Group	AMBROXOL Group	
		Scheme A	Scheme B
≤ 30	● ● ● ● ● ● ○ ○	○	○ ●
31	○ ○ ○ ○ ○ ○		○
32	○ ○ ○		○ ○ ○ ○
33	● ● ○ ○ ○ ○ ○ ○ ○ ○ ○ ○	○ ○	● ● ○ ○ ○
34	● ○ ○ ○ ○ ○ ○	○ ○	○ ○ ○
35	○	○ ○ ○	○ ○ ○ ○
36	○ ○ ○ ○ ○ ○	○	○ ○ ○

● RDS

○ no RDS

Fig. 1. Incidence of RDS in liveborn infants ≤36 weeks gestation according to gestational age and treatment.

DISCUSSION

Previous reports showed that ambroxol is able to reduce RDS incidence in preterm infants. Lowenberg et al. (9) and Wauer et al. (10) found a statistically significant reduction ($p < 0.01$) of RDS incidence after the 32nd week of gestation, but before that time not statistically significant, after antenatal administration of ambroxol compared to placebo.

Our lower RDS incidence both before and after the 32nd week of gestation after antenatal administration of ambroxol than of betamethasone, was not statistically significant.

It should be noted that infants in the betamethasone group had a significantly lower ($p < 0.05$) birth weight and gestational age at birth than infants in the ambroxol group and that both of these two factors significantly influenced RDS incidence in our study population.

However other factors influencing development of RDS were not significantly different in the two groups. Furthermore, since treatment was randomized and gestational age at entry was not significantly different in the two groups, one cannot exclude that ambroxol treatment may have a tocolytic effect, perhaps because of the fluid intake that it requires.

Up to this time there have been no reports of other maternal and neonatal adverse effects than nausea and headache in the mother (10,12).

The only significant modification of maternal laboratory tests after ambroxol treatment in our study was a reduction in urinary specific gravity that was probably due to the fluid intake that the therapy required, and no neonatal short time adverse effects were seen.

However other investigations are necessary to evaluate long term adverse effects on infants after antenatal use of this drug.

In conclusion, preliminary results of our study suggest that ambroxol may be at least as beneficial as betamethasone in reducing RDS incidence.

Its only limitation appears to be the relatively long duration of the treatment by schedule A and the probably lower effectiveness of the treatment by schedule B.

However it is possible to formulate the hypothesis that ambroxol may be used successfully in place of steroids at least for cases in which steroids are less effective, such as after the 32nd week of gestation or after PROM.

In all other cases it may be a suitable alternative to steroids or it may be used together with them to increase the efficacy of the prophylaxis.

ACKNOWLEDGEMENTS

We thank Prof. D. Pecorari, Dr. L. Samaia, Dr. M. Abrate for their contribution to the study.

We thank the Department of Biometry of Istituto De Angeli S.p.A. Milan, for the statistical analysis performed with Wang 2200 MVP Computer.

REFERENCES

1. Liggins, G.C. and Howie, R.N. (1972) Pediatrics, 50, 515

2. Quirk, J.G. Jr., Raker, R.K., Petrie, R.H. and Williams, A.M. (1979) Am. J. Obstet. Gynecol., 134, 768

3. Collaborative group on antenatal steroid therapy (1981) Am. J. Obstet. Gynecol., 141, 276

4. Garite, T.J., Freeman, R.K., Linzey, E.M., Braly, P.S. and Dorchester, W.L. (1981) Am. J. Obstet. Gynecol., 141, 508

5. Taeusch, H.W. (1975) J. Pediatrics, 87, 617

6. Taeusch, H.W., Frigoletto, F., Kitzmiller, J., Avery, M.E., Mehre, A., Fromm, B., Lawson, E. and Neff, R.K. (1979) Pediatrics, 63, 64

7. Corbet, A.J., Flax, P., Alston, C. and Rudolph, A.J. (1978) Pediatrics Res., 12, 797

8. Mashiach, S., Barkai, G., Sack, J., Stern, E., Goldman, D., Brish, M. and Serr, D.M. (1978) Am. J. Obstet. Gynecol., 130, 289

9. Lowenberg, E., Jimenez, L., Martinez, M. and Pommier, M. (1981) Prog. Resp. Res., 15, 240

10. Wauer, R.R., Schmalisch, G., Menzel, K., Schroder, M., Muller, K. and Tiller, R. et al. (1982) Biological Research in Pregnancy, 3, 84

11. Dubowitz, L.M.S., Dubowitz, V. and Goldberg, C. (1970) J. Pediatr., 77, 1

12. Luerti, M., Stefanoni , S., Zavattini, G. and Pintaudi, M. (1982) In: "Il liquido amniotico" - G. Vecchietti e G.C. di Renzo. Piccin Ed., Padova

© 1983, Elsevier Science Publishers B.V.
Pulmonary Surfactant System, E.V. Cosmi
and E.M. Scarpelli eds.

PREVENTION OF THE RESPIRATORY DISTRESS SYNDROME WITH AMBROXOL

PROF.EDUARDO LOWENBERG, FERNANDO ESCOBEDO,LOURDES JIMENEZ.
20th of November Medical Center. ISSSTE. MEXICO CITY.

INTRODUCTION

It has been shown that Respiratory Distress Syndrome (RDS)
is caused by lung surfactant deficiencies.(1,5).

Administration of glucocorticoids has proved useful in the
prevention of the RDS in spite of severe contraindications and
the unknown long-term effects (2,3,8,12).

Research of drugs which may induce fetal lung maduration has
been the trend of many Perinatal Centers, where prematurity
has a high incidence and RDS is the first component of perinatal
morbidity and mortality.

In a previous report (14) we concluded upon the usefulness
of Ambroxol (Bromhexine Metabolite NA 872) and the need of more
investigation in view of the drug's satisfactory tolerance and
lack of known contraindications.

A four years follow-up of such babies has shown no adverse
effects.

Following the same line of investigation, we have been using
Ambroxol in women with threatened preterm labor or women who
required interruption of gestation between the 30th and 35th
weeks.

Diagnosing fetal lung maturity by means of amniocentesis and
thin layer bidimensional chromatography has proved an excellent
study that related closely with newborn pulmonary health (6,7,9).

In the former study we evaluated the effects of Ambroxol on
surfactant content in amniotic fluid before and after drug
administration, in the present study which included the group
published previously no second sample was needed, since we evaluated only the presence of RDS in the newborn.

AMBROXOL (NA 872) has pharmacological studies which have shown
a stimulating action on bronchial secretions, but the most
important fact is that the drug increases the alveolar surfactant
activity, this function is essential when dealing with premature
newborns (4,10,11,13,15,16).

MATERIAL AND METHOD

148 patients received Ambroxol and formed the treated group.

The Control Group comprised 108 patients in whom no inductors of fetal lung maturation were used.

Admittance diagnosis of both groups are shown in Table 1.

TABLE 1

PRINCIPAL ADMITTANCE DIAGNOSIS

	AMBROXOL GROUP	CONTROL GROUP
Threatened Preterm Labor	83	62
Dangerous Fetal Condition	18	10
Prem. Rupture of Membranes	16	6
Hypertension/toxemia	16	11
Diabetes Mellitus	7	5
Urosepsis	5	8
Isoimmunization	3	6
	148	108

Gestational age at trial start is shown in Table 2.

TABLE 2

GESTATIONAL AGE AT RIAL START

WEEKS	AMBROXOL GROUP	CONTROL GROUP
30 or less	9	10
31	9	13
32	16	15
33	21	13
34	36	16
35	57	41
	148	108

Patients age, parity, pathology in previous gestations were similar in both groups.

The group under treatment included patients with threatened preterm labor of unknown etiology and patients with complications of gestation who were advised to terminate pregnancy.

Tocolytic agents (Betamimetic Drugs) were used in most of the cases of threatened preterm labor. In all cases amniotic fluid was obtained for phospholipids analysis. Ambroxol was used if immaturity data was found.

The control group included patients with similar diagnosis made on admission on whom only tocolytic drugs were used. Of these patients, as in the treated group, amniotic fluid was obtained for analysis.

Criteria for immaturity of fetal lung was: lecithin/sphingo myelin ratio (L/S) equal to or lower than 2 with no phospho glycerol (PG).

The treated group was handled as follows: after tocological evaluation a betamimetic drug was infused, as soon as uterine contractions were inhibited an amniocentesis was performed to determine the phospholipids content. Tocolytics were discontinued. 1000 mg of Ambroxol was administered diluted in 250 ml of a 5% glucose solution with the aid of an infusion pump, in a two hours drip. The treatment was repeated every day until a maximun of 5 doses. If the patient did not give birth the treatment was repeated every week until labor was establish or until the 35th week of gestational age when all treatment was stopped.

When pregnandy was interrupted for obstetrical reasons the same Ambroxol treatment was used, after verification of fetal lung immaturity. Usually these patients received few doses.

Patients gave birth at different gestational ages (Table 3), and received a different number of Ambroxol doses.

All groups received the same obstetrical care and were kept under biweekly observation until childbirth.

Weight, Apgar Score at 1 and 5 minutes, presence of RDS, morbidity and mortality rate due to RDS were recorded. Chi square analysis were used to find differences between groups.

RESULTS

Side Effects. Nausea and vomiting were common during Ambroxol infusion (31%) but only infrequently was it necesary to stop treatment for this reason.

Slight tachycardia was observed during treatment (8%).Fetal tachycardia was recorded in 26% of the cases.

TABLE   3

GESTATIONAL AGE AT DELIVERY

WEEKS	AMBROXOL GROUP	CONTROL GROUP
30 or less	5	6
31	4	7
32	6	12
33	17	12
34	24	18
35	46	36
36 or more	46	17

When used alone Ambroxol did not cause changes in blood pressure. Decrease blood pressure were reported in 2 cases out of 5 in which Ambroxol and tocolytic drugs were used at the same time.

Weight and Apgar Score were similar in both groups (Tables 4,5).

TABLE 4

AVERAGE WEIGHT OF NEWBORNS

WEEKS	AMBROXOL GROUP	CONTROL GROUP
30 or less	1150 g	1120 g
31	1200	1225
32	1280	1230
33	1620	1590
34	1950	1900
35	2560	2620
36 or more	2930	3050

Weight of the babies in both groups were within normal limits for gestational age and there were 12 hypotrophic babies in the treated group against 10 in the control group.

Presence of RDS according with the number of doses of Ambroxol used is shown in Table 6.

Fetal deaths occured with no difference in both groups.

Neonatal mortality diminished in the treated group and so did the perinatal mortality (Tables 7,8).

TABLE 5

AVERAGE APGAR SCORE

WEEKS	AMBROXOL GROUP		CONTROL GROUP	
	1'	5'	1'	5'
30 or less	7.2	8.1	5.4	7.4
31	6.5	8.8	6.3	7.8
32	7.1	8.0	6.5	8.2
33	7.4	7.9	7.6	8.2
34	7.8	8.4	8.0	8.6
35	8.3	8.8	8.1	8.7
36 or more	8.1	8.5	8.3	8.8

39 cesarean section were performed in the treated group (26.3%) against 32 in the control group (29.6%).

TABLE 6

NUMBER OF DOSES OF AMBROXOL
USED AND PRESENCE OF RDS

DOSES	n	RDS
1	22	3
2	23	2
3	39	1*
4	37	1*
5	27	1*

* Some repeat treatment
every week until the 35th
week gestational age.

TABLE 7

PERINATAL MORBIDITY AND MORTALITY

	AMBROXOL GROUP	CONTROL GROUP	SIGNIFICANCE p less than
RDS	8	19	0.01
RDS MORTALITY	4	10	0.01
FETAL DEATHS	2	3	ns
NEONATAL DEATHS	8	17	0.01
PERINATAL MORTALITY	10	20	0.01
SURVIVING	138	88	

RDS was statistically significant less in the treated group, (p<0.01).

As many pregnancies in both groups were prolonges due to toco-lytic drugs, we compared the results of Ambroxol in those cases in which delivery occurred during the week of the first treatment and the results were statistically significant (p<0.01) (Table 8).

TABLE 8

PERINATAL MORBIDITY AND MORTALITY FOR RDS
DURING THE WEEK OF THE FIRST TREATMENT

	AMBROXOL GROUP	CONTROL GROUP	SIGNIFICANCE p less than
RDS	4	16	0.025
RDS MORTALITY	3	11	0.025
No RDS	56	63	
FETAL DEATHS	1	1	n.s.
NEONATAL DEATHS	3	17	0.01
PERINATAL DEATHS	4	18	0.01
SURVIVING	56	61	

RDS and RDS mortality by gestational age is shown in Table 9.

TABLE 9

RDS AND RDS MORTALITY BY GESTATIONAL AGE

WEEKS	AMBROXOL GROUP		CONTROL GROUP	
	RDS	RDS MORT.	RDS	RDS MORT.
30 or less	2	1	4	2
31	1	1	4	2
32	2	1	3	2
33	1	1	5	2
34	1	0	3	0
35	1	0	1	1
36 or more	0	0	1	1
TOTAL	8	4	19	10

COMMENTS

Disadvantages and caution in the use of glucocorticoids as in-ducer of fetal lung maturation has led investigators to new drugs. Ambroxol a bromhexine metabolite has enough background research to be used in clinical trials.

Our previous work showed an improvement in amniotic fluid phospholipids when Ambroxol was administered to patients before term. Conversion from immaturity (L/S ratio equal or less than 2 and absence of PG) to maturity (L/S ratio more than 2 and pre sence of PG) was observed more frequently.

In the present study all cases were documented with immaturity data and although no further amniotic fluid analysis was performed, presence of RDS decreased in a statistically significant number.

Perinatal mortality diminished and the number of survivings improved when Ambroxol was used.

No immediate adverse effects were seen with Ambroxol and follow up of the babies until now (1982) showed no problems after 4 years of using the drug.

Data showed a better prognosis no matter how many doses of Ambroxol were used but best results were obtained when the 5 doses were applied, specially when the treatment was repeated every week until the baby was born.

No difference was observed when Ambroxol was administered in different pregnancy complications, altough when used in those pathologies that per se accelerate fetal lung maturation the results were better. No statistical analysis support this latter personal criteria.

With glucocorticoids best results were achieved between the 28th and 32th weeks gestational age; with Ambroxol no difference was found, but we think that more cases are needed to confirm statistically this probability.

No side effects in mothers were recorded. Normal bleeding during cesarean section was reported.

REFERENCES

1. Brown,B.J.,Gorbert,H.A.,Stenchever,M.A.:Respiratory distress syndrome, surfactant biochemistry and acceleration of fetal lung maturity. A review. Obstet.Gynec.Surv. 30:71,1975.

2. Caspi,E., Schreyer,P., Weinraub,S., Bukovsky,I., Tamir,I.: Changes in amniotic fluid lecithin/sphingomyelin ratio following maternal dexamethasone administration. Am. J. Obstet. Gynec. 122:327,1975.

3. De Lemos,R.A.,Shermata,D., Knelson,J.H., Kotas,R.V., Avery,M.E. Acceleration of appearance of pulmonary surfactant in the fetal lamb by administation of corticoids. Am.Rev.Resp.Dis.102:358 1971.

4. Agberts,J., Fontijne,K.,Wamsteker,J.: Indication of increase of the lecithin/sphingomyelin (L/S) ratio in lung fluid of lambs maternally treated with metabolite VIII of Bisolvon. Biol. Neonate 29:315,1976.

5. Farrel,P.M.,Avery,M.E.: Hyaline membrane diseases. Am.Rev. Resp.Dis. 111:657,1975.

6. Gluck,L., Kulovich,M.,Borer,R.C., Brenner,P.H.,Anderson,C., Spellacy,W.N.:Diagnosis of the respiratory distress syndrome by amniocentesis. Am.J.Obstet.Gynec. 109:440,1971.

7. Gluck,L.,Kulovich,M.: Lecithin/sphingomyelin ratios in amniotic fluid in normal and abnormal pregnancies. Am.J.Obstet.Gynec. 115:539,1973.

8. Gluck,L.; Administration of corticoids to induce maturation of fetal lung. Am.J.Dis.Child. 130:976,1976.

9. Hallman,M., Gluck,L.: Development of the fetal lung. J.Perinatal Med. 5:3,1977.

10.Kapanci,T.,Cerutti,P.: Morphometric evaluation of type II epithelial-cell changes in the lung of rats, produced by a metabolite of bromhexine. (Unpublish).

11.Krieglsteiner,P.,Lohninger,A.,Munnich,W.,Erhard,W.,Neiss,A., Blumel,G.: Effekt von Betamethason und Bromhexin-Metabolit VIII auf die fetale Surfactantbiosynthese. (Unpublish).

12.Liggins,G.C.,Howie,R.N.: A controlled trial of ante-partum glucocorticoid treatment for prevention of the respiratory distress syndrome in premature infants. Pediatrics. Spingfield 50:515,1972.

13.Lorenz,U.,Ruttgers,H.,Fux,G.,Kubli,F.: Fetal pulmonary surfactant induction by bromhexine metabolite VIII. Am.J.Obstet. Gynec. 119:1126, 1974.

14.Lowenberg,E.,Jiménez,L.,Martínez,M.,Pommier,M.:Effects of Ambroxol (NA 872) on biochemical fetal lung maturity and prevention of the respiratory distress syndrome.Prog.Resp.Res. Vol 15.pp 240. Karger,Basel 1981.

15.Puschmann,S.,Engelhorn,R.:Pharmakologische Untersuchungen des Bromhexin-Metaboliten Ambroxol. Arzneimittel Forsch. 5a 889 (Drug Res.)

16.Zahn,U.,Zach,H.P.,Sigmund,R.: Uber die Moglichkeit der prenatalen Behanlung des Atemnotsyndroms bei Fruhgeburten mit Ambroxol. Atemwegs-LungenKr. 4:35,1978.

© 1983, Elsevier Science Publishers B.V.
Pulmonary Surfactant System, E.V. Cosmi
and E.M. Scarpelli eds.

THE PREMATURE NEWBORN RABBIT AS EXPERIMENTAL R.D.S. MODEL

ROLAND NILSSON

Department of Pediatric Pathology, Karolinska Institutet,
Stockholm, Sweden.

INTRODUCTION

The cause of the neonatal respiratory distress syndrome (RDS)
or hyaline membrane disease (HMD), is almost certainly a deficiency of surface-active lung phospholipids (surfactant) (36). Morphologically, HMD is characterized mainly by atelectasis, bronchiolar
epithelial necrosis. and hyaline membranes. This pattern is
seen irrespective of whether artificial ventilation has been
applied or not (4,8). However, even short periods of artificial
ventilation have been found to provoke bronchiolar epithelial
necrosis in surfactant-deficient, immature newborn experimental
animals (19,33). Treatment of RDS with artificial ventilation
therefore probably could aggravate already existing epithelial
lesions. The long-term complication of HMD, known as bronchopulmonary dysplasia (BPD), was originally interpreted as due to oxygen
toxicity (32), but a number of retrospective studies indicate
that high-dose oxygen treatment is not directly correlated to
the development of BPD (18,28,29,34,35). It seems that intermittent positive pressure ventilation (IPPV) can induce BPD even
with low oxygen dose and low insufflation pressure (18), but
the severity of BPD is well correlated to the peak pressure
level used during artificial ventilation (37).

The aim of this paper is to give a brief description of an
experimental model of RDS developed in our laboratory and to
review a number of studies in which this model has been applied
These studies concerned the pathogenesis and morphogenesis of
the bronchiolar epithelial lesions as well as the efficacy of
various therapeutic methods, such as surfactant replacement
and different types of artificial ventilation.

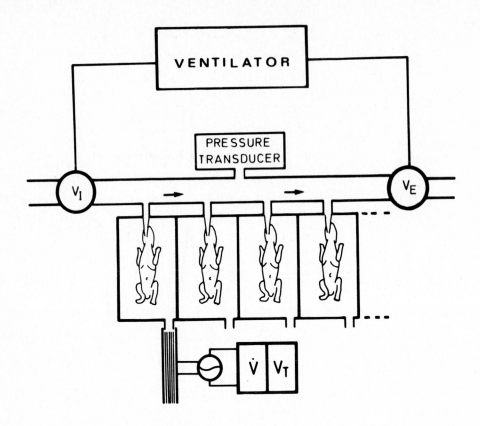

Fig. 1. Diagram of respirator system for ventilation of multiple animals at standardized P_I. Flow ($\dot{V}$) and V_T are recorded
by a differential pressure transducer connected to each body
plethysmograph via a Fleisch tube. P_I is recorded close to the
connections of the tracheal tubes. V_I and V_E are inspiratory
and expiratory valves.

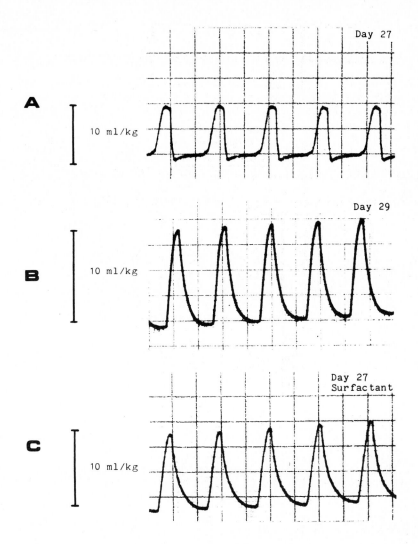

Fig. 2. Volume recordings from three rabbit neonates ventilated
with standardized V_T (10 ml/kg). The two animals from gestational
day 27 are littermates. A. Gestational age 27 days, untreated
animal. The volume recording has a delayed onset and a rapid
expiration phase (immature volume recording). B. Gestational
age 29 days, untreated animal. The deflation loop of the volume
tracing has a curved shape, reflecting prolonged expiration
(mature volume recording). C. Gestational age 27 days, surfactant-
-treated animal showing mature type of volume recording. (From
Nilsson 1982).

THE EXPERIMENTAL MODEL

As experimental animals we use premature rabbit neonates at
a gestational age of 27 days (full term = 31 $\pm$ 1 days). The
animals are tracheotomized and kept in volume- or pressure-
-constant body plethysmographs at 37°C (Fig. 1). They are subjected to IPPV, using standardized tidal volume (V_T) or standardized
insufflation pressure (P_I). V_T is calculated from the pressure
variations in the volume-constant type of plethysmograph. When
the plethysmograph is of pressure-constant type, V_T and air
flow are recorded with a specially designed Fleisch-tube, a
differential pressure transducer and an integrator unit. After
the experiment the animals are killed and the lungs fixed by
vascular perfusion. Paraffin sections from the lungs are examined
microscopically, and the degree of alveolar expansion and the
prevalence of bronchiolar epithelial lesions are determined
morphometrically (22). Programmes have also been developed for
computerized morphometry (30).

APPLICATIONS OF THE EXPERIMENTAL MODEL

Fetal maturity vs. epithelial lesions and lung compliance

One of our earlier experimental series (21) included newborn
rabbits from gestational days 27-30. All animals from day 27
were here found to be immature, i.e. they had low lung-thorax
compliance and abundant bronchiolar epithelial lesions. All
animals from days 29 and 30 were mature; their lung-thorax compliance was high and there were no epithelial lesions. Alveolar
air expansion, determined morphometrically, was clearly higher
in mature animals. Animals from day 28 constituted a mixed group
of immature and mature animals. These studies also revealed
that mature and immature animals have different types of V_T
recordings: In the mature animals there is an immediate onset
of inspiration and a prolonged expiration phase, and in the
immature animals a delayed onset of inspiration and a very rapid
expulsion of air during expiration (Fig. 2.)

These results are concordant with earlier studies on surfactant
production and static pressure-volume characteristics of the
fetal rabbit lung during late gestation (9.10,13,14). They show,

in addition, that there is a close relation between in-vivo
lung mechanics, alveolar expansion, and the liability to develop
epithelial lesions during artificial ventilation.

Since only fetuses from day 27 were consistently immature,
such animals were used in our subsequent experiments for analysing
the pathogenesis of the epithelial lesions, and for testing
therapeutic regimens of potential clinical significance.

Early development of bronchiolar epithelial lesions

In a combined light and electron microscopic study (24), immature newborn rabbits were ventilated for periods varying from
1 to 30 min. Bronchiolar epithelial necrosis was observed in
all animals ventilated for 5 min or more (Fig. 3.). Even in
some animals ventilated for only 1 min, pyknotic bronchiolar
epithelial cells were found. With longer periods of ventilation,
necrotic epithelial cells coalesced and formed typical hyaline
membranes.

These findings confirm earlier observations in showing the
very rapid development of epithelial lesions in artificially
ventilated immature newborn experimental animals (19,33). The
lesions are of the same type as seen in early human HMD (4,8).
As mentioned above, these observations suggest that ventilator
treatment can aggravate already existing lung lesions in HMD,
and increase the risk of BPD (18,29,34,35).

Surfactant treatment

When immature newborn rabbits were given homologous natural
surfactant in the tracheal cannula before being connected to
the ventilator system, lung-thorax compliance increased as compared to littermate controls (Fig. 4) (23,25). This effect was
observed irrespective of whether the animals were ventilated
with standardized V_T or standardized P_I. Treatment with surfactant
also protected the animals from developing epithelial lesions
and improved alveolar aeration, evaluated morphometrically.

In another study (27) the immature animals were first ventilated for 10 min to allow the development of early epithelial
lesions. Thereafter, 1-4 doses of natural surfactant were given
at 30-min intervals. With this treatment, lung compliance usually

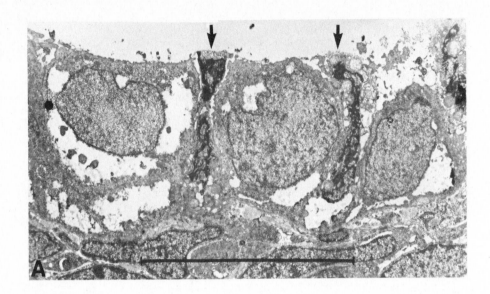

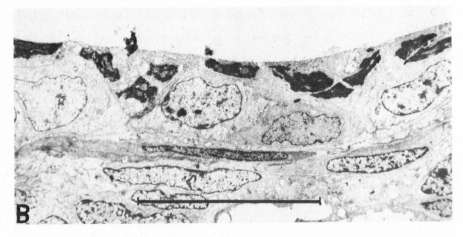

Fig. 3. Ultrastructure of bronchiolar epithelial cells in fetuses ventilated for 5 min. Two pyknotic epithelial cells are
indicated with arrows in A. The field shown in B represents
a more advanced type of lesion with multiple necrotic, desquama-
ted, and flattened epithelial cells.
Horizontal bar = 10 μ. (From Nilsson et al 1980a).

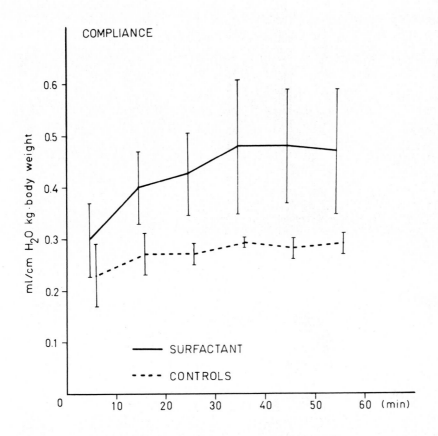

Fig. 4. Lung-thorax compliance $\bar{X}\pm$SD) in surfactant-treated immature newborn rabbits and littermate controls (gestational age
27 days) at various intervals after onset of IPPV with standardized V_T (10 ml/kg) (Based on data from Nilsson et al. 1978).

did not increase significantly until after the second treatment
(Fig. 5). Bronchiolar epithelial lesions were, as expected,
found in all animals including those receiving surfactant. However, these lesions were clearly less widespread in surfactant-
-treated animals than in littermate controls. The development
of epithelial lesions in surfactant-treated animals also seemed
to have been arrested at an early stage (Fig. 6). The degree
of alveolar aeration was again higher than in control animals.

When lung mechanics were evaluated during spontaneous ventilation (15), surfactant treatment before the first breath had
the same beneficial effects on lung mechanics and morphology
as outlined above. In recordings of the first breaths, surfactant-
-treated animals retained more air at end-expiration, indicating
that the presence of surfactant facilitates the establishment
of functional residual capacity (FRC).

The combined results of these studies show that treatment
of the immature rabbit neonate with surfactant increases lung
compliance, facilitates lung aeration and prevents (23,25) or
arrests (27) the development of bronchiolar epithelial necrosis
and hyaline membranes.

Effects of positive end-expiratory pressure (PEEP)

In similar experiments on immature newborn rabbits, a low
level of PEEP (5 cm H_2O) was applied during the period of artificial ventilation (26). This treatment resulted in a significant
improvement in lung-thorax compliance in comparison with littermate controls, ventilated without PEEP. Recordings of air flow
revealed that there was an immediate onset of accelerating inspiratory flow in the PEEP-treated group, while control animals
had a delayed onset of inspiration. Maximal expiratory flow
was lower in animals ventilated with PEEP. Morphometry showed
no difference in alveolar aeration between the groups, but epithelial lesions were clearly reduced in animals treated with PEEP.
These results thus show that the effects of PEEP on lung mechanics
and lung morphology are similar to those of surfactant.

The influence of frequency and inspiration:expiration (I:E) ratio

In a series of experiments reported by Lachmann et al (16), premature rabbit neonates were ventilated with varying frequency (20-60/min) and varying duration of the inspiration phase (20-80 %). At all frequencies tested, compliance increased almost linearly with increasing I:E ratio. It was also obvious from the volume tracings that at high frequency and low I:E ratio the duration of the inspiration phase was too short to allow adequate aeration of the lungs. At high frequency and high I:E ratio the expiration phase was short enough to prevent zero flow before the onset of the next inspiration; this means that the lungs were not allowed to collapse at end-expiration. The results thus document the beneficial effect of high I:E ratio (> 1:1) during artificial ventilation of surfactant-deficient lungs, confirming the clinical observations previously reported by Reynolds et al (29).

In another series of experiments, Lachmann et al (17) studied the combined effects of prolonged inspiration phase and surfactant replacement in immature newborn rabbits. Again, animals treated with surfactant had a much higher compliance than controls, irrespective of the I:E ratio. Lung-thorax compliance reached a maximal value at 60 % inspiration time and frequency 40/min, and decreased at higher I:E ratio. This decrease in compliance may be due to an increase in FRC. Histological lung sections from surfactant-treated animals showed that alveolar air expansion increased with the I:E ratio, suggesting that alveolar recruitment is enhanced by prolongation of the inspiration phase. As in previous experiments, surfactant treatment prevented the development of bronchiolar epithelial lesions. Lachmann et al (17) emphasized that the setting of the ventilator system should be carefully adjusted with respect to the therapeutic response, in RDS patients treated with surfactant.

Pathogenesis of bronchiolar epithelial lesions and the prophylactic effect of surfactant and PEEP

The cause of bronchiolar epithelial lesions in clinical and experimental HMD may be related to at least three mechanisms:

222

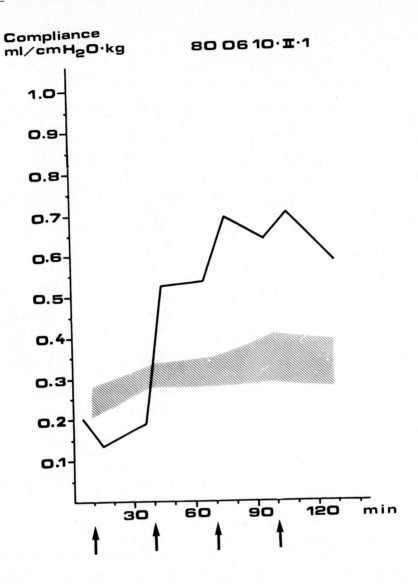

Fig. 5. Lung-thorax compliance in one experimental animal at various intervals after onset of artificial ventilation. Surfactant administration is indicated with arrows. Compliance levels ($\overline{X} \pm SEM$) for non-treated littermate group are shown as a hatched zone. (From Nilsson et al 1981).

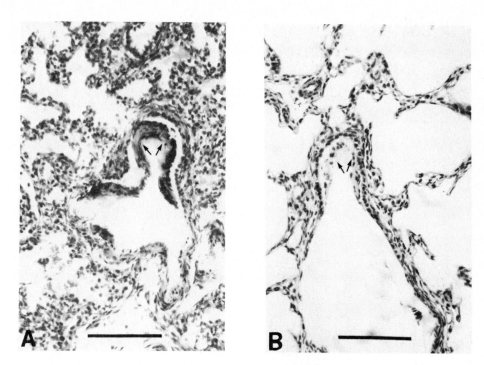

Fig. 6. Histologic lung sections from non-treated animal (A)
and from littermate treated with surfactant (B). Both animals
were ventilated for 130 min; the experimental animal received
4 doses of surfactant. In the non-treated animal there is advanced
shedding of bronchiolar epithelium with hyaline membrane formation
(A, arrows). An early type of bronchiolar lesion is seen in
the surfactant-treated animal, characterized by necrosis and
desquamation of pyknotic epithelial cells without prominent
exudative reaction (B, arrows). Hematoxylin and eosin. Horizontal
bar = 100 µ. (From Nilsson et al 1981).

to structural immaturity per se, to barotrauma and to overdistension of conducting airways. The findings that treatment with surfactant or PEEP protects the immature lung against the development of epithelial lesions, even during high pressure ventilation, seems to eliminate the first two possibilities. The third mechanism, bronchiolar overdistension, remains likely. In surfactant deficiency, resistance to aeration is high due to capillarity in the finer conducting airways and a high P_I is therefore required to push the air-liquid interface into alveoli. This might imply a risk of bronchiolar overdistension during the inspiration phase, with consequent mechanical disruption of the airway epithelium (3,31). Furthermore, since airway dimensions depend upon the expansion pattern of the surrounding parenchyma (12), an irregular expansion pattern may in itself cause shear stress in the airway mucosa. Treatment with surfactant or PEEP keps the air-liquid interface at alveolar level throughout the ventilatory cycle. This reduces the resistance to aeration and promotes a more uniform expansion of the alveolar compartment. In accordance with the principles outlined above, both these effects reduce the risk of bronchiolar epithelial injury during artificial, or spontaneous, ventilation.

Application of the experimental model for evaluation of other surfactant preparations

The experimental model has also been used to investigate the effect of different synthetic surfactant preparations. These include emulsified synthetic surfactant (11) and dry artificial surfactant (1). When given intratracheally, both preparations had a beneficial effect on lung compliance. The effect was, however, not as prominent as that of natural surfactant, especially as the synthetic preparations did not seem to prevent the development of bronchiolar epithelial lesions (11,20).

The model has also been applied by Fujiwara et al for evaluation of a semi-synthetic surfactant (5), which seemed to have the same physiological effects as natural surfactant (6). This semi-synthetic surfactant has also been tested in artificially ventilated RDS-patients, with dramatically good results (7). This indicates that surfactant treatment is effective also clinically

in infants with severe HMD. The recent observation that natural
surfactant retains its important physiological properties after
removal of most protein components (2) may render surfactant
substitution more easily acceptable in clinical practice.

SUMMARY

When immature newborn rabbits, delivered at a gestational
age of 27 days, are subjected to artificial ventilation, bronchiolar epithelial lesions develop within 1-5 min after the onset
of ventilation. These lesions are similar to those in early
human HMD. Surfactant instillation in the tracheal cannula prevents or arrests the development of such epithelial lesions,
increases lung-thorax compliance and improves the alveolar air
expansion. These beneficial effects are seen even during ventilation with standardized high insufflation pressure. Similarly,
the application of a low level of PEEP causes increased compliance
and reduces the development of epithelial lesions. Artificial
ventilation with prolonged inspiration phase also has a beneficial
effect on lung-thorax compliance, especially in combination
with surfactant replacement. It seems likely that the epithelial
lesions result from a combination of bronchiolar overdistension
and shear stress in the airway mucosa caused by irregular aeration
of the alveolar compartment. The same mechanisms probably cause
the corresponding epithelial lesions in human HMD.

ACKNOWLEDGEMENT

This work was supported by The Swedish National Association
against Heart and Chest Diseases.

REFERENCES

1. Bangham, A.D., Morley, C.J. and Phillips, M.C. (1979) The
    physical properties of an effective lung surfactant.
    Biochim. Biophys. Acta 573: 552-556.

2. Berggren, P., Grossmann, G., Nilsson, R., Tollbom, Ö.,
    Thunell, S. and Robertson, B. (1981) A protein-free physiolo-
    gically active preparation of natural lung surfactant.
    IRCS Med. Sci. 9: 283-284.

3. Enhörning, G. and Robertson, B. (1972) Lung expansion in
    the premature rabbit fetus after tracheal deposition of
    surfactant. Pediatrics 50: 58-66.

4. Finlay-Jones, J.-M., Papadimitriou, J.M. and Barter, R.A.
    (1974) Pulmonary hyaline membrane: Light and electron micro-
    scopic study of the early stage. J. Pathol. 112: 117-124.

5. Fujiwara, T., Tanaka, Y. and Takei, T. (1979) Surface proper-
    ties of artificial surfactant in comparison with natural
    and synthetic surfactant lipids. IRCS Med. Sci. 7: 311.

6. Fujiwara, T., Maeta, H., Chida, S. and Morita, T. (1979)
    Improved lung-thorax compliance and prevention of neonatal
    pulmonary lesion in prematurely delivered rabbit neonates
    subjected to IPPV after tracheal instillation of artificial
    surfactant. IRCS Med. Sci. 7: 313.

7. Fujiwara, T., Chida, S., Watabe, Y., Maeta, H., Morita,
    T. and Abe, T. (1980) Artificial surfactant therapy in hya-
    line-membrane disease. Lancet 1: 55-59.

8. Gandy, G., Jacobson, W. and Gairdner, D. (1970) Hyaline
    membrane disease. I: Cellular changes.
    Arch. Dis. Child. 45: 289-310.

9. Gluck, L., Motoyama, E.K., Smits, H.L. and Kulovich, M.V.
    (1967) The biochemical development of surface activity in
    mammalian lung. I. The surface-active phospholipids; the
    separation and distribution of surface-active lecithin in
    the lung of the developing rabbit fetus.
    Pediat. Res. 1: 237-246.

10. Grossmann, G. (1977) Expansion pattern of terminal air-spaces
    in the premature rabbit lung after tracheal deposition of
    surfactant. Pflügers Arch. 367: 205-209.

11. Grossmann. G., Larsson, I., Nilsson, R., Robertson, B.,
    Rydhag, L. and Stenius, P. (1979) Emulsified synthetic surfac-
    tant; surface properties and effect on neonatal lung expansion
    during artificial ventilation. Path. Res. Pract. 165: 100.

12. Hughes, J.M.B., Hoppin, F.G. and Mead, J. (1972) Effect
    of lung inflation on bronchial length and diameter in excised
    lungs. J. Appl. Physiol. 32: 25-35.

13. Humphreys, P.W. and Strang, L.B. (1967) Effects of gestation
    and prenatal asphyxia on pulmonary surface properties of
    the foetal rabbit. J. Physiol. (London) 192: 53-62.

14. Kikkawa, Y., Motoyama, E.K. and GLuck, L. (1968) Study of
    the lungs of fetal and newborn rabbits.
    Am. J. Pathol. 52: 177-192.

15. Lachmann, B., Grossmann, G., Nilsson, R. and Robertson,
    B. (1981) Effect of supplementary surfactant on in vivo
    lung mechanics in the premature rabbit neonate.
    Eur. J. Pediatr. 136: 173-179.

16. Lachmann, B., Grossmann, G., Freyse, J. and Robertson, B.
    (1981) Lung-thorax compliance in the artificially ventilated
    premature rabbit neonate in relation to variations in inspira-
    tion:expiration ratio. Pediat. Res. 15: 833-838.

17. Lachmann, B., Berggren, P., Curstedt, T., Grossmann, G and Robertson, B. (1982) Combined effects in surfactant substitution and prolongation of inspiration phase in artificially ventilated premature newborn rabbits. Pediat. Res. 16: 921-927.

18. Lindroth, M., Svenningsen, N.W., Ahlström, H. and Jonson, B. (1980) Evaluation of mechanical ventilation in newborn infants. II. Pulmonary and neuro-developmental sequelae in relation to original diagnosis. Acta Pediatr. Scand. 69: 151-158.

19. McAdams, A.J., Coen, R., Kleinman, L.I., Tsang, R., and Sutherland, J. (1973) The experimental production of hyaline membranes in premature rhesus monkeys. Am. J. Pathol. 70: 277-284.

20. Morley, C., Robertson, B., Lachmann, B., Nilsson, R., Bangham, A., Grossmann, G. and Miller, N. (1980) Artificial surfactant and natural surfactant. Comparative study of the effects on premature rabbit lungs. Arch. Dis. Child. 55: 758-765.

21. Nilsson, R. (1979) Lung compliance and lung morphology following artificial ventilation in the premature and fullterm rabbit neonate. Scand. J. Resp. Dis. 60: 206-214.

22. Nilsson, R. (1982) The artificially ventilated preterm rabbit neonate as experimental model of hyaline membrane disease. Acta Anaesth. Scand. 26: 89-103.

23. Nilsson, R., Grossmann. G. and Robertson, B. (1978) Lung surfactant and the pathogenesis of neonatal bronchiolar lesions induced by artificial ventilation. Pediat. Res. 12: 249-255.

24. Nilsson, R., Grossmann, G. and Robertson, B. (1980a) Bronchiolar epithelial lesions induced in the premature rabbit neonate by short periods of artificial ventilation. Acta Path. Microbiol. Scand. Sect. A. 88: 359-367.

25. Nilsson, R., Grossmann, G. and Robertson, B. (1980b) Pathogenesis of neonatal lung lesions induced by artificial ventilation; evidence against the role of barotrauma. Respiration 40: 218-225.

26. Nilsson, R., Grossmann, G. and Robertson, B. (1980c) Artificial ventilation of premature newborn rabbits; effects of positive end-expiratory pressure on lung mechanics and lung morphology. Acta Pediatr. Scand. 69: 597-602.

27. Nilsson, R., Grossmann, G., Berggren, P. and Robertson, B. (1981) Surfactant treatment in experimental hyaline membrane disease. Eur. J. Respir. Dis. 62: 441-449.

28. Pusey, V.A., MacPherson, R.I. and Chernick, V. (1969) Pulmonary fibroplasia following prolonged artificial ventilation of newborn infants. Canad. Med. Assoc. J. 100: 451-457.

228

29. Reynolds, E.O.R., and Taghizadeh, A. (1974) Improved prognosis of infants mechanically ventilated for hyaline membrane disease. Arch. Dis. Child. 49: 505-515.

30. Rigaut, J.-P., Berggren, P. and Robertson, B. (in press) Automated techniques for the study of lung alveolar stereological parameters with IBAS image analyser on optical microscopy sections. J. Microsc.

31. Robertson, B. (1976) Current and counter-current theories on lung surfactant. Scand. J. Resp. Dis. 57: 199-207.

32. Rosan, R.C. (1975) Hyaline membrane disease and a related spectrum of neonatal pneumopathies. In Perspectives in Pediatric Pathology, H.S. Rosenberg & R.P. Bolande (Eds), Year Book Medical Publishers, Chicago, vol. 2, pp. 15-60.

33. Stahlman, M., Lequire, V.S., Young, W.C., Merrill, R.E., Birmingham, R.T., Payne, G.A. and Gray, J. (1964) Pathophysiology of respiratory distress in newborn lambs. Am. J. Dis. Child. 108: 375-393.

34. Stocks, J., and Godfrey, S. (1976) The role of artificial ventilation, oxygen, and CPAP in the pathogenesis of lung damage in neonates: Assessment by serial measurements of lung function. Pediatrics 57: 352-362.

35. Stocks, J., Godfrey, S. and Reynolds, E.O.R. (1978) Airway resistance in infants after various treatments for hyaline membrane disease: Special emphasis on prolonged high levels of inspired oxygen. Pediatrics 61: 178-183.

36. Strang, L.B. (1977) Neonatal respiration. Physiological and clinical studies. Blackwell Scientific Publications, Oxford, pp. 181-218.

37. Taghizadeh, A. and Reynolds, E.O.R. (1976) Pathogenesis of bronchopulmonary dysplasia following hyaline membrane disease. Am. J. Pathol. 82: 241-264.

ADULT RESPIRATORY DISTRESS SYNDROME AND OTHER LUNG DISEASES

© 1983, Elsevier Science Publishers B.V.
Pulmonary Surfactant System, E.V. Cosmi
and E.M. Scarpelli eds.

SURFACTANT REPLACEMENT THERAPY IN THE EXPERIMENTAL ADULT
RESPIRATORY DISTRESS SYNDROME (ARDS)

BURKHARD LACHMANN, TETSURO FUJIWARA, SHOICHI CHIDA, TOMOAKI
MORITA, MINEO KONISHI, KOZI NAKAMURA AND HARUO MAETA
(Research Institute for Lung Diseases, 1115 Berlin-Buch,
Karower Str. 11, GDR, and Department of Pediatrics, Iwate
Medical University, Morioka, Japan)

INTRODUCTION

In earlier experimental and clinical investigations we could
show that alterations of the surfactant system of the lung are
an important factor in the development of severe respiratory
insufficiency in adult respiratory distress syndrome (for review
see 1).

Despite optimal of ventilatory therapy and application of
extracorporeal oxygenation these symptomatic therapeutic regimens are not very succesful in most severe forms of ARDS (2).

Since the surfactant system employs central significance in
the development of ARDS (1), the aim of our studies was to show
whether it was possible to improve gas exchange in an animal
model with combined severe respiratory insufficiency and surfactant deficiency by tracheal instillation of surfactant phospholipids.

MATERIAL AND METHODS

22 guinea pigs weighing 230 - 250 g were used. The animals
were anaesthetized, paralyzed and ventilated with a pressure
generated respirator (3). The inspiratory pressure was 28 cm
of water, PEEP was 5 cm of water, the I/E-ratio was 1:1, frequency was 20 per minute and the $F_I O_2$ was 1.

To produce the acute RDS the animals were lavaged 8 times
with warm saline to remove alveolar surfactant according to
Lachmann et al. (4). The volume of lavage fluid was 40 ml per kg
body weight. 10 and 40 minutes after the last lavage procedure
1 ml of surfactant was instilled into the airways.

The surfactant that we have used contained 56 % of dipalmy-
toyllecithin, 21 % unsaturated lecithin 10 % phosphotidylglyce-

232

rol as well as 6 % of other phospholipids normally present in lung surfactant.

It also contained 5 % neutral lipids and about 1 % protein (5).

Blood samples were taken from a catheter inserted in the carotid artery for measurements of blood gases.

RESULTS AND COMMENTS

The first instillation of surfactant produced a striking improvement in oxygenation in comparison to the controls (Fig. 1).

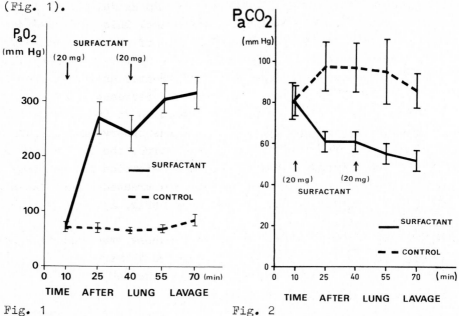

Fig. 1   Fig. 2

Behaviour of PaO_2 (X ± SD) (Fig. 1) and $PaCO_2$ (X ± SD) (Fig. 2) in adult guinea pigs with severe RDS after tracheal instillation of surfactant in comparison to controls.

However, after the first instillation a small decrease of arterial oxygenation occurred. That means that 20 mg Phospholipids was not enough to stabilize all alveoli in these surfactant deficiency lungs. The second instillation, 30 minutes later, led to a further improvement of the arterial oxygenation with nearly stable values. The mean difference in the arterial oxygen tension was finally more than 250 mm Hg.

We could also demonstrate in several animals that the same effect after surfactant instillation could be obtained when the interval between the last lung lavage and the surfactant instillation was over two or three hours (Fig. 3). This means, that respiratory failure of prolonged duration can be removed by substitution of surfactant within few minutes.

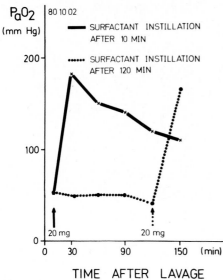

Fig. 3
Course of PaO$_2$ in two animals with ARDS. In one guinea pig surfactant instillation was performed 10 minutes after lung lavage, and in the other one two hours after the lavage period.

Arterial CO$_2$-tension in the controls increased from 80 to about 95 mm Hg following the last lavage. This indicates the existence of massive respiratory acidosis. On the other hand, however, treated animals demonstrated a decrease of CO$_2$-tension from 80 to 50 mm Hg by the end of the observation period. At that time, the mean difference of CO$_2$-tension between controls and treated animals was 35 mm Hg (Fig. 2).

At autopsy, the lungs of controls were "liver-like" in appearance, whereas the lungs of the treated animals were well aerated.

The lung weight (Fig. 4) and the ratio of lung to body weight (Fig. 5) indicates that mean fluid content in lungs of surfactant-treated animals was higher than that in controls. This was caused by the instillation of 2 ml of fluid, containing the surfactant phospholipids. This results also indicates, that the massive improvement of the arterial oxygen- and CO$_2$-tension was not caused by diminished intraalveolar or interstitial fluid but only by a decrease of intrapulmonary shunt.

These experimental results show that it is possible to depo-

234

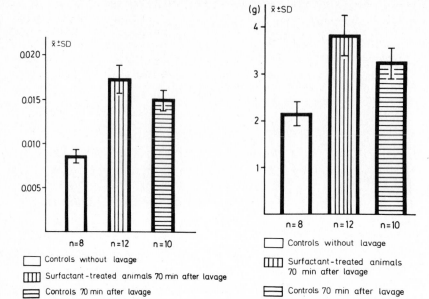

Fig. 4   Fig. 5
Lung weight (Fig. 4) and lung weight to body weight-ratio
(Fig. 5) in adult guinea pigs.

sit surfactant phospholipids in surfactant-deficiency adult
lungs in vivo.

It is evident that progressive atelectasis occurs in ARDS,
regardless of its etiology. We believe, that surfactant can be
used to treat the atelectasis which is the common factor in
ARDS regardless of etiology.

We also believe, that the instillation of surfactant begins
a new era in the therapy of ARDS.

REFERENCES

1. Lachmann, B. and Danzmann, E. (1983) Adult respiratory dis-
   tress syndrome in: Robertson, B., Van Golde, L.M.G. and
   Batenburg, J.J. (Ed.), Pulmonary Surfactant, Elsevier/North-
   Holland Biomedical Press, Amsterdam, in press.

2. Pontoppidan, H. and Rie, M.A. (1982) Pathogenesis and therapy
   of acute lung injury. In: O. Prakash (Ed.) Applied Physiology
   in Clinical Respiratory Care, Martinus Nijhoff Publishers,
   The Hague-Boston-London, pp. 55-73.

3. Merker, G., Lachmann, B., Oddoy, A., Robertson, B., Grossmann, G. and Vogel, J. (1981) Aufbau und Einsatzmöglichkeiten
   eines Steuergerätes für Magnetventile zur tierexperimentellen

Beatmung. Anaesthesiol. u. Reanimat., 6, 157-164.

4. Lachmann, B., Robertson, B. and Vogel, J. (1980) In vivo lung lavage as an experimental model of the respiratory distress syndrome. Acta Anaesth. Scand., 24, 231-236.

5. Fujiwara, T., Chida, S., Watabe, Y., Maeta, H., Morita, T. and Abe, T. (1980) Artificial surfactant therapy in hyaline-membrane disease. Lancet, 1, 55-59.

THE EFFECT OF AMBROXOL IN NEWBORN AND ADULT ANIMALS WITH SURFACTANT DEFICIENCY

BURKHARD LACHMANN
Research Institute for Lung Diseases, 1115 Berlin-Buch
Karower Str. 11, GDR

INTRODUCTION

The role of pulmonary surfactant in the pathogenesis of many lung diseases, particularly in respiratory distress syndrome of newborn infants as well as in adult respiratory distress syndrome, is well established (for review see 1, 2).

Because a surfactant replacement therapy in RDS was not under discussion up to recently it was tried to influence the synthesis and/or the discharge of surfactant phospholipids by various pharmacologic agents such as ambroxol (NA 872), corticosteroids, aminophylline, ß-adrenergic agonists, thyroxine, pilocarpine, etc. (for review see 3).

In the last years we have investigated by in vivo and in vitro methods the effect of ambroxol in different animal models with surfactant deficiency.

1. EXPERIMENTS IN PREMATURE NEWBORN ANIMALS

1.1. EXPERIMENTS ON IMMATURE NEWBORN RABBITS ON DAY 27 OF GESTATION

MATERIALS AND METHODS

The experiments were carried out on a total of 139 immature newborn rabbits, obtained from 18 does. Since these immature fetuses usually do not exhibit the vigorous ventilatory efforts that are required to expand the lungs at birth (4) they have to be ventilated artificially to be kept alive under well-standardized conditions.

8 does were treated with intravenous injections of ambroxol (50 mg/kg/day in two doses) on days 24-26 of gestation. A seventh dose of ambroxol (25 mg/kg) was given early on day 27. Control animals received intravenous injections with saline. About 2 h after the last treatment, the doe was killed and the premature rabbits were delivered by hysterotomy.

The animals were tracheostomized, kept in plethysmographs at 37 °C, and ventilated artificially for 10 minutes with pure oxygen, insufflation pressure 30 cm H_2O, frequency 40/min., and varying inspiration time (20, 40, 60, or 80 %), (for details see 5, 6).

RESULTS

Body weight was the same in ambroxol-treated litters and controls (31 ± 5 and 32 ± 6 g, respectively; mean ± SD). Lung-thorax compliance increased with inspiration time in both ambroxol-treated animals and controls, but there was no difference in compliance between treated and non-treated litters (Fig. 1).

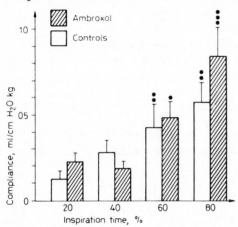

Alveolar expansion, evaluated morphometrically in histological sections, was enhanced in ambroxol-treated animals ventilated with prolonged inspiration phase (60 or 80 %); such a difference was not found in the non-treated group (Tab. 1).

Fig. 1 Lung-thorax compliance (mean ± SEM) related to inspiration time in ambroxol-treated premature newborn rabbits and controls, excluding animals with pneumothorax. Asterisks indicating levels of statistical significance (✶ = $p < 0,05$; ✶✶ = $p < 0,01$; ✶✶✶ = $p < 0,002$) refer to differences vs. compliance values for inspiration time 20 %. Differences between ambroxol-treated animals and controls are not statistically significant (from 5).

1.2. EXPERIMENTS ON IMMATURE NEWBORN RABBITS ON DAY 28 OF GESTATION

MATERIALS AND METHODS

These experiments were carried out on a total of 102 immature newborn rabbits obtained from 14 does. 8 does were treated with ambroxol on days 25-27 of gestation. Immediately after birth the neonates were tracheotomized, and 30, 60, and 120 minutes after delivery the lung mechanics were registered during spontaneous

Tab. 1   The alveolar expansion index (I_a, defined as volume of alveolar spaces/volume of solid parenchyma) related to inspiration time in ambroxol-treated animals and controls. Among ambroxol-treated animals, the difference between the combined groups ventilated with short inspiration time (20 and 40 %) and those ventilated with longer inspiration time (60 and 80 %) is statistically significant ($p < 0,05$). Differences within the non-treated group and differences between ambroxol-treated animals and controls are not statistically significant (from 5).

Treatment	I_a ($X \pm$ SEM)/inspiration time			
	20 %	40 %	60 %	80 %
Ambroxol	$0,67 \pm 0,11$ (n = 15)	$0,38 \pm 0,04$ (n = 15)	$0,88 \pm 0,12$ (n = 14)	$0,92 \pm 0,18$ (n = 14)
Controls	$0,57 \pm 0,07$ (n = 20)	$0,64 \pm 0,08$ (n = 14)	$0,78 \pm 0,17$ (n = 9)	$0,67 \pm 0,14$ (n = 13)

ventilation, according to principles described in detail elsewhere (4).

RESULTS

The 30, 60, and 120 minutes survival rate was increased in ambroxol-treated neonates, in comparison to saline-treated controls (Tab. 2).

Tab. 2   Survival rate and body weight of immature fetuses from ambroxol-treated animals and controls, (chi-square test).

	Time after delivery (min)	Group		P<
		Ambroxol	Saline (control)	
Survival rate	30	59 / 64	28 / 38	0,01
	60	58 / 64	20 / 38	0,01
	120	55 / 64	20 / 38	0,01
Number		64	38	
Body weight (g, X ± SD)		34 ± 7	42 ± 10	

Compared with controls, the treated animals also had improved tidal volume, dynamic lung compliance, and inspiratory and expiratory resistance 30 minutes after birth (Tab. 3). Morphometric analysis of histologic lung sections showed, in addition, that alveolar air expansion was enhanced in ambroxol-treated animals (Tab. 3).

Tab. 3   Frequency(f/min), tidal volume (V_T/kg), lung compliance (C_{dyn}/kg), Resistance (R_L insp, R_L ex), and morphometric parameters ($X \pm SD$) of immature fetuses from ambroxol-treated animals and controls from day 28 of gestation, (Wilcoxon test).

	Time after delivery (min)	Group		P <
		Ambroxol	Saline	
f/min	30	106 ± 61	55 ± 52	0,05
	60	96 ± 49	84 ± 44	NS
	120	83 ± 48	96 ± 48	NS
V_T/kg (ml/kg)	30	1,97 ± 0,73	2,21±1,25	NS
	60	2,03 ± 0,87	3,12±1,22	0,05
	120	2,30 ± 0,99	3,33±2,13	0,05
C_{dyn}/kg (ml/cm H_2O x kg)	30	1,09 ± 0,72	0,653±0,537	0,05
	60	1,24 ± 0,67	1,248±0,65	NS
	120	1,41 ± 0,95	1,283-0,687	NS
R_L insp (cm H_2O/ml x sec^{-1})	30	0,71 ± 0,87	2,19 ± 2,85	0,05
	60	0,61 ± 0,59	0,48 ± 0,28	NS
	120	0,70 ± 0,63	0,58 ± 0,45	NS
R_L ex (cm H_2O/ml x sec^{-1})	30	1,28 ± 1,11	2,09 ± 1,79	0,05
	60	1,34 ± 1,18	1,31 ± 1,13	NS
	120	1,11 ± 0,97	0,89 ± 0,89	NS
Alveolarexp. Index	–	0,45 ± 0,16 (n = 28)	0,35 ± 0,10 (n = 20)	0,05

COMMENT

In contrast to the fetuses from day 28, the data from fetuses delivered on day 27 showed no significant improvement of lung-thorax compliance. To some extent, this discrepancy might reflect important differences in the maturation of the surfactant system in the immature lung between 27 and 28 days of gestation. However, the morphometric analysis showed, that alveolar expansion was enhanced in both groups treated with ambroxol.

It is an apparent paradox that the same ambroxol-treated animals from day 27 that failed to show any significant improvement of lung-thorax compliance had significantly enhanced alveolar air expansion when the lungs were fixed following ventilation with prolonged inspiration phase. This paradox can be solved if we assume that there is, indeed, an increased amount of alveolar surfactant phospholipids in the ambroxol-treated animals. Although not sufficient to improve lung-thorax compliance under dynamic conditions and short periods of observation, these phospholipids might slowly form a stabilizing film in the alveolar air-liquid interface under static conditions - as for instance when the lungs are fixed at end-inspiration. The shape and size of the alveolar air bubbles, initially expanded at a pressure of 30 cm H_2O, are then determined by the solubility of the entrapped gas in the surrounding fluid and by the surface tension of the air-liquid interface. If the air-liquid interface is not stabilized by a film of surfactant phospholipids, the air bubble will shrink as gas becomes dissolved in the surrounding fluid, and the decreasing radius will in turn lead to increased retraction force due to surface tension etc. - until the bubble in the alveolar space has disappeared. Since the diaphragm is mobile, such events could lead to a gradual postmortem collapse of surfactant-deficient lungs during the period of fixation. Lungs generating a stabilizing film of surfactant phospholipids in the air-expanded alveoli, on the other hand, will tend to remain aerated upon fixation(5).

The increased survival rate and the improvements in lung mechanics in fetuses on day 28 of gestation suggest, that lung adaptation was improved by ambroxol probably by increased synthesis and/or discharge of surfactant phospholipids. The reason that there were no differences in lung mechanics between treated animals and controls at time intervals of 60 respectively 120 minutes after delivery is, that all control animals with a bad lung adaptation died before 60 minutes. This means that control animals surviving 60 minutes are a selected group of animals with improved lung adaptation from day 28 of gestation and therefore no difference between these controls and treated animals exists. This result suggests further, that antenatal treatment with ambroxol might have a stimulating effect on the synthesis and/or on release of surfactant phospholipids improving alveolar stability in the premature lung. However, these effects are inferior to that obtained with direct instillation of surfactant into the airways (1).

2. EXPERIMENTS IN ADULT ANIMALS WITH SURFACTANT DEFICIENCY
2.1. STUDIES ON AUTOTRANSPLANTED DOG LUNGS

MATERIALS AND METHODS

The alveolar surfactant system was investigated in 15 dogs 6-24 months after autotransplantation of one lung. 5 dogs received 50 mg/kg bromhexine intravenously 24 hours before killing the animals. The survival time of the treated dogs was 8, 9, 10, 14, and 15 months. Surface tension measurements and phospholipid analysis were performed from the upper and lower lobe of the transplanted and non-transplanted lung.

RESULTS

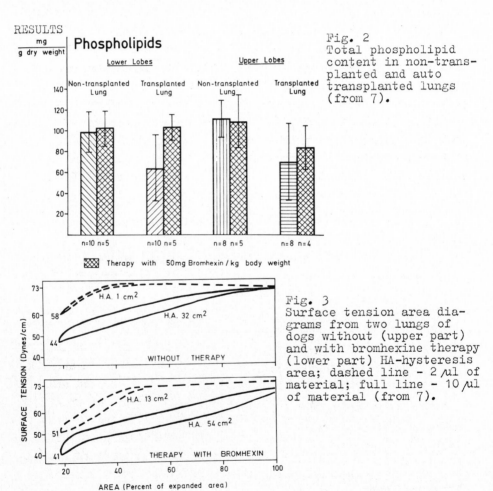

Fig. 2
Total phospholipid content in non-transplanted and auto transplanted lungs (from 7).

Fig. 3
Surface tension area diagrams from two lungs of dogs without (upper part) and with bromhexine therapy (lower part) HA-hysteresis area; dashed line - 2 µl of material; full line - 10 µl of material (from 7).

Postmortem the phospholipid content in the transplanted lung was decreased (Fig. 2), the water content was increased (78, 75 in the non-transplanted lung and 80, 56 in the transplanted lung) and surface tension measurements showed an altered surfactant system (Fig. 3). In the bromhexin-treated animals there were no significant differences between transplanted and non-transplanted lungs in parameters mentioned above.

2.2. RDS CAUSED BY INTRAVENOUS ADMINISTRATION OF HETEROLOGOUS ANTI-LUNG SERUM

MATERIALS AND METHODS

The experiments were carried out on a total of 29 guinea pigs. 18 animals got an intravenous injection of anti-lung serum. From this group 8 animals died within 3 hours on acute respiratory insufficiency. 5 animals which survived the anti-lung serum injection were intraperitoneally treated with 100 mg/kg B.W. ambroxol 2, 8, and 22 hours after anti-lung serum injection. 5 control animals received intraperitoneal injections of saline. 24 hours after anti-lung serum injection blood samples were taken for blood gas analysis, lung mechanics were recorded, and phospholipids in the whole lung were analyzed as well as surface activity was measured (for details see 8).

RESULTS

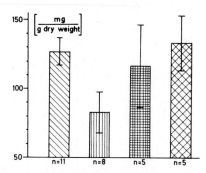

controls, killed 24 hours after saline inject.

died 20min.-3 hours after ALuS inject.

survived ALuS inject., killed after 24 hours

survived ALuS inject., therapy with 100 mg/kg Na 872, killed after 24 hours

Fig. 4
Total phospholipid content in guinea pigs with and without ambroxol treatment after injection of anti-lung serum (from 8).

There were no differences in blood gases and lung mechanics between ambroxol-treated animals and controls which survived the anti-lung serum injection. However, the total phospholipid content was increased in treated animals in contrast to the controls (Fig. 4).

Furtheron, surface activity was also improved in the ambroxol-treated animals (hysteresis area 52 ± 6 cm^2 vs. 37 ± 18 cm^2, min $37 \pm 0,7$ vs. $41 \pm 4,4$ dyn/cm).

2.3. RDS INDUCED BY REMOVAL OF ALVEOLAR SURFACTANT WITH BRONCHIAL LAVAGE

MATERIALS AND METHODS

2.3.1. Using our lung lavage model (9) we studied the effects of ambroxol in 3 different animal groups. We studied 8 guinea pigs lavaged every 15th minute, to find out, whether the amount of phospholipids removed by repeated lavages and the surface activity of the lavage fluid can be influenced by ambroxol. The animals received intraperitoneal ambroxol (50 mg/kg/day in two injections) in the last 2 days before first lung washing. 7 non-treated animals were used as controls. We analyzed from each animal individual samples from the 2nd, 4th, 7th, and 10th washing, as well as pooled samples representing the other intervals.

2.3.2. In order to clarify the mechanism by which lung phospholipids increase following treatment with ambroxol, C^{14}-labeled cholin (20 μC) was administered intraperitoneally in guinea pigs one hour before the first lung lavage. 5 animals were used as controls. The protocol of therapy was the same as in group one.

2.3.3. The effect of ambroxol on lung mechanics and blood gases were analyzed before and about 10-12 hours after the lavage procedure in 10 animals. 5 guinea pigs were used as controls. The protocol of therapy was the same as in group one. All animals were ventilated with pure oxygen, insufflation pressure of 28 cm H$_2$O, PEEP of 8 cm H$_2$O and a frequency of 32/min.

RESULTS

2.3.1. Total phospholipids obtained in lavage fluid at various intervals from animals treated with ambroxol are shown in Fig. 5. The amount of phospholipids in animals treated with ambroxol recovered by the second lavage was about three times higher than in controls; the differences between treated animals

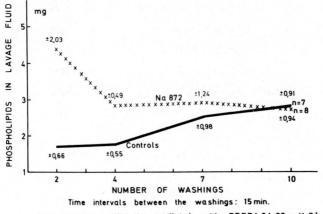

Time intervals between the washings: 15 min.

Animals were artificially ventilated with PEEP (+8/+28 cmH₂O)

— Controls without treatment

xx Start of treatment with Na 872 (50 mg/kg/d) 48 hours before lavage

Fig. 5
Course of phospholipid content in lavage fluid in dependence to the number of washings from ambroxol-treated animals and controls.

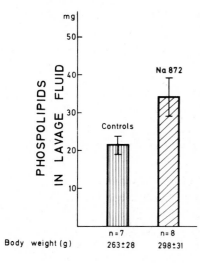

Fig. 6
Total phospholipid content in the lavage fluid from all washings from ambroxol-treated animals and controls.

and controls decreased at subsequent intervals and were no longer statistically significant after the 4th lavage. These findings are summarized in Fig. 6, which gives the total amount of phospholipids that could be removed by repeated lavages in treated animals and controls.

The surface properties of the lavage fluid obtained at various intervals showed no statistically significant differences between treated animals and controls.

2.3.2. The results obtained from these studies are summarized in Tab. 4. In animals treated with ambroxol the total activity as well as the activity from the recovered lecithin and the specific activity is

Tab. 4   Activity in total phospholipids (DPM tot), activity of lecithin (DPM lec) and specific activity of lecithin (DPM/mg lec) in the lavage fluid from ambroxol-treated animals and controls (unpublished obersations from Malmqvist and Lachmann).

No of washing	Ambroxol		
	DPM tot	DPM lec	DPM/mg lec
1	$88,18 \cdot 10^3$ $\pm 132,5 \cdot 10^3$	$45,02 \cdot 10^3$ $\pm 66,15 \cdot 10^3$	$21,22 \cdot 10^3$ $\pm 24,68 \cdot 10^3$
2	$13,09 \cdot 10^3$ $\pm 11,51 \cdot 10^3$	$8,7 \cdot 10^3$ $\pm 7,67 \cdot 10^3$	$11,93 \cdot 10^3$ $\pm 5,49 \cdot 10^3$
3,4,5	$68,24 \cdot 10^3$ $\pm 94,39 \cdot 10^3$	$40,30 \cdot 10^3$ $\pm 62,28 \cdot 10^3$	$27,24 \cdot 10^3$ $\pm 11,24 \cdot 10^3$
6	$35,19 \cdot 10^3$ $\pm 33,51 \cdot 10^3$	$13,39 \cdot 10^3$ $\pm 10,22 \cdot 10^3$	$25,74 \cdot 10^3$ $\pm 10,8 \cdot 10^3$
7,8	$79,29 \cdot 10^3$ $\pm 96,23 \cdot 10^3$	$36,37 \cdot 10^3$ $\pm 51,33 \cdot 10^3$	$29,03 \cdot 10^3$ $\pm 13,25 \cdot 10^3$
9,10	$119,7 \cdot 10^3$ $\pm 95,04 \cdot 10^3$	$71,62 \cdot 10^3$ $\pm 59,04 \cdot 10^3$	$42,3 \cdot 10^3$ $\pm 13,0 \cdot 10^3$

No of washing	Control		
	DPM tot	DPM lec	DPM/mg lec
1	$1,40 \cdot 10^3$ $\pm 1,13 \cdot 10^3$	$1,31 \cdot 10^3$ $\pm 0,72 \cdot 10^3$	$3,15 \cdot 10^3$ $\pm 0,51 \cdot 10^3$
2	$1,73 \cdot 10^3$ $\pm 0,78 \cdot 10^3$	$1,5 \cdot 10^3$ $\pm 0,6 \cdot 10^3$	$3,43 \cdot 10^3$ $\pm 0,77 \cdot 10^3$
3,4,5	$8,02 \cdot 10^3$ $\pm 9,05 \cdot 10^3$	$4,62 \cdot 10^3$ $\pm 5,94 \cdot 10^3$	$7,95 \cdot 10^3$ $\pm 7,53 \cdot 10^3$
6	$9,56 \cdot 10^3$ $\pm 11,15 \cdot 10^3$	$7,6 \cdot 10^3$ $\pm 10,96 \cdot 10^3$	$13,71 \cdot 10^3$ $\pm 12,57 \cdot 10^3$
7,8	$10,2 \cdot 10^3$ $\pm 5,20 \cdot 10^3$	$3,97 \cdot 10^3$ $\pm 3,2 \cdot 10^3$	$15,03 \cdot 10^3$ $\pm 10,15 \cdot 10^3$
9,10	$9,72 \cdot 10^3$ $\pm 6,64 \cdot 10^3$	$3,68 \cdot 10^3$ $\pm 3,78 \cdot 10^3$	$15,88 \cdot 10^3$ $\pm 13,26 \cdot 10^3$

highly significantly increased in ambroxol-treated animals in comparison to control animals. This difference exists already in the first lavage fluid. That means, that not only the discharge of surfactant phospholipids was stimulated but also the new synthesis of phospholipids.

2.3.3. Animals treated with ambroxol showed only a little improvement of lung function in comparison to control animals. However, these differences were not statistically significant, neither for blood gases nor for lung mechanics after ten to twelve hours after lung lavage.

COMMENT

In our experimental models with surfactant deficiency it was evident that ambroxol always leads to an increase of surface active phospholipids and improved surface activity. These findings are in agreement with studies from other authors (for review see 3). Improvements in lung mechanics and blood gases could also in part be proved, but in most cases these changes were statistically not significant in comparison to nontreated animals. That means, that the raised synthesis of phospholipids in these models do not lead to an improvement of alveolar stability. Causes could be, that the amount of total phospholipids in surfactant deficient lungs was not enough to interrupt the vicious circle - permeability disturbance of the alveolar-capillary membrane, surfactant inactivation, surfactant wash-out into the blood stream, decrease of functional residual capacity and compliance, inhibition of the production of new surfactant by hypoxia and acidosis, etc. It seems to be that this vicious circle can be interrupted by exogenous instillation of surfactant only (10). Because we could show that ambroxol stimulates the new synthesis of surface active phospholipids and also the discharge of phospholipids into the alveolar space, therefore a combination of surfactant instillation and pharmacologic stimulation of surfactant phospholipids, for instance by ambroxol, could be useful in the treatment of most severe forms of respiratory distress syndrome.

REFERENCES

1. Robertson, B. (1983) Pathology and pathophysiology of neonatal surfactant deficiency ("Respiratory Distress Syndrome", "Hyaline Membrane Disease". In: B. Robertson, L.G.M. Van Golde, J.J. Batenburg (Ed.), Pulmonary Surfactant, Elsevier/North-Holland Biomedical Press, Amsterdam, in press.

2. Lachmann, B. and Danzmann, E. (1983) Adult respiratory distress syndrome. In: B. Robertson, L.G.M. Van Golde, J.J. Batenburg (Ed.), Pulmonary Surfactant, Elsevier/North-Holland Biomedical Press, Amsterdam, in press.

3. Robertson, B. (1981) Neonatal pulmonary mechanics and morphology after experimental therapeutic regimens. In: E.M. Scarpelli, E.V. Cosmi (Ed.), Review in Perinatal Medicine Vol. 4, Raven Press, New York, pp. 337-380.

4. Lachmann, B., Grossmann, G., Nilsson, R. and Robertson, B. (1979) Lung mechanics during spontaneous ventilation in premature and fullterm rabbit neonates. Respir. Physiol. 38, 283-302.

5. Lachmann, B., Tischer, A.-B., Grossmann, G. and Robertson, B. (1981) Lung compliance and alveolar expansion in the artificially ventilated premature newborn rabbit after maternal treatment with ambroxol. Respiration, 42, 209-216.

6. Lachmann, B., Grossmann, G., Freyse, J., Robertson, B. (1981) Lung-thorax compliance in the artificially ventilated premature rabbit neonate in relation to variations in inspiration: expiration ratio. Pediat. Res., 15, 833-838.

7. Lachmann, B., Winsel, K., Eckert, H., Engelmann, C., Franz, W.-D., Kaltwasser, K., Danzmann, E., Noack, K., Voigt, H. and Vogel, J. (1976) Das alveoläre Surfactant-System in der autotransplantierten Hundelunge und seine Beeinflussbarkeit durch Bromhexin. Dtsches Gesh.-wesen, 31, 1289-1296.

8. Lachmann, B., Bergmann, K.-Ch., Winsel, K., Müller, E., Petro, W., Schäfer, C. and Vogel, J. (1975) Experimentelles Atemnotsyndrom nach Injektion von Anti-Lungenserum. Pädiatrie u. Grenzgeb., 14, 211-233.

9. Lachmann, B., Robertson, B. and Vogel, J. (1980) In vivo lung lavage as an experimental model of the respiratory distress syndrome. Acta anaesth. scand., 24, 231-236.

10. Lachmann, B., Fujiwara, T., Chida, S., Morita, T., Konishi, M., Nakamura, K. and Maeta, H.
Surfactant replacement therapy in the experimental adult respiratory distress syndrome (ARDS), in this book.

© 1983, Elsevier Science Publishers B.V.
Pulmonary Surfactant System, E.V. Cosmi
and E.M. Scarpelli eds.

METHODOLOGICAL APPROACHES TO EXPERIMENTAL ADULT RESPIRATORY DISTRESS SYNDROME

CARLO SAITTO[1], ALAN J. MAUTONE[2] and ERMELANDO V. COSMI[1]

1 II Department of Obstetrics and Gynecology, University of Perugia, Perugia, Italy
2 Pediatric Pulmonary Division, Albert Einstein College of Medicine, 1300 Morris
  Park Avenue, Bronx, New York 10461, U. S. A.

INTRODUCTION

The Adult Respiratory Distress Syndrome (ARDS) was recognized as a distinct clinical entity in 1967 (1) and it has since been found to be both relatively common and very often lethal. Infact, it affects more than 150,000 persons each year and more than half of these die despite aggressive supportive treatment (2).

This syndrome is a complex sequela of massive trauma, shock, systemic sepsis, viral pulmonary infections and many other acute insults. It is characterized, clinically, by reduced pulmonary compliance, bilateral lung infiltrates and a low PaO_2, which is sustained by large intrapulmonary shunts and ventilation/perfusion mismatches; and which is often resistant to mechanical ventilation with high FiO_2 and PEEP. In many instances pulmonary vascular resistance tends to increase early in the course of the disease in the presence of normal or below normal Pulmonary Artery Wedge Pressure (PAWP). This picture of extensive acute pulmonary injury precociously results in permanent lung lesions; some kind of functional pulmonary deficit is a long term common sequela for patients who survive.

A variety of pathological pictures, like extensive epithelial cell necrosis alveolar lining layer abnormalities, proliferating immature type 2-pneumocytes, vascular damage and diffuse pulmonary fibrosis have been observed in ARDS (3). This broad range of pathophysiological findings is not surprising, considering the numerous acute diseases which can result in this syndrome and the different timing of pathological observations with respect to the onset of ARDS, initiation of mechanical ventilation and application of PEEP. (Table 1).

TABLE 1

HUMAN ARDS

Preceding Event Or Disease

Shock, Systemic sepsis, Battlefield trauma, Multiple bone fractures, Viral respiratory infections.

Clinical Picture

Reduced pulmonary C_L, V/Q mismatch, Lung infiltrates, Low PaO_2 resistant to high FiO_2 and Peep.

Pathology

Extensive pneumocyte damage, Preserved basement membrane, Alveolar lining layer abnormalities, Vascular lesions, Proliferating immature granular pneumocytes, Pulmonary fibrosis.

EXPERIMENTAL APPROACHES TO ARDS

The disappointing results of current supportive treatments, as well as of extracorporeal membrane oxygenation stimulated the development of experimental models of human ARDS in order to achieve a better understanding of the disease processes and to devise more effective methods of prevention and treatment (2). The variety of abnormalities and clinical presentations makes it very difficult to propose a single hypothesis for the pathogenesis of ARDS. In fact, a number of different experimental models have been proposed claiming to mimic the most relevant aspects of the disease. These models can be related to three distinct experimental approaches: (1) the vascular approach; (2) the alveolar approach and (3) the systemic approach. The first two approaches relate to the alveolo-capillary unit as the main anatomic target of the pulmonary injury while the systemic approach does not assume any specific target but tries to reproduce either in vivo or in vitro some pathological processes of human ARDS. (Table II)

The Vascular Approach.

The observation that normal PAWP and indirect radiological and clinical evidence of increased lung water are both usually present in human ARDS prompted some investigators to consider the disease, regardless of its cause, as a

TABLE II

EXPERIMENTAL APPROACHES TO ARDS

Anatomic target	Pulmonary microvasculature	Alveolar cells	
Method	Toxic chemicals Glass beads	Toxic chemicals Bronchial lavage	Drugs Toxins Coagulation byprod.
Pathologic process	Direct injury (?) (Complement activation) (DIC)	Direct injury	DIC-Fibronolysis Oxygen radicals Complement activ.
Pathogenesis of pulmonary insult	Increased vascular permeability	Surfactant deficiency	Increased permeability Cell damage (?) Surfactant deficiency (?)

particular form of noncardiogenic, non homogeneous pulmonary edema, due to

increased permeability of the air-blood barrier. (Table III).

TABLE III

VASCULAR APPROACH

Method

Oleic acid, Ethchlorvynol (ECV), αNaphtylthiourea (ANTU), Glass microspheres (200 μ)

Physiology

Increased lung water, Increased albumin-rich lymph flow, Decreased DL (improves wit PEEP), Low PaO2, Normal surface forces

Pathology

Endothelial necrosis, Basement membrane damage, Intravascular plugging, Epithelial damage

Staub and coworkers laid the basis for the study of different types of pulmonary edema by developing an animal model in which the caudal mediastinal lymph duct of the sheep was cannulated to obtain lung lymph (4). Under steady state conditions the composition of lung lymph is assumed to be identical to that of water and solutes crossing the pulmonary endothelium. Alterations in the rate of flow and in the concentration and molecular size of the transferred proteins can be mathematically related to the interaction between driving pressure and membrane permeability. It then becomes possible to identify hydrostatic (or cardiogenic) and permeability (or non-cardiogenic) pulmonary edema.

Several kinds of toxic substances have proved capable of increasing pulmonary vascular permeability and have been administered intravenously to simulate ARDS (5). In some cases a study of mechanical lung properties or of the morphological appearance of the lungs were also performed. Recently Grossman and his group studied lung mechanics in adult rabbits after inducing non-cardiogenic pulmonary edema by intravenous administration of oleic acid (6). They investigated the contribution of several factors that could cause the decreased static lung compliance found in this experimental model. They observed a 115% increase in lung water and 38% decrease in functional residual capacity (FRC). They concluded that loss of ventilatable units, secondary to alveolar flooding, accounted for virtually all the 47% decreased static lung compliance. Any effect of interstitial edema on compliance was excluded since no difference was found between saline pressure-volume curves of normal and edematous lungs. The role of increased surface tension could not be directly determined, but the comparison of air pressure-volume curves of normal and edematous lungs suggested it was negligible. A similar increase in lung water was never observed in human ARDS notwithstanding comparable decrease in lung compliance.

Gill and McNiff administered ethchlorvynol intravenously to rabbits. Ethchlorvynol is a mild oral hypnotic agent which has been reported to induce respiratory distress after intravenous self administration in humans (7,8). They performed several morphologic studies showing variable intraalveolar hemorrhagic edema, with modest interstitial edema, and irregular diffuse vascular plugging by degranulated platelets, fibrin, erythrocytes and leucocytes. A comparatively higher degree of endothelial rather than epithelial damage was also observed. They suggested that localized vascular injury rather than a diffuse increase in permeability can cause early alveolar flooding in human ARDS. Although these reports advance the possibility that alveolar flooding can occur without relevant interstitial edema the pathologic features of this model are in many aspects different from those observed in human ARDS. Moreover, a thorough physiological study assessing the functional impact of the observed lesions was not performed.

Havill and coworkers studied the pulmonary vascular injury produced by another toxic chemical, αNaphtylthiourea (ANTU), after intravenous administration to sheep (9). They used the experimental technique developed by Staub (4) and observed an increase flow rate of protein-rich pulmonary lymph up to 4 hours after the ANTU administration. They recovered large amounts of fibrin degradation products in the pulmonary lymph but not in plasma and observed a significant but transient decrease in the number of circulating leukocytes. They concluded that the increase in vascular permeability is dependent on intravascular clotting and, possibly, a specific complement activation. They also observed diffuse endothelial thinning, capillary engorgement, sparse epithelial damage and modest intraalveolar flooding by proteinaceous fluid. Extravascular lung water was not significantly increased and only a transient decrease in arterial oxygen tension was observed. This model apparently results in minor physiological derangements and peculiar pathologic changes.

Vascular injury and pulmonary edema also follow the injection of glass microspheres in the main pulmonary artery of sheep in a model of acute respiratory distress developed by Malik and his group (10). Recently (11) they compared the effects of microspheres of two different diameters, 200 and 500 μ. They observed that although both calibers actually induce pulmonary edema only the injection of 500 μ microspheres is followed by an increase of PAWP and filtration pressure. They suggest that microembolization of the sheep pulmonary vasculature by 200 μ microspheres increases vascular permeability by diffuse intravascular clotting and release of vasoactive products.

All these models of pulmonary vascular injury can produce a variable degree of non-cardiogenic pulmonary edema and occasionally duplicate very unusual clinical circumstances. However, the pathologic process of the vascular injury is generally poorly understood or still a matter of speculation. Moreover, the pathological appearance of these lungs only partially resembles human ARDS. Finally, these models propose too simplistic a view of the lungs as a specialized vascular bed and not as the complex, metabolically active tissue they are. Their functional derangements are not solely due to hydraulic phenomena and thus cannot be explained only by the "Starling Hypothesis". The vascular approach to experimental ARDS has so far provided some very important information and interesting suggestions but falls short of ensuring a deeper insight into the disease or proper clues to its treatment.

The Systemic Approach.

The observation that ARDS is very often the pulmonary expression of morbid events occurring somewhere else in the body, prompted many investigators to explore the effects on the lungs of a wide range of well defined systemic pathologic processes. (Table IV). These processes, like immune reactions, disseminated intravascular coagulation, free oxygen radicals production, bacterial toxins release and bacterial blood dissemination can be initiated by many specific and non-specific insults. Although they are not directed against the lung they could be capable of offending the lungs as well. In many instances this has been proved to be the case, either in vivo or in isolated tissue preparations.

Manwaring and coworkers (12) administered intravenously to dogs and rabbits a purified fibrin-fibrinogen degradation product; D-antigen, a monomer of low molecular weight which has been found to be markedly elevated in patients with ARDS. They observed tachypnea, hypoxemia and an increase in lung water and pulmonary lymph flow. The animals were only partially protected from

---

TABLE IV

SYSTEMIC APPROACH

Method	Physiology	Pathology
DIC-Fibrinolysis (FGD, AMCA, Thrombin)	Increased lymph flow in vivo Hypoxemia	Intravascular plugging
Oxygen radicals (PMA, Purine-xantine oxidase)	Increased permeability in vivo and in vitro	Cell damage
Bacterial toxins (Esc. Coli)	Increased lymph flow in vivo	
Complement activation (Killed 7 pneumococci)	Increased permeability in vitro	

---

developing these changes when thrombocytopenia was preliminarily induced. Similar results were observed after intravenous thrombin infusion to dogs in a study by Malik and coworkers, who also observed diffuse fibrin-platelet plugs in the pulmonary vasculature (13). Gerdin reports the occurrence of respiratory insufficiency 60 minutes after the administration of trans-4-Aminoethil-cicloesano Carboxylic Acid (AMCA) to rats (14). AMCA is a fibrinolysis inhibitor and its administration is followed by production of incomplete degradation products of fibrin. Thus both the particulate and the soluble products of intravascular coagulation and fibrinolysis can cause ARDS-like pictures in laboratory animals. Although these factors probably contribute to human ARDS, they can hardly be considered its main cause. Infact, relatively minor physiological changes have been reported in these models and respiratory distress can still be experimentally induced after heparin, fibrinogen depletion and platelet depletion (2).

Shasby and coworkers (15) considering the accumulation of inflammatory cells in the alveoli and microvessels of ARDS lungs suspected that the release of peroxides by granulocytes could be partly responsible for tissue damage and increased vascular permeability. Therefore, they treated rabbits with Phorbol Myristate Acetate (PMA), as PMA causes granulocytes to adhere, aggregate and

release oxygen radicals and granular enzymes. They studied the effects of
PMA on the lungs in vivo, in normal and granulocytopenic animals, and in vitro
by perfusing isolated lungs with normal granulocytes and with chronic granulomatous disease granulocytes which are deficient in oxygen radical production.
In both experimental settings increased vascular permeability and pulmonary
edema developed only when normal granulocytes were present. In a separate
study direct injection of oxygen radicals precursors in leucocytes-depleted
isolated lungs also caused permeability edema and vasoconstriction (16). This
interesting model, while stressing the toxicity of O2 radicals and the risk of
using high FiO2 in the treatment of ARDS, does not pretend to provide a comprehensive explanation for all the physiological and pathological abnormalities of this syndrome.

Intravenous administration of bacterial toxins or killed bacteria is also
capable of reproducing some features of ARDS. Brigham and coworkers (17)
demonstrated increased lung vascular permeability after infusion of E.Coli
endotoxin to sheep. The sustained increase in protein-rich pulmonary lymph-
flow was reported to be dependent on the dose of endotoxin administered.
Another possibility of indirect bacterial pulmonary insult has been advanced
by Hoshea and his group (18) who observed that 20% of intravenously injected
(killed) type 7 pneumococci were trapped in the lungs of normal animals while
only 6% were trapped in complement depleted animals. These investigators were
also able to correlate the amount of trapping with the increase in pulmonary
vascular permeability in vitro.

While the vascular approach provides   far from ideal models of ARDS, the
systemic approach provides a host of well defined pathologic processes, most
of which are probably operating in vivo. Most of these systemic models are
capable of producing some form of pulmonary injury. However, none of these
models individually results in the full blown picture of human ARDS. This is
really an expected finding since, as with acute failure in other organ systems,

we must consider ARDS as a multifactorial metabolic insult to all the cell populations of the lung. Indeed, ARDS can be defined as the most acute metabolic disease of lung parenchyma.

The Alveolar Approach.

The goal of simulating an acute metabolic insult to lung cells has been addressed by the alveolar approach to ARDS. The predominant metabolically active cell population of the lung is represented by the surfactant producing type 2 alveolar pneumocytes. Abnormally aggregated surfactant as well as functionally inactive phospholipids from the surfactant system have been recovered in the bronchoalveolar lavage fluids from patients with ARDS (19,20). On this basis the alveolar approach to experimental ARDS mainly consists of studying surfactant depleted lungs. (Table V).

TABLE V

ALVEOLAR APPROACH

Methods

N-nitroso-N-methylurethane (NNNMU), Bronchial lavage, Phosgene

Physiology

Reduced C_L (resistant to PEEP), V/Q mismatch, Low PaO_2, Increased surface forces, Little increase in lung water

Pathology

Epithelial damage, Disrupted alveolar lining layer, Preserved basement membrane, Proliferating granular pneumocytes, Some endothelial damage

---

In a series of separate studies, Ryan and coworkers (21,22) were able to demonstrate that subcutaneous injection of N-nitroso-N-methylurethane (NNNMU) to mongrel dogs will induce, over a 2 to 4 days period, a clinical picture closely resembling human ARDS. Lung mechanics, ventilation/perfusion mismatch and histological sections appear very similar and sometimes indistinguishable from those of human ARDS. The decrease of pulmonary compliance was paralleled by progressive destruction of pneumocytes and by decreasing amounts of pulmonary surfactant phospholipids in the fluid from bronchoalveolar lavage, while only modest increase of lung water was transiently observed. When progressive recovery occurred, after 15 to 20 days, active regeneration of immature granular pneumocytes, progressive cellular differentiation and active production and release of new surfactant in the alveolar space were also observed. Remarkably very little damage to basement membrane and endothelial cells occurs in this model, which is also consistent with human ARDS. Reportedly, the effects of NNNMU administration are restricted to lung cells and are reproducible and dose-dependent. Notwithstanding its resemblance to ARDS, NNNNMU pulmonary injury can still be subjected to major criticism. NNNNMU is a toxic chemical and a very potent carcinogen, the mechanisms of its actions are largely unknown, and it should not be expected to possess such a selective cell target. The evolution of NNNMU lesions is characterized by early, "irreversible" alveolar closure followed by fibrosing alveolitis which apparently confirm a more extensive toxic tissue damage. The progressive decrease in compliance, which was determined by mechanical ventilation with increasing PEEP, suggests that alveolar closure, as shown histologically, has a significant physiologic impact. Moreover, a PEEP-dependent decrease in compliance is a very unusual clinical observation. In human ARDS the application of PEEP is more often followed by an increase in compliance which is supposedly due to recruitment of less compliant alveoli. Nevertheless the NNNMU model of ARDS duly stresses the importance of the surfactant system in lung homeostasis and how acute lung failure results from its deficiency.

Further support of the importance of surfactant, not only in neonatal but in adult RDS as well, comes from the reports of Lachmann and coworkers (22) and, more recently, from our group (24). Both groups observed severe respiratory insufficiency, in guinea pigs and in rats respectively, after repeated bilateral lung lavage. If has been well documented that substantial amounts of surfactant can be washed out of the lungs, in vivo, by repeated lavage, without any structural damage to lung parenchyma. This experimental procedure has therefore been considered to produce a pure surfactant-deficiency model of ARDS. Lachmann intermittently ventilated guinea pigs for as long as 8 hours after lung lavage and reported both physiologic and morphologic findings similar to human ARDS. Thirty minutes after lavage respiratory rate had increased 4 times, pulmonary compliance was reduced to 15% of control values and PaO_2 was 61 mmHg with an FiO_2 of 1.0. Notably, necrosis and desquamation of membranous pneumocytes were seen by electron microscopy in all animals while the denuded intact basement membranes were partially covered with cell debris and phospholipid complexes. Our findings in rats partially confirmed Lachmann's observations about the effects of lung lavage on pulmonary mechanics and respiratory blood gases in a different experiment setting. We mechanically ventilated the animals with a constant respiratory rate, an FiO_2 of 0.6 to avoid direct oxygen toxicity. We did not perform any morphological studies. We observed a prompt deterioration of pulmonary compliance, acid-base status and blood gases during and immediately after lavage but a clear trend to recovery was evident as soon as 30 minutes after lavage, during which time significant endogenous surfactant replacement seems unlikely. Therefore, we suggest that variable alveolar flooding, secondary to lavage procedure, together with surfactant deficiency contributes to abnormal lung function and that early recovery depends on fluid adsorption by the pulmonary circulation. The pulmonary lavage model confirms that ARDS-like pulmonary injury, including cell necrosis and desquamation, can result from surfactant deficiency. However, lung lavage is not equivalent to surfactant deficiency as alveolar flooding with its effects on pulmonary circulation are likely. Moreover, the amount of resulting injury is not easily reproducible and the nature of the insult itself is not comparable to common clinical situations.

The observation that phosgene inhalation causes lethal respiratory distress in humans prompted some investigators to evaluate the pulmonary injury after phosgene inhalation as a possible model of ARDS (25). Pawlowski et al (25) observed that selective alveolar lining layer disruption and alveolar cells necrosis with preserved basement membranes and endothelial cells represent early changes after inhalation of phosgene in dogs. We have observed (26) that the decrease in compliance and the increase in intrapulmonary shunt paralleled the amount of toxic gas which was actually ventilated. Artificial surfactant administration caused an impressive improvement in lung morphology and partially restored to normal the pulmonary mechanics. This study, although related to a very specific clinical situation, points to the relevance of surfactant deficiency in respiratory distress and also suggests that surfactant supplementation can promptly ameliorate very sick lungs.

The alveolar approach to ARDS relies mainly on the assumption that pneumocyte injury and surfactant deficiency can account for most features of human ARDS. This may indeed be an oversimplification, but the pathologic and physiologic abnormalities which are observed in the presented models resemble the human disease more closely than any other animal model.

CONCLUSIONS

In conclusion, although the "quintessential model" of human ARDS does not yet exist. The large amount of experimental work that has been done on this subject in the last few years has enormously increased our understanding of this complex disease and offers new clues to its prevention and treatment. ARDS must now be considered the result of vascular injury, parenchymal damage and surfactant deficiency; the relative importance of each varying over a wide range of clinical presentations. A thoroughly adequate experimental model should provide a reproducible and controlled degree of all these kinds of pulmonary insult, assess their relative contribution, and their eventual interdependence. (Table VI).

The essential role of surfactant deficiency in ARDS must be emphasized since surfactant (1) reduces the tendency toward atelectasis, (2) reduces the stress in the alveolar septa, (3) increases the compliance of the alveolar capillary sheet, thereby reducing the resistance to blood flow, and (4) contributes to prevention of accumulation of fluid in alveoli by lowering alveolar surface tension (27).

TABLE VI

GOALS OF EXPERIMENTAL ARDS

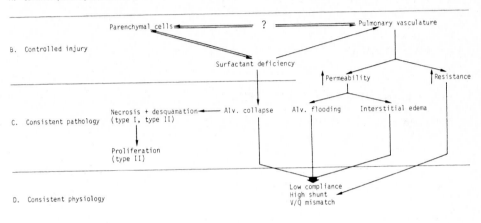

A. Definite pathologic process (?)

B. Controlled injury

C. Consistent pathology

D. Consistent physiology

REFERENCES

1. Ashbaugh, D.C., Rigelow, D.B., Petty, T.L. and Levin, B.E. (1967) Lancet, 2, 319.

2. Rinaldo, J.E. and Rogers, R.M. (1982) N. Engl. J. Med., 306, 900.

3. Pratt, P.C., Vollmer, R.T., Shelburne, J.D. and Crapo, J.D. (1979) Am. J. Pathol., 95, 191.

4. Staub, N.C. (1971) Circ. Res., 28(S1), 1.

5. Ashbaugh, D.E. and Vzaura, T. (1968) J. Surg. Res., 8, 417.

6. Grossman, R.F., Jones, J.G., and Murray, J.F. (1980) J. Appl. Physiol., 48, 1045.

7. Gil, J., Silage, D.A. and McNiff, J.M. (1981) J. Appl. Physiol., 50, 334.

8. Gil, J. and McNiff, J.M. (1982) Am. Rev. Resp. Dis., 126, 701.

9. Havill, A.M., Gee, M.H., Washburne, J.D., Pumkumar, A., Ottaviano, R., Flynn, J.T. and Spath, J.A., Jr. (1982) Am. J. Physiol., 243, H505.

10. Malik, A.B., Lee, B.C., van der Zee, H. and Johnson, A. (1979)
    Circ. Res., 45, 120.

11. Johnson, A., van der Zee, H. and Malik, A.B. (1981) J. Appl. Physiol.,
    51, 461.

12. Manwaring, D., Thorning, D., and Curreri, P.W. (1978) Surgery 84, 45.

13. Malik, A.B. and van der Zee, H. (1977) Thromb. Res., 11, 497.

14. Gerdin, B. (1981) Eur. Surg. Res., 13, 402.

15. Shasby, M.D., Vanbenthuysen, K.M., Tate, R.M., Shasby, S.S., McMurtry, I.F.
    and Repine, J.E. (1982) Am. Rev. Resp. Dis., 125, 443.

16. Tate, R.M., Vanbenthuysen, K.M., Shasby, M.D., McMurtry, I.F. and Repine,
    J.E. (1982) Am. Rev. Resp. Dis., 126, 802.

17. Brigham, K.L., Bowers, R.E. and Haynes, J. (1979) Circ. Res., 45, 292.

18. Hoshea, S., Brown, E., Hammer, C. and Frank, M. (1980) J. Clin. Invest.,
    66, 375.

19. Petty, T.L., Silvers, G.W., Paul, G.W. and Stanford, R.E. (1979)
    Chest, 75, 571.

20. Petty, T.L., Reiss, O.K., Paul, G.W., Silvers, G.W. and Elkins, N.D.
    (1977) Am. Rev. Resp. Dis., 115, 531.

21. Baret, C.R., Jr., Loomis Bell, A.L., Jr., and Ryan, S.F. (1981) Am. Rev.
    Resp. Dis., 124, 705.

22. Baret, C.R., Jr., Loomis Bell, A.L., Jr., and Ryan, S.F. (1979)
    Chest, 75,705.

23. Lachmann, B., Robertson, B. and Vogel, J. (1980) Acta Anaesth. Scand.,
    24, 231.

24. Saitto, C., Gristine, G.R., Barbati, A. and Cosmi, E.V. (1983) In:
    Internatl. Symp. on The Surfactant System of the Lung, Rome.

25. Pawlowski, R. and Frosolono, M.F. (1977) Arch. Environ. Health, 32, 278.

26. Mautone, A.J., Katz, Z. and Scarpelli, E.M. (1983) Submmitted to J.
    Clin. Toxicol. (In press).

27. Pattle, R.E. (1955) Nature, 175, 1125.

ACKNOWLEDGEMENTS

This work was supported by the Italian Council for Research and Ministry for
Public Instruction.
This research is under the auspices of the U.S.A.-Italy cooperative science
program NIH-CNR.

© 1983, Elsevier Science Publishers B.V.
Pulmonary Surfactant System, E.V. Cosmi
and E.M. Scarpelli eds.

AMBROXOL AND SURFACTANT SECRETION. Experimental Studies on the Incorporation of ^{3}H-Palmitate into Pulmonary Surfactant.

YUSUF KAPANCI AND GABRIELLA ELEMER

Department of Pathology, Faculty of Medicine, University of Geneva, CH-1211 Geneva 4, Switzerland

INTRODUCTION

Recently several reports have suggested that Ambroxol: metabolite VII of the secretolytic agent Bromhexine (Bisolvon^R, Boehringer), exerts a stimulatory effect on lung surfactant production (1-8). Experimentally it has been shown in lambs and rabbits that fetal or maternal administration of Ambroxol results in a significant increase in lecithin/sphingomyelin ratio in the tracheal washing fluids (1,2). When administered intravenously to women threatened by premature labour, this drug induces a significant rise in amniotic fluid lecithin level (3). Furthermore in experimental (7) or human acute respiratory distress syndrome (ARDS), Ambroxol appeared to improve pulmonary functions (8).

In a previous report, we suggested that one of the possible effects of Ambroxol was to cause type II epithelial hypertrophy (4). Others observed "in vitro" that lecithin synthesis in lung tissue slices was enhanced and that the phospholipid composition of alveolar lavage fluids was modified (6).

The present investigation was done to determine the effects of Ambroxol on the incorporation of ^{3}H-palmitate into alveolar tissue in adult rats. Palmitate is a constituent of phosphatidylcholine which in turn is a major surface-active phospholipid in surfactant. Its incorporation into lung cells and fluids was appreciated by EM autoradiographic studies and also by biochemical analyses of lung tissues and alveolar lavage fluids. A preliminary report on autoradiographic findings has been previously published (9).

MATERIALS AND METHODS

Seventy-two pathogen free Wistar rats (Ivanovas, West Germany) weighing about 100 g were divided into two groups: 1) rats treated with Ambroxol at a dose of 200 mg/kg/day; 2) rats treated with the solvent of Ambroxol, namely 0.9% NaCl. The drug and saline were administered per os, during 3 days, after which all animals were fasted for 15 hours. On the 4th morning they were given a unique i.v. dose of 9, 10 palmitic acid-^{3}H (New England Nuclear Corporation SA, 17 Ci/mmole) complexed to bovine serum albumin as a potassium salt, in 0.15 ml saline. Each animal destinated to autoradiographic studies received 0.5 mCi of palmitic acid-^{3}H, those to biochemical analyses 0.16 mCi.

For autoradiographic studies 27, and for biochemical studies 45 rats were employed. One, 4 and 8 hours after injection of palmitic acid-^{3}H, the rats were anesthetized with sodium pentobarbital (Nembutal^R, 0.15 ml/100 g b.w., i.p.) and under arterficial ventilation (10), the thorax was opened, the pulmonary artery canulated and rinsed shortly with 0.9% NaCl.

For **autoradiographic studies,** the lungs were fixed by 2.5% glutaraldehyde perfusion (10); then small tissue blocks were cut from each lobe, washed in cacodylate buffer at 4°C and postfixed in 2% OsO$_4$ (in S-collidine buffer, pH 7.4). In order to diminish the loss of labelled lipids, a short dehydration was made (11); the blocks were then embedded in Epon. 500 Å thick sections were covered with Ilford L-4 emulsion; the exposition was maintained for 3 months. They were then developed in Microdol X developer (12), stained with lead citrate and examined with a Philips EM-300 microscope. Electron micrographs were taken randomly from all experimental and control groups (4 tissue blocks per rat, 20 pictures per block) at constant magnification of 6'840. The grain density, which can be defined as the number of grains per unit volume of a structure, was determined: a) in type II epithelial cells, b) in the rest of alveolar tissue, c) in the organelles of type II cells. The volume of different structures was appreciated by standard morphometric methods (13).

For **biochemical studies** lungs were washed 6 times with 5 ml of 0.9% NaCl in order to remove the material on the alveolar surface. The lavage fluid from each lung was then pooled, centrifuged and the supernatant was kept for further analysis. To prepare pulmonary tissue extracts lungs were homogenized in chloroform-methanol (2:1, v/v) and the total lipids were extracted according to the method of Folch et al. (14). They were separated into neutral fat and phospholipids by column chromatography using silicic acid (15). Phospholipids were then separated by thin layer chromatography on Silica Gel coated plates (Merck, 0.2 mm thick). Five individual phospholipids were identified by comparison with reference substances (Sigma): lysophosphatidylcholine, sphingomyelin, phosphatidylcholine, phosphatidylserine and phosphatidylethanolamine. Radioactivity of total lipids, total and individual phospholipids in alveolar lavage fluids and lung homogenates was determined using a liquid scintillation counter (Beckman 3100). The statistical relevance of the results was estimated by means of Student's t-test.

RESULTS

Autoradiographic studies. Silver grains representing the incorporated ^{3}H-palmitate showed the same distribution pattern in Ambroxol-treated and control animals; they seemed however more numerous in experimental lungs. Grains were concentrated on type II epithelial cells and were seen sporadically on some capillary endothelial cells, alveolar type I cells and septal connective tissue cells. In type II epithelial cells they labeled predominently the lamellar bodies, but were also observed occasionally on mitochondria, endoplasmic reticulum and cell membranes (Fig. 1). In the lungs of rats sacrificed 8 hours after injection of ^{3}H-palmitate, tubular myelin visible in occasional alveoli appeared labelled (Figs. 1b and 2). Morphometric evaluations demonstrated that in Ambroxol-treated as well as in control animals the grains (^{3}H-labeled palmitate) were concentrated over the type II epithelial cells. There was a significant increase in grain density in Ambroxol injected rats (p < 0.01) and this higher level of labeling appeared at all experimental periods investigated (Fig. 3). The ratio of grain density of type II cells to the rest of alveolar tissue was much higher in Ambroxol group and the labeling was most manifest at the level of lamellar bodies (Fig. 4). Between experimental and control rats the difference in incorporation of ^{3}H-palmitate into lamellar bodies was statistically significant at all 3 periods investigated (p < 0.01). However there was a manifest decrease at 4 hours and a further drop at 8 hours (Fig. 5).

Biochemical studies. In lung homogenates as well as in alveolar lavage fluids the incorporation of ^{3}H-palmitate was significantly increased in Ambroxol-treated rats (Fig. 6). In the parenchyma this increase involved total lipids as well as the phospholipid portion (Fig. 7). The amount of radioactivity dropped parallely both in experimental and control groups at 4 hours, and a further decrease occurred at 8 hours (Fig. 7). A remarkable finding consisted in the opposite time-course pattern in phosphatidylcholine radioactivity in lung homogenates and in lavage fluids. In fact while in lungs homogenates the radioactivity was reduced between 1 and 4 hours and lesser thereafter, in lavage fluids, on the contrary, it was increased during the same period (Fig. 6). Table I summarizes the biochemical data concerning the incorporation of ^{3}H-palmitate into phosphatidylcholine fraction which represents about 80% of surface active material in surfactant.

266

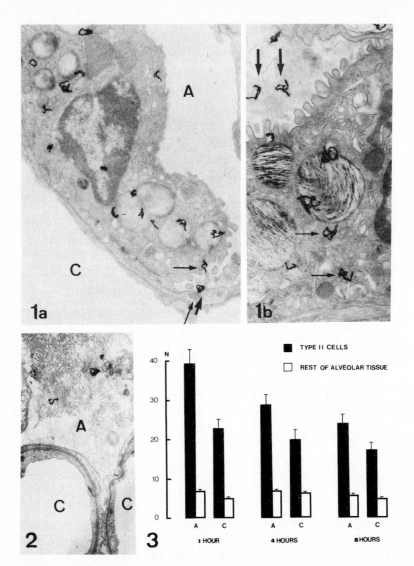

Fig. 1. Autoradiograph of a type II epithelial cell of an Ambroxol-treated rat: a) 1 hour after injection of ^{3}H-palmitate, b) 8 hours after injection of ^{3}H-palmitate with labeling of intraalveolar fluid (heavy arrows). Note grains over lamellar bodies and occasional labeling of other organelles (light arrows) and of a type I cell (light and heavy arrow). A = alveolar space; C = capillary.

Fig. 2. Autoradiograph showing alveolar space with tubular myelin, labeled by grains in an Ambroxol-treated rat 4 hours after injection of ^{3}H-palmitate. A = alveolus; C = capillary.

Fig. 3. Grain density of alveolar tissue. A = Ambroxol; C = control.

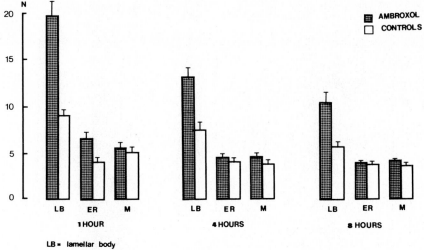

LB = lamellar body
ER = endoplasmic reticulum
M = mithochondria

4

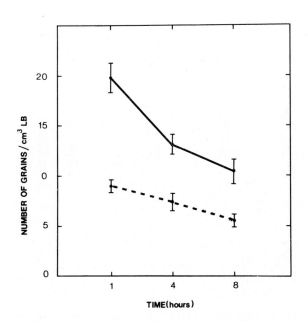

5

Fig. 4. Grain density in type II epithelial cells.
Fig. 5. Grain density in LB. Full lines: Ambroxol. Dashed lines: control.

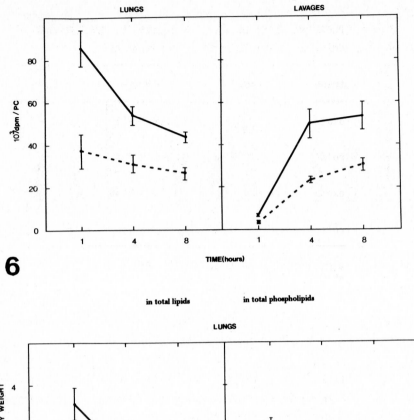

6

in total lipids   in total phospholipids

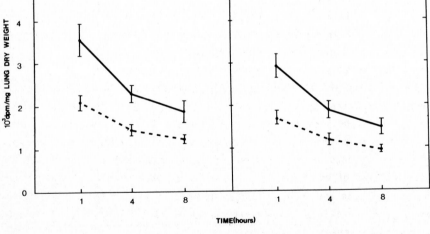

7

Fig. 6 Radioactivity in phosphatidylcholine of lung homogenates and alveolar lavages. Full lines: Ambroxol. Dashed lines: control.
Fig. 7 Radioactivity in total lipids and total phospholipids extracted from lung homogenates. Full lines: Ambroxol. Dashed lines: Control.

TABLE I

RADIOACTIVITY IN PHOSPHATIDYLCHOLINE OF LUNG HOMOGENATES AND ALVEOLAR
LAVAGES AT DIFFERENT TIMES AFTER INJECTION OF ^{3}H-PALMITATE

	Treatment	1 hour	4 hours	8 hours
Lungs[a]	Ambroxol	2612 ± 274	1692 ± 156	1322 ± 73
	Controls	1240 ± 200	972 ± 134	794 ± 99
Lavages[b]	Ambroxol	6668 ± 660	49500 ± 6960	52992 ± 6858
	Controls	3222 ± 326	22878 ± 1590	29964 ± 2937

The data are averages ± SE of five lungs and lavages
[a]dpm/mg lung dry weight
[b]dpm/total lavage

DISCUSSION

There is a general agreement that type II alveolar cells of lungs synthesize the pulmonary surfactant and their characteristic lamellar inclusions
are the intracellular storage phase of the surface-active material (16-21).
Our data obtained by quantitative autoradiography demonstrate that Ambroxol
can increase the incorporation of ^{3}H-palmitate into type II epithelial cells
and more specifically into the lamellar bodies of these cells.

Von Wichert et al. (5) have found that in rabbits, 2 to 6 hours after intravenous administration of Ambroxol, the DNA content of lung tissue slices
increases in respect to controls. They raised the question as to whether
this increase might be related to a specific cell proliferation. Our previous investigations (4) using morphometrical measurements suggest that Ambroxol treatment of adult rats is followed by an increase in the lamellar bodies in respect to the total volume of alveolar tissue; some of our data indicate a possible cellular hypertrophy which in turn may bear some relationship with the synthesis of surfactant.

It has been well established that pulmonary surfactant is largely composed
of phospholipids and that the principal surface-active component is diplami-
toylphosphatidylcholine (15-17,22,23). Our biochemical analyses of lung
homogenates indicate that Ambroxol stimulates the incorporation of ^{3}H-palmi-
tate into lung phospholipids, particularly into phosphatidylcholine. These

data corroborate the results of von Wichert et al. (5) who have reported increased incorporation of labeled palmitate into pulmonary lecithin of Ambroxol-treated rabbits.

The morphological and biochemical findings of the present study show a parallelism in the time course in respect to incorporation of ^{3}H-palmitate. Indeed, the grain density of lamellar bodies and the amount of radioactivity of lung phospholipids exhibit the highest value at 1 hour after injection of palmitate and decrease subsequently. On the contrary, in the alveolar lavage fluid, an opposite pattern is observed (Fig. 6): the level of radioactivity is highest at 8 hours. It is noticeable that, at 8 hours period, some labeling of tubular myelin is seen on EM micrographs (Fig. 2). It seems thus that there is full agreement between autoradiographic and biochemical results.

In concluding, it should be pointed out that EM autoradiography provides evidence in favor of intracellular source of surfactant in type II epithelial cells (19,21) but gives poor insight into the secretion. Tubular myelin figures are believed to represent the morphological equivalent of the extracellular comportment of surfactant (24,25). Their labeling in late phases of the experiment bears hence some relevance.

SUMMARY

Ambroxol (metabolite VIII of the secretolytic agent Bisolvon^R) was administered to adult rats which were subsequently injected with ^{3}H-palmitate. One, 4 and 8 hours after injection, the localization of the label in lung tissue was evaluated by electron microscopic autoradiography using morphometric methods; its incorporation into lipids extracted from lung homogenates and alveolar lavage fluids was also measured. Our findings indicate that Ambroxol stimulates the rate of incorporation of ^{3}H-palmitate into lamellar bodies of type II epithelial cells and into the major surfactant lipid, phosphatidylcholine.

RIASSUNTO

Dei ratti adulti sono stati trattati con Ambroxol (metabolita dell'agente secretolitico Bisolvon^R) per os durante tre giorni e sono stati sacrificati al quarto giorno 1, 4 e 8 ore dopo aver ricevuto un'iniezione di palmitato-H^3. La localizzazione del palmitato-H^3 è stata valutata quantitativamente per mezzo dell'autoradiografia al microscopio elettronico utilizzando dei metodi morfometrici. L'incorporazione del palmitato-H^3 negli estratti lipidici degli omogenati polmonari e dei liquidi di lavaggio alveolare è stata valutata biochemicamente. I risultati indicano che l'Ambroxol stimola l'incorporazione del palmitato-H^3 nei corpi lamellari delle cellule epiteliali di typo II et nella fosfatidilcolina, uno dei lipidi principali del surfattante.

ACKNOWLEDGEMENTS

The authors are grateful to Prof. A. Junod for helpful advices and encouragement. This work was supported by the Swiss National Science Foundation, Grant No 3.382.078, and by K. Thomae GmbH.

REFERENCES

1. Egbert, F., Fontijne, P. and Warmsteher, K. (1976) Biol. Neonate, **29**, 315.

2. Van Petten, G.R., Mears, G.J. and Taylor, P.J. (1980) Am. J. Obstet. Gynecol. **130**, 35.

3. Lorenz, U., Rüttgers, H., Fux, G. and Kubli, F. (1974) Am. J. Obstet. Gynecol. **119**, 1126.

4. Cerutti, P. and Kapanci, Y. (1979) Respiration, **37**, 241.

5. Von Wichert, P., Bavendamm, U., Von Teichmann, M., Müller, G., Thalheim, E., Wilke, A. and Wiegers, U. (1977) Naunyn-Schiedeberg's Arch. Pharmacol. **297**, 269.

6. Prevost, M.C., Soula, G. and Douste-Blazy, L. (1979) Respiration **37**, 215.

7. Dauberschmidt, R., Kuckelt, W., Bender, V., Hieronymi, U., Urochen, H., Winzel, H., Zinsmeyer, J. and Meyer, M. (1980) Bull. Europ. Physiopathol. Resp. **16**, 135.

8. Kuckelt, W., Dauberschmidt, R., Scharfenberg, J., Winsel, K., Lachmann, B., Frenzke, H., Hieronymi, U., Urochen, H. and Meyer, M. (1980) Respiration **39**, 264.

9. Elemer, G. and Kapanci, Y. (1981) Progr. Resp. Res. **15**, 234.

10. Assimacopoulos, A. and Kapanci, Y. (1974) J. Microsc. **100**, 227.

11. Stein, O. and Stein, J. (1967) J. Cell Biol. **33**, 319.

12. Salpeter, M.M. and Bachmann, L. (1964) J. Cell Biol. **22**, 469.

13. Weibel, E.R. (1969) Int. Rev. Cytol. **26**, 235.

14. Folch, J., Lees, M. and Stanley, G.H.S. (1957) J. Biol. Chem. **226**, 497.

15. Young, S.L. and Tierney, D.F. (1972) Am. J. Physiol. **272**, 1539.

16. Goerke, J. (1974) Biochem. Biophys. Acta **344**, 241.

17. Tierney, D.F. (1974) Ann. Rev. Physiol. **36**, 209.

18. Faulkner, C.S. and Rochester, N.Y. (1969) Arch. Pathol. **87**, 521.

19. Askin, F.B. and Kuhn, C. (1971) Lab. Invest. **25**, 260.

20. Batenburg, J.J., Post, M., Oldenborg, V. and Van Gelde, L.M.G. (1980) Exp. Lung. Res. **1**, 57.

21. Chevalier, G. and Collet, A.J. (1972) Anat. Rec. **174**, 289.

22. Van Golde, L.M.G. (1976) Am. Rev. Resp. Dis. **114,** 977.

23. King, K.J. and Clements, J.A. (1972) Am. J. Physiol. **223,** 715.

24. Williams, M.C. (1977) J. Cell Biol. **72,** 260.

25. Sanders, R.L., Ilasset, K.J. and Vatter, A.E. (1980) Anat. Rec. **198,** 485.

© 1983, Elsevier Science Publishers B.V.
Pulmonary Surfactant System, E.V. Cosmi
and E.M. Scarpelli eds.

CHEST RADIOGRAPHIC PATTERNS OF R.D.S. IN ADULT PATIENTS

CARLO GIUNTINI[1], MASSIMO PISTOLESI[2] and MASSIMO MINIATI[2]

[1]2nd Medical Clinic of the University of Pisa and [2]CNR Institute of Clinical
Physiology, Pisa, Italy

INTRODUCTION

The radiographic pattern of pulmonary edema in patients with cardiac disease
has been well established (1-5). Direct comparison between the amount of extravascular lung water measured by a modified indicator dilution method and an
x-ray score of pulmonary interstitial edema has shown that chest roentgenogram
is the most sensitive method to detect and quantitate hydrostatic lung edema in
the clinical setting (6,7). On the contrary, the role of chest roentgenogram in
patients with increased permeability pulmonary edema is not yet firmly defined.
Previous reports on this subject failed to provide a systematic analysis of the
relative prevalence of various radiographic findings and of their significance
(8-10). Recently we observed that chest roentgenogram is able to reflect the
clinical course in R.D.S. patients and that chest radiographic findings can be
used to differentiate increased permeability from hydrostatic pulmonary edema
(11).

Aim of this paper is to further define the radiographic appearance of R.D.S.,
describe changes   occurring throughout the evolution of the syndrome and, final
ly, to identify possible peculiar findings that could be related to the underlying pathophysiologic mechanisms.

MATERIALS AND METHODS

We analyzed 206 chest radiographs of 40 patients with R.D.S. admitted consecu-
tively to the intensive care units of the University of Pisa. R.D.S. was diagnosed on the basis of clinical and hemogasanalytic evidence of acute respiratory
failure and the presence of increased radiographic density. In all the patients
R.D.S. was the complication of various definite diseases or accidental events.
Clinical diagnosis, age, prevalence and survival of all the patients are listed

Supported in part by CNR National Cardiorespiratory Group Grant CT 81.00063.04

274

in Table 1. No patient had a previous history of cardiac or respiratory disease or clinical, electrocardiographic and serum enzymes data compatible with present cardiac disease. In 8 patients lung perfusion scan ruled out the diagnosis of pulmonary embolism.

TABLE 1

CLINICAL DIAGNOSIS, AGE, PREVALENCE AND SURVIVAL OF 40 PATIENTS WITH R.D.S.

Diagnosis	Age	Prevalence	Survived
Head trauma	22 ± 9	10	4
Multiple long bone fractures	20 ± 3	10	6
Non traumatic brain lesions (hemorrhage, tumor)	36 ± 17	8	0
Burns (25-80% extension)	31 ± 12	7	3
Other (infective, systemic lupus, post-partum R.D.S.)	25 ± 7	5	3
	26 ± 12	40	16

Bedside radiographs were obtained keeping the patient as erect as possible in bed. X-ray tube conditions were set to keep the exposure time at a minimum for each radiograph. In sequential radiographs of each patient the same setting was maintained when possible. The follow-up period from the first to the last radiograph (the last available for those who died and the last with significant abnormalities for those who survived) was 6.3 ± 5.4 days.

The radiographs were examined by two observers employing a reading table conceived in order to reduce intra and interobserver variability. The reading table contains (Table 2): description of the heart and hilar vessel characteristics; analysis of the increased lung density qualitative feature (diffuse, patchy, white lung); its extension to one or both lungs (unilateral, predominantly unilateral, bilateral); and its regional distribution along the horizontal (peripheral, central, central plus peripheral) and vertical (upper, mid, lower) axes of the lung. Other radiographic findings known to be common in pulmonary edema such as widening of fissurae, pleural effusion, peribronchial and perivascular cuffs, air bronchogram and septal lines were recorded when present.

TABLE 2

PREVALENCE OF RADIOGRAPHIC FINDINGS IN 206 RADIOGRAPHS OF 40 PATIENTS WITH R.D.S

Heart size		Hilar abnormalities	
Right heart enlargement	54%	Not clearly visualized [a]	12%
Bulging of the common trunk of the pulmonary artery	39%	Increased size	36%
		Increased density	30%
Left heart enlargement	0%	Blurring	20%
Right and left heart enlargement	13%		

Lung density increase	78%				
Qualitative feature		Extension		Regional distribution	
Diffuse increase	53%	Unilateral	24%	Peripheral 20%	Upper 50%
Patchy increase	30%	Predominantly unilateral	12%	Central 10%	Mid 89%
White lung	17%	Bilateral	64%	Peripheral + central 70%	Lower 90%

Other findings	
Widening of the fissurae	29%
Pleural effusion	5%
Peribronchial and perivascular cuffs	5%
Air bronchogram	32%
Septal lines	1%

[a] for technical defects or increased lung density.

The prevalence of the various radiographic findings observed in the chest x-ray at diagnosis (DXR) and in the last chest x-ray with significant abnormalities (LXR) has been compared by chi square test (exact test of Fisher) in all the patients, in the 16 patients who survived and in the 24 patients who died. Furthermore, the prevalence of radiographic findings in the 20 patients with head trauma and/or bone fractures was compared with that of the remaining patients. We accepted $p < 0.05$ as indicating statistical significance.

RESULTS

Radiographic findings of pulmonary edema appeared together with or immediately after the clinical onset of respiratory failure and were in no instance predictive of R.D.S. development. However, in each patient, the chest radiograph matched the clinical and hemogasanalytic course of the disease.

Heart size

Enlargement of the right heart cavities was observed frequently in the radiographs of our patients (Table 2). It was one of the earliest radiographic findings to appear(Figure 1), and was more frequent in patients with head and/or long bone traumatic lesions ($p < 0.001$). In the presence of right heart enlargement the most characteristic alteration was the marked bulging of the second arch on the left cardiac border, i.e., the common trunk of the pulmonary artery (Figure 1). This finding as well prevailed significantly in patients with trauma ($p < 0.001$). Left heart enlargement alone was not seen, whereas the joint right and left heart enlargement was found in 13% of the radiographs. The highest prevalence of this finding was observed in the 7 burned patients (42%), being only 6% in the remaining patients.

Hilar abnormalities

The prevalence of these findings is listed in Table 2. Loss of definition of hilar borders (blurring) occurred less frequently than hilar enlargement and increase of density. When considering DXR and LXR in all the patients,hilar size was larger in DXR than in LXR ($p < 0.05$), whereas hilar blurring was less frequent in DXR with respect to LXR ($p < 0.001$). In the 16 patients who survived, we confirmed the previous observation made on the entire population as far as hilar size and blurring are concerned, furthermore the increased hilar vessel density was, in these patients, significantly less represented in LXR (Figure 2). In the 24 patients who died there were no significant differences between DXR and LXR

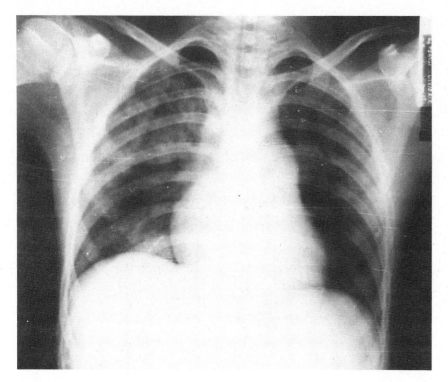

Fig. 1. Fourteen year old male patient admitted unconscious following a car accident in which he reported head trauma and bone fractures of lower extremities. The radiograph reveals right heart enlargement (bulging of the first and second arch on the right and of the second arch on the left). Diffuse increase of density in the upper regions of the right lung.

in hilar size and density increase. Hilar abnormalities were more frequent in patients with head trauma and/or long bone fractures with respect to the remaining patients (p<0.001).

Lung density increase

Qualitative feature. An increased density was found in 78% of all the radiographs (Table 2). Density increase was distinguished in diffuse (a non shaped increase of density that allows the underlying structures to be seen), patchy (a shaped increase of density), and white lung (self-explanatory). These fea-

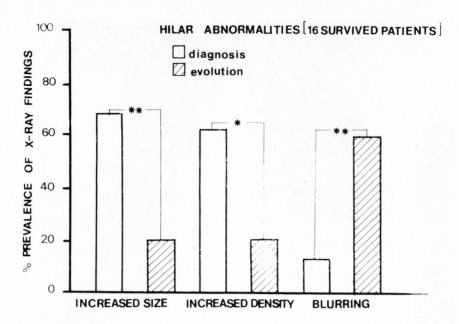

Fig. 2. Relative prevalence of hilar abnormalities in DXR (diagnosis) and LXR (evolution) in the 16 survived patients.** = p<0.01;* = p<0.05.

tures where chosen in order to define three different degrees of lung involvement in high permeability pulmonary edema (from interstitial phase to alveolar involvement and extensive lung consolidation). The overall prevalence of these features is reported in Table 2. An example of diffuse increase of density is given in Figure 1. Patchy increase of density is shown in Figure 3 and white lung in Figure 4. When comparing DXR and LXR in all the patients we observed a lower prevalence of patchy increase of density in LXR (p<0.05). The same trend was found in surviving patients, that showed also a higher prevalence of the diffuse increase of density feature in LXR (Figure 5). On the contrary, white lung prevailed (p<0.05) in LXR of patients who died.

Extension. The extension of the increased lung density was on the whole bilateral (Table 2). Unilateral or predominantly unilateral extension was observed above all in the 20 traumatic patients: 42 over 81 radiographs (52%). In the other 20 patients, unilateral or predominantly unilateral extension was observed only in 18 over 80 radiographs (23%). The difference was more striking when considering unilaterality alone. Indeed, 41% of traumatic patients radiographs

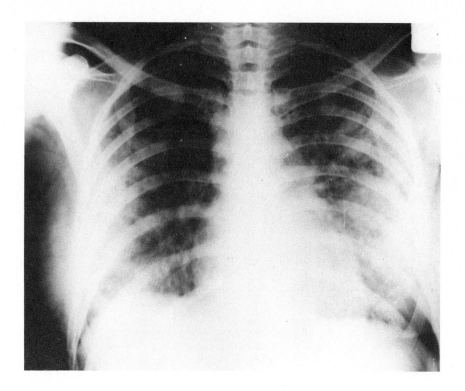

Fig. 3. Twenty year old female patient admitted following a car accident in which she reported bone fractures of lower extremities. The radiograph taken five days after admission shows right heart enlargement and patchy increase of density in the peripheral regions of both lungs.

showed unilateral distribution of the increased lung density with respect to 9% of the other patients radiographs (p<0.001).

  Regional distribution. Lung density increase was   distributed both in the central and the peripheral lung regions. However, considering all the pa-tients, the regional distribution of the increased lung density was considerably more often peripheral in DXR with respect to LXR, where a predominantly central distribution was observed (p<0.05). A more central distribution in LXR with respect to DXR was also observed in the surviving patients (Figure 5). No sig-nificantly different regional distribution of the increased lung density was observed, between DXR and LXR, in patients who died. The radiographic pattern of

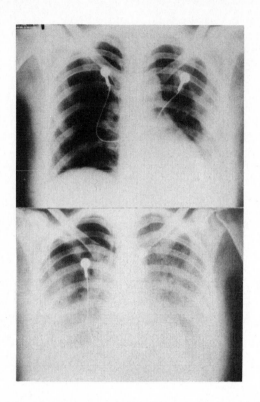

Fig. 4. Twentyeight year old
female patient admitted unconscious following head trauma
(subdural hematoma and frontal
laceration). The radiograph
taken two days after admission
(upper frame) shows white lung
in the peripheral regions of
the left lung. The evolution
radiograph (lower frame) shows
progressive involvement of both
lung fields. Density is more
markedly increased in the peripheral regions.

patchy increase of density was more peripherally distributed with respect to
that of diffuse increase of density (p<0.001). The regional distribution along
the vertical axis of the lung demonstrated a prevalent involvement of mid and
lower regions with respect to the upper ones (Table 2). However, upper regions
were more involved in patients with head trauma and/or long bone fractures
(p<0.001). A reduced involvement of the upper regions was observed in LXR of
patients who survived (Figure 5).

Other findings

The prevalence is listed in Table 2. Widening of fissurae was observed in all
the instances at the level of the horizontal fissura. Air bronchogram must be
differentiated from peribronchial cuffing. In the former instance, the cast of
the bronchial tree is shown   by the increased density of the surrounding lung
parenchyma, while in the latter the bronchial walls themselves stand out as a

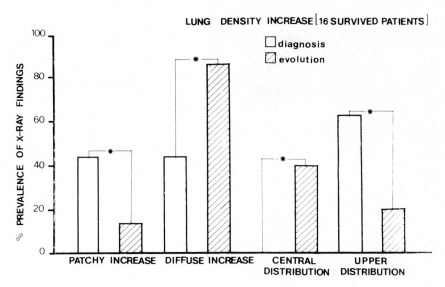

Fig. 5. Relative prevalence of qualitative features and regional distribution of the increased lung density in DXR (diagnosis) and LXR (evolution) of patients who survived. *= p<0.05

consequence of fluid accumulation in the surrounding connective tissue. Septal lines were observed only in the radiographs of a patient affected by viral pneumonia. In this patient, Kerley A lines radiating from hila appeared in 2 radiographs.

DISCUSSION

Heart size

The high prevalence of right heart enlargement suggests that increased pulmonary vascular resistance is a common feature in our series of patients. This finding is in keeping with data obtained in humans (12) and animals (13-15) showing that pulmonary vascular resistance is consistently elevated in clinical and experimental R.D.S. Right heart enlargement is frequently observed when the radiographic involvement of the lung fields is not yet fully developed (Figure 1).

This may reflect the early hemodynamic alterations that, as shown in experimental studies, precede the increase in microvascular permeability (13-16). The higher prevalence of right heart enlargement in patients with head trauma and/or long bone fractures could be related to a more severe involvement of the pulmonary vascular bed. Indeed, in these patients, both massive sympathetic discharge (17,18) and bone marrow microemboli (19,20) could be specific triggers of the increased vascular resistance. Bulging of the common trunk of the pulmonary artery can be considered the most reliable sign to detect right heart enlargement, being less influenced by factors, such as patient supine position, loss of lung volume and increased circulating blood volume, that can modify the shape of the first and second arch on the right cardiac border. The higher prevalence of a joint right and left heart enlargement in burned patients may be explained by the positive balance of fluids to which these patients were subjected. In contrast fluid intake was generally reduced in the remaining patients.

Hilar abnormalities

The observed prevalence of hilar abnormalities was, on the whole, less than that reported in a population of 45 patients with acute myocardial infarction in whom hilar size and density increase and blurring were respectively 75,79, and 80% of 132 radiographs (6). The loss of definition of hilar border (blurring) is widely accepted in the literature as an early specific sign of pulmonary edema (2-4). In the aforementioned population of cardiac patients hilar blurring was present in 85% of the radiographs taken on admission and in 25% of those taken at discharge. In this series of R.D.S. patients, hilar blurring prevailed in the evolution chest x-ray (52%) with respect to the diagnostic one (10%), thus pointing to different accumulation and reabsorption patterns of pulmonary edema fluid in the two conditions. Hilar enlargement and increase of density are not specific of pulmonary edema and the prevalence we observed in our R.D.S. patients can be regarded as an index of increased pulmonary vascular resistance, as well as right heart enlargement. This is in keeping with the reduced prevalence of both findings in the radiologic evolution of patients who survived, where pulmonary vascular resistance can be expected to return within normal limits (12). As a matter of fact the same trend was not observed in patients who died. The presence in the diagnostic chest x-ray of an increased hilar size and density can not be considered, per se, as an index of poor prognosis, as we found a higher prevalence of both signs at diagnosis in the group of patients who subsequently survived. In this respect more prognostic value

may be assigned to the persistance of this finding throughout the evolution of
the disease.

Lung density

Qualitative features of increased lung density are related to the severity of
pulmonary involvement in R.D.S. This can be surmised from the reduced prevalence
of the patchy pattern in the evolution chest x-ray of the surviving patients as
well as from the increased prevalence of white lung in that of patients who
died. Furthermore, the diffuse pattern, that is expression of prevalent interstitial fluid accumulation, prevailed in the evolution chest x-ray of patients
subsequently surviving.

The observed unilateral extension of the increased lung density in patients
with head trauma and/or long bone fractures may be related to direct chest con-
tusion and/or aspiration of gastric content, events that are likely to occur
in these patients.

Regional distribution of lung density in R.D.S. patients deserves special attention, since its peripheral increase appears as a distinctive radiographic
pattern. Indeed, lung periphery was involved in 90% of the radiographas that
presented an increased lung density. In the course of injury pulmonary edema
vascular permeability to water and solute increases, with a consequent accumulation of protein-rich fluid in the interstitial space close to the leaking
vessels. Owing to its rapid accumulation and its high protein content (13,21-
23), this fluid cannot be removed easily from the site of production towards
the loose connective tissue around large vessels and airways. Indeed, the diffusion of water molecules along the extravascular tissue space is hampered by
the high oncotic activity of the extravasated protein molecules. Moreover, these
large molecules, despite the considerable oncotic gradient established between
the site of their primary accumulation and the loose connective tissue, cannot
easily negotiate a path through the dense meshwork of fibrils interspersed within the connective ground substance (24). Therefore, their regional clearance
appears to be mostly related to the function of the lymphatic system. Lymphatic
vessels, however, have been shown to respond slowly to an increase in the net
transvascular fluid filtration rate (25) and furthermore, their function may be
impaired during R.D.S. (26). Hence, as long as the microvascular injury persists,

the lymphatic system cannot satisfactorily remove the excess of fluid and solute.
From the radiographic standpoint these events are in agreement with the observed
predominantly peripheral distribution of lung density increase (i.e. in the lung
cortex where the network of microvessels is extensively developed) in the diagno
stic chest x-ray of all the patients. Likewise, the patchy configuration of the
increased lung density, that must be regarded as a sign of alveolar involvement,
prevailed in the peripheral regions with respect to the diffuse configuration.
If the microvascular injury eventually subsides, lymphatics are allowed to drain
the fluid from the extravascular space towards the hilum. This accounts for the
higher prevalence of a central distribution of the increased lung density in the
evolution chest x-ray of the surviving patients.

Even if in the overall population the increased lung density seems to be grav-
itationally distributed, we found that in patients with trauma the upper regions
were more frequently involved than in the remaining patients. This, again, may
be probably ascribed to the relative higher values of pulmonary vascular resistance in these patients with consequent recruitment of the whole pulmonary vascular bed.

Other findings

Peribronchial and perivascular cuffs were seldom encountered in our R.D.S.
population. This is in contrast with the high prevalence of this finding in patients with cardiogenic pulmonary edema (6). Septal lines were observed in only
one patient and this, again, is in contrast with the higher figures reported in
patients with myocardial infarction in whom Kerley A, B and C lines were observed in 20, 14 and 17% respectively. Different prevalence of peribronchovascu-
lar cuffs and septal lines in the two population stresses, to a further extent,
the difficulty for high permeability pulmonary edema fluid to diffuse within the
interstitial connective tissue. Air bronchogram was, on the contrary, more frequently observed in R.D.S. patients than in cardiac patients, thus reflecting a
higher degree of lung density increase in the former group. As far as pleural
effusion is concerned the low prevalence of this finding in our R.D.S. patients
should be considered with caution as a distinctive feature, because most of our
radiographs were performed with the patient lying close to the supine position.

CONCLUSIONS

From the analysis of our data the following conclusive remarks can be drawn: chest x-ray in R.D.S. patients shows a peculiar configuration mainly related to the regional distribution (peripheral) and qualitative feature of the increased lung density (patchy, white lung) in the presence of sparse radiographic signs of interstitial fuid accumulation. Heart size and hilar abnormalities, though cannot be regarded as specific findings, may provide an insight into the patient hemodynamic status. Despite a lack of predictive value in patients at risk for developing R.D.S., chest x-ray has been found to be a reliable tool to cope with the problem of R.D.S. monitoring in the intensive care units.

REFERENCES

1. Kerley, P.(1957) Lung changes in acquired heart disease. Am. J. Roentgenol. 80, 256-263.

2. Logue, R.B., Rogers, J.V. and Gay, B.B. (1963) Subtle roentgenographic signs of left heart failure. Am. Heart J., 65, 464-473.

3. Harrison, M.O., Conte, P.J. and Heitzman, E.R. (1971) Radiological detection of clinically occult cardiac failure following myocardial infarction. Br. J. Radiol., 44, 265-272.

4. Chait, A.(1972) Interstitial pulmonary edema. Circulation, 45, 1323-1330.

5. Chait, A., Cohen, H.E., Meltzer, L.E. and VanDurme, J.I. (1972) The bedside chest radiograph in the evaluation of incipient left heart failure. Radiology, 105, 563-566.

6. Pistolesi, M. and Giuntini, C. (1978) Assessment of extravascular lung water. Radiol. Clin. North Am., 16, 551-574.

7. Giuntini, C, Pistolesi, M., Pollastri, A., Begliomini, E., Ballestra, A.M. and Maseri, A. (1979) Chest x-ray versus dilution method in the assessment of pulmonary edema in patients with coronary artery disease. In: Giuntini, C. and Panuccio, P. (Eds.), Cardiac Lung, Piccin Medical Books, Padova, pp. 251-262.

8. Dick, D.R. and Zylak, C.J. (1973) Acute respiratory distress in adults. Radiology, 106, 487-501.

9. Joffe, N. (1974) The adult respiratory distress syndrome. Am. J. Roentgenol., 122, 719-731.

10. Ostendorf, P., Birzle, H., Vogel, W. and Mittermayer, C. (1975) Pulmonary radiographic abnormalities in shock. Radiology, 115, 257-263.

11. Pistolesi, M., Miniati, M., Ravelli, V. and Giuntini, C. (1982) Injury versus hydrostatic lung edema: detection by chest x-ray. Ann. N.Y. Acad. Sci.

384, 364-380.

12. Zapol, W.M. and Snider, M.T. (1977) Pulmonary hypertension in severe acute respiratory failure. New Engl. J. Med., 296, 476-480.

13. Brigham, K.L., Woolverton, W.C., Bland, L.H. and Staub, N.C. (1974) Increased sheep lung vascular permeability caused by Pseudomonas bacteremia. J. Clin. Invest., 54, 792-804.

14. Gee, M.H. and Havill, A.M. (1980) The relationship between pulmonary perivascular cuff fluid and lung lymph in dogs with edema. Microvasc. Res., 119, 209-216.

15. Porcelli, R., Foster, W.M., Bergofsky, E.H., Bicker, A., Kaur, R., Demeny, M. and Reich T. (1974) Pulmonary circulatory changes in pathogenesis of shock lung. Am. J. Med. Sci., 268, 251-261.

16. Demling, R.H. (1982) Role of prostaglandins in acute pulmonary microvascular injury. Ann. N.Y. Acad. Sci., 384, 517-534.

17. Thedore, J. and Robin, E.D. (1976) Speculations on neurogenic pulmonary edema (NPE). Am. Rev. Resp. Dis., 118, 783-786.

18. Ingram, R.H., Szidon, J.P., Skalak, R. and Fishman, A.P. (1968) Effects of sympathetic nerve stimulation on the pulmonary arterial tree of the isolated lobe perfused in situ. Circ. Res., 22, 801-815.

19. Jacobs, R.R. and McClain, O. (1979) The role of embolic fat in post-traumatic pulmonary insufficiency. Internat. Orthop., 3, 71-75.

20. Barie, P.S., Minnear, F.L. and Malik, A.B. (1981) Increased pulmonary vascular permeability after bone marrow injection in sheep. Am. Rev. Resp. Dis., 123, 648-653.

21. Vreim, C.E. and Staub, N.C. (1976) Protein composition of lung fluids in acute alloxan edema in dogs. Am. J. Physiol., 230, 376-379.

22. Fein, A., Grossman, R.F., Jones, J.G., Overland, E., Pitts, L. and Staub, N.C. (1979) The value of edema fluid protein measurement in patients with pulmonary edema. Am. J. Med., 67, 32-38.

23. Bachofen, M., Bachofen, H. and Weibel, E. (1979) Lung edema in the adult respiratory distress syndrome. In: Fishman, A.P. and Renkin, E.M. (Eds.), Pulmonary Edema, American Physiological Society, Bethesda, pp. 242-252.

24. Comper, W.D. and Laurent, T.C. (1978) Physiologic function of connective tissue polysaccharides. Physiol. Rev., 58, 255-315.

25. Gee, M.H. and Spath J.A. (1980) The dynamics of the lung fluid filtration system in dogs with edema. Circ. Res., 46, 796-801.

26. Halmagyi, D.F.J. (1978) Role of lymphatics in the genesis of " shock lung". In: Staub, N.C. (Ed.), Lung Water and Solute Exchange, Marcel Dekker Inc., New York, pp. 423-435.

PULMONARY SURFACTANT AND MINERAL-INDUCED DISEASES

ROY RICHARDS, JENNIFER HUNT AND GERWYN GEORGE
Department of Biochemistry, University College of Cardiff, P.O. Box 78
Cardiff CF1 1XL, Wales, U.K.

INTRODUCTION

A number of minerals are known to produce pathological responses upon deposition in lung tissue as indicated by the formation of inflammatory areas
followed by the later development of fibrosis and in some instances tumour
formation.   The final lesion which develops relies on a number of factors
including the physical and chemical nature of the minerals and the amount
deposited, both of which may control the clearance from the lung.   Attempts
have been made to understand the precise cellular and biochemical changes which
occur in lung tissue following mineral deposition.   In particular the role of
the alveolar macrophage in both acute inflammation and fibrogenesis has been
an area of intense investigation with relatively less attention being given to
the possible changes in other cell types and components of the alveolar surface
and in the lung interstitium.   However early in vitro studies (1) showed that
pulmonary surfactant could protect red blood cells from mineral-induced lysis
and other work (2) suggested that, following exposure to a fibrogenic quartz,
animals developed severe lipoproteinosis.   It was therefore decided to
determine whether minerals could alter the levels of pulmonary surfactant,
whether any such effect was specifically related to fibrogenic dusts and what
consequences the alterations in surfactant levels could have on lung tissue or
cells.   This communication reviews the effects of a number of dusts of
different cytotoxic and fibrogenic potency following their inhalation or
instillation on the levels of isolated alveolar surface surfactant.   In
addition, the effects of pulmonary surfactant on the metabolism of stationary
phase lung fibroblasts, maintained in vitro, is described.

EXPERIMENTAL

Alveolar surfactant isolation and composition.   Isolation of alveolar
surface surfactant is achieved by a modification of the method described by
Abrams (3).   Following lung lavage removal of the free cells at 300g and
further centrifugation of the supernatant at 1000g to remove approximately 80%
of the soluble surface protein, a small pellet of material is obtained which
when suspended in 4M saline and recentrifuged (1500g), separates into 3 layers.

The top, floating layer or pellicle is designated pulmonary surfactant and this can be dialysed, freeze-dried and weighed (4). Analysis of this material from several animal species reveals that it is composed of approximately 90% lipid and 10% protein (Table 1). Lipid analysis indicates that the major component is phosphatidylcholine (70-80%) and fatty acid analysis of this component reveals that a high level (75%) of palmitic (hexadecanoic) acid is present suggesting that a major proportion of the phosphatidylcholine material exists as a dipalmitoyl form (4, Table 1).

TABLE 1
COMPOSITION OF ALVEOLAR SURFACE SURFACTANT

	Rat	Rabbit
Protein (% w/w)	10	8
Lipid (% w/w)	88	90
Triacylglycerol (% lipid)	4.6	4.1
Fatty acid	2.6	1.6
Phosphatidylethanolamine	4.1	1.1
PHOSPHATIDYLCHOLINE	72.6	83.4
Phosphatidylglycerol	4.5	2.5
Phosphatidylinositol	4.5	1.6
Lysophosphatidylcholine	0.2	trace
Sphingomyelin	2.1	2.0
Cholesterol	3.2	3.3
Other	1.6	0.4
Palmitate (16:0) (% PC component)	72.8	78.4

When rats inhale chrysotile asbestos (a known cytotoxic and fibrogenic dust in humans) alveolar surface surfactant accumulates over a 15 week exposure period such that treated animals have between 6 and 12 times the amount of material found in normal rats (5,6). Removal of animals from the inhalation chamber resulted in some reduction in surfactant levels with clearance time but such levels did not return to those found in normal rats (5). Exposure to 'low' amounts of chrysotile does not promote surfactant accumulation in rats (7) and furthermore the isolated surfactant composition is very similar

in both normal and chrysotile-treated rats (6).   Amosite asbestos (a fibrogenic mineral) produces similar, although less extensive affects than chrysotile whereas fibreglass (weak or non-fibrogenic) produces only a small,
transient increase in surfactant levels which return to normal levels following
clearance (7).   Polyvinyl chloride dust, a man-made paste polymer, produces
small granulomatous areas following dust inhalation at nuisance dust levels
(10 mg/m^3) (8).   However, this dust induces little or no change in pulmonary
surfactant levels and shows no evidence of initiating any fibrogenic reaction
in the lung tissue (8).   Further experiments with rats inhaling DQ12 αquartz
(highly fibrogenic) showed that even after a 16 week clearance period from
first exposure (over 8 weeks) the dust-treated animals had 16 times the amount
of alveolar surface surfactant detected in control animals (Hardy and Richards
unpublished data, 9).

The conclusion drawn from these inhalation studies is that dusts which are
highly fibrogenic (particularly in human subjects) appear to promote the accumulation and maintain high levels of alveolar surfactant even following clearance in the experimental animal model.   In view of the fact that inhalation
studies are expensive, are not readily available to many investigators and are
difficult to adapt to dose response studies it was decided to repeat and extend
the above investigations using a simplified procedure of dust administration
known as instillation.   Most preliminary investigations were carried out to
determine the effects of low, instilled doses of dust.   The effects of an
amorphous silica (A380, considered weak or non-fibrogenic in humans) and an
αquartz (DQ12, highly fibrogenic) at 1 and 4 weeks after a single instillation
of any given dose on surfactant levels is shown (Fig. 1).   Little distinction
between the effects of the compounds is detected at 1 week except at a 5mg dose
but at 4 weeks animals exposed to 5mg of A380 have two times whereas those
exposed to quartz have 15 times the amount of surfactant found in normal
animals.   At this latter time period the amount of surfactant accumulated is
related to the dose of quartz instilled.   A number of dusts will slightly
elevate surfactant levels one week after instillation and therefore to obtain
better distinction between the relative biological reactivity of each compound
the effects of the particles were examined at 4 and 15 weeks after instillation
(Fig. 2).   Dusts of little or no fibrogenic potential (titanium dioxides,
PVC's and different man-made calcium silicates, A-C) have little if any effects
on surfactant levels.   Amorphous silicas (R972, A380 and Cabosil) which are
quite cytotoxic but probably only weakly fibrogenic produce a small, but
transient increase in surfactant levels which is not maintained over a 15 week

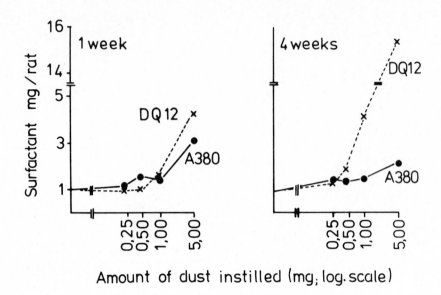

Amount of dust instilled (mg; log. scale)

Fig. 1. Amounts of alveolar surface surfactant in rats at 1 and 4 weeks following a single intratracheal instillation of different doses of amorphous silica (A380) and α quartz (DQ12).

period and strongly contrasts with the extensive promotion and maintenance of high surfactant levels in the fibrogenic quartz-treated rats.

The conclusions drawn from both instillation and inhalation experiments with minerals were therefore identical. Dusts could promote the levels of alveolar surface surfactant, the reaction is dependent on such factors as dose, particle /fibre size distribution, mineral surface chemistry and that the dusts with the greatest fibrogenic potential in humans produced the most extensive effects. These results raised a number of questions. What are the cellular sequence of events which lead to surfactant accumulation? Why is the synthetic/degradative balance of surfactant disturbed by dusts? Does the wounded lung have more need of pulmonary surfactant and what are the consequences of accumulating large amounts of this material? It can be inferred that a cytotoxic dust, when deposited in sufficient quantity, probably damages the Type I cell barrier; as Type I cells are not rapidly replaced Type II cells replicate quickly to 'plug' the epithelial gap. The number of Type II cells would thus increase resulting in the production of more surfactant, which in the absence of

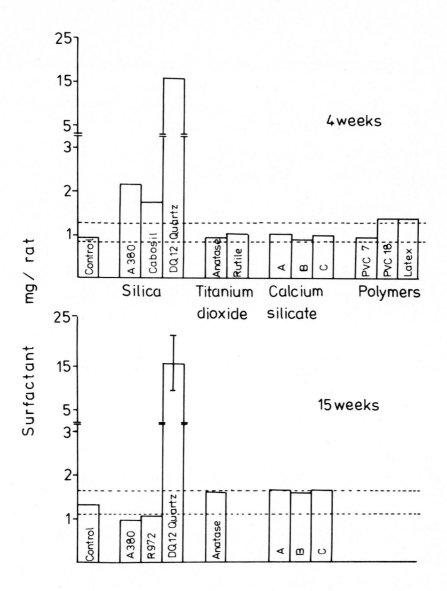

Fig. 2. Amounts of alveolar surface surfactant in rats instilled with 5mg quantities of dusts and examined after 4 and 15 weeks exposure. The standard deviation from the mean control level is shown by the dashed lines. A - C are 3 forms of calcium silicate products.

sufficient increase in the degradative capacity of the lung tissue would lead to surfactant accumulation. Additional surfactant at the lung surface would help prevent damage to cell membranes by adsorption reactions between the dusts and surfactant (1). In addition an increase in the amount of lipid products may well increase the influx of macrophages (10) which could then assist in the clearance of offending dust particles. One further attractive hypothesis is that surfactant accumulation may act as a 'trigger' to the interstitial connective tissue either by stimulating fibroblast growth or increasing the ability of such cells to synthesise and deposit collagen. This possibility was examined experimentally by exposing stationary phase lung fibroblast cells to different concentrations of pulmonary surfactant and its major component dipalmitoylphosphatidylcholine (DPPC) in the presence of ^{3}{H}-thymidine and ^{14}{C}-proline for 24h. Little alteration was found in the uptake of ^{3}{H}-thymidine into DNA in any cultures suggesting no changes were induced by the components in DNA 'synthesis'. However protein 'synthesis' as adjudged by incorporation of ^{14}{C}-proline into cell mat protein was depressed with increasing doses of surfactant but not with its major component, DPPC (Fig. 3). Similarly all doses of surfactant reduced the levels of radiolabelled hydroxy-proline containing moieties ('soluble' collagen) in the culture medium and the 2 highest doses of lipoprotein produced a similar effect in the cell mat ('deposited' collagen). Once again, the DPPC component was without significant effect on the formation of radiolabelled hydroxyproline moieties, except for those in the medium where cells had been exposed to the two lowest concentrations of the material (Fig. 3). It is concluded from these experiments that, at least under in vitro conditions, increasing doses of pulmonary surfactant suppress both protein and collagen synthesis by fibroblast cells and as such the lipoprotein material is an unlikely promoter of fibrogenesis. It also seems reasonable to conclude that DPPC alone, the major component of surfactant, does not interfere with protein synthesis in these stationary phase cells.

Further instillation studies using 5mg quantities of different minerals (α quartz-fibrogenic; titanium dioxide - non fibrogenic) were carried out to determine the long term effects on surfactant levels in comparison with hydroxy-proline estimations (biochemical fibrogenesis) in the lung tissue. These experiments have yet to be completed but details are shown for the effects produced by the 3 minerals up to a 45 week exposure time (Fig. 4). Animals exposed to titanium dioxide show no changes in surfactant levels, only minimal changes in total lung hydroxyproline after 36 weeks and histological sections show no abnormalities or evidence of fibrosis throughout the period of exposure.

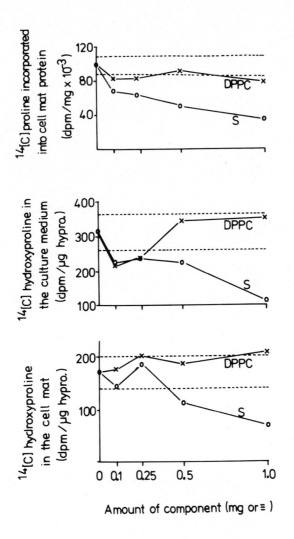

Fig. 3.   The effects of rabbit alveolar surface surfactant (**S**) and dipalmitoyl-phosphatidylcholine (DPPC) on stationary phase lung fibroblasts incubated with [3]{H}-thymidine and [14]{C}-proline.

Cells were incubated in Waymouth's medium MB752/1 containing 0.3μCi/ml of [3]{H} and 0.2μCi/ml of [14]{C}.   Full details of analysis are given by George (11). Standard deviation of control samples are shown by dashed lines; Ξ equals amount of DPPC present in any given amount of pulmonary surfactant.

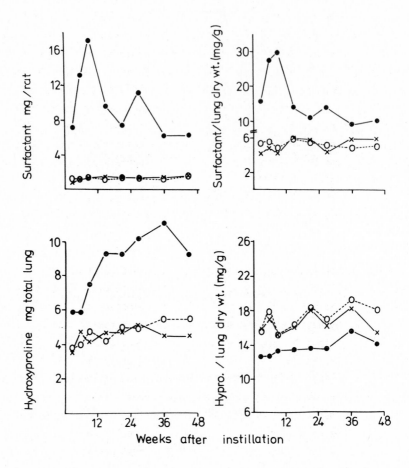

Fig. 4. Alveolar surface surfactant and hydroxyproline levels in lavaged lungs of rats exposed for different time periods following a single instillation (at time 0) of 5mg of DQ12 quartz (● ——— ●) or titanium dioxide (anatase, O ——— O) compared with control animals (X ——— X).

By contrast, alveolar surface surfactant levels are elevated extensively in quartz-exposed animals over the first 9 weeks after which there is a reduction but even after 45 weeks the mineral-treated rats have approximately 4 times the amount of lipoprotein found in normal animals.   Total lung hydroxyproline is also significantly elevated in quartz-treated rats particularly after 9 weeks although if hydroxyproline is expressed in terms of dried lung weight then these treated animals have less hydroxyproline (and presumably therefore less collagen -like material) per given mass of tissue than that found in control animals. Such a result may be equated by the fact that in the quartz-treated lungs a large proportion of the increase in total mass is due to the presence of lipid components.   Some evidence of additional, patchy deposition of collagen is detected by Anilene blue staining at 45 weeks in quartz-exposed rats.   This effect is much less marked at 15 and 28 weeks after exposure to the quartz (5mg) again suggesting that the formation of fibrotic areas is unlikely whilst an extensive lipoproteinosis is occurring in the lung (2).

CONCLUSIONS

The deposition in the lung of a fibrogenic dust creates changes in epithelial lining cell metabolism resulting in the accumulation of alveolar surface (and possibly intracellular, see Ref. 2) pulmonary surfactant.   This primary effect may have the advantage of reducing dust toxicity and promoting macrophage influx thus initiating clearance and reducing the possibility of dust directly entering the interstitium.   A second protective function for surfactant may be that it has a role in the regulation of lung protein synthesis and thus increasing amounts of lipoprotein may depress collagen formation/ deposition and reduce the likelihood of fibrogenesis.   However, in quartz-treated lungs, the continual provocation of Type II cells and excessive accumul-ation of pulmonary surfactant may aid in trapping dust particles and accumul-ating 'foamy cell' macrophages at the alveolar surface thus impairing clearance. The initiation of a reepithelialisation process following damage by any agent deposited in the lung would seem to be of paramount importance in preventing fibrogenesis.   An example of this has been shown in the combined effects of butylated hydroxytoluene and oxygen on lung tissue (12).   In quartz-exposed lungs, the reepithelialisation process may be very slow and the restoration of the normal Type I to Type II cell ratio never completely achieved.   Failure to maintain an efficient epithelial barrier in localised areas of the lung may well result in extensive quartz particle entry to the interstitium.   This could be the primary step in the initiation of fibrogenesis.

ACKNOWLEDGEMENTS

  Two of us (RJR, JH) would like to thank the Ministry of Defence for financial support and Drs. Gall and Lee for helpful suggestions.   GG is also grateful to the Medical Research Council for financial support.

REFERENCES

1. Desai, R. and Richards, R.J. (1975) Life Sciences, 16, 1931.

2. Heppleston, A.G., Fletcher, K. and Wyatt, I. (1974) Br. J. exp. Path., 55 384.

3. Abrams, M.E. (1966) J. App. Physiol., 21, 718.

4. Harwood, J., Desai, R., Hext, P.M., Tetley, T.D. and Richards, R.J. (1975) Biochem. J., 151, 707.

5. Tetley, T.D., Hext, P.M., Richards, R.J. and McDermott, M. (1976) Br. J. exp. Path., 57, 505.

6. Tetley, T.D., Richards, R.J. and Harwood, J.L. (1977) Biochem. J., 166, 323.

7. Tetley, T.D. and Richards, R.J. (1981) in: von Wichert, P. (Ed.), Progress in Respiratory Research 15, Karger, Basel, pp. 93-103.

8. Richards, R.J., Rose, F.A., Tetley, T.D., Cobb, L.M. and Hardy, C.J. (1981) Arch. Env. Hlth., 36, 14.

9. Hardy, C.J. (1981) Some responses of rat lung to inhaled glass fibres. Ph.D. Thesis, University of East Anglia, Norwich.

10. Heppleston, A.G. (1969) Brit. Med. Bull., 25, 282.

11. George, G. (1981) Proteins on the lung surface.   Ph.D. Thesis, University of Wales.

12. Haschek, W.M. and Witschi, H. (1979) Toxicol. App. Pharmacol., 51, 475.

SMOKING AND LUNG SURFACTANT

BY

THEODORE N. FINLEY, M.D.

THEODORE N. FINLEY, MD,FACP
Clinical Professor of Medicine
UC Davis Medical School, California
P.O. Box 266
Deer Park, Ca. 94576   USA

INTRODUCTION

The studies reported here were performed over ten years ago
using the then new technique of broncho-pulmonary lavage.(1)
We found the sediment obtained from broncho-pulmonary lavage
in normal smokers and nonsmokers was strikingly different.

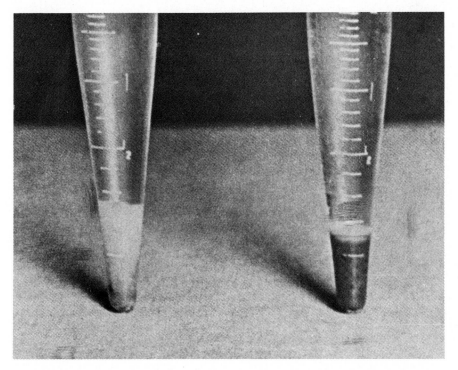

Fig. 1.   Lavage sediments from a nonsmoker (left) and a smoker
(right)

Figure 1 shows the sediment obtained from broncho-pulmonary lavage in a nonsmoker and a smoker lavage sediment. There is a predominance of a non-cellular white layer in the nonsmoker and a predominance of a cellular brown layer in the smoker. We have shown in dogs that the non-cellular white layer is predominantly lipid, is highly surface active and is similar to alveolar lining material in vivo.

The brown layer is a cellular and is predominantly alveolar macrophages. We feel that the white layer in Figure 1 is obtained from the alveolar walls in humans and may represent a reduction in pulmonary surfactant in normal cigarette smokers. This reduction may represent increased ingestion of pulmonary surfactant during phagocytosis by the alveolar macrophages.

MATERIAL & METHOD

We performed broncho-pulmonary lavage using a 19F Metras catheter (Figure 2). It was inserted into a lower lobe by the oral or nasal route under local anesthesia in normal volunteers. The balloon at the end of the Metras catheter was inflated and the catheter was secured in a lower lobe. Three 100 ml. aliquots of 0.9% saline were individually lavaged in and out of the catheter and collected. The catheter was then removed. There were no ill effects to the volunteer. Similarly fiberoptic bronchoscopy allows one to do more selective lavage and this has been reported in a number of papers. (3-5) lavage fluid was then centrifuged at 3,000 times gravity at 0° centigrade for five minutes. The supernatant was removed with the white layer and was separated by pipeting and all supernatants were then centrifuged to 25,000 times gravity for twenty minutes to sediment all the white layer. The sediment consisted of a lower cellular brown layer predominantly alveolar macrophages and an upper non-cellular white layer. The white layer had the surface tension behavior of pulmonary surfactant.

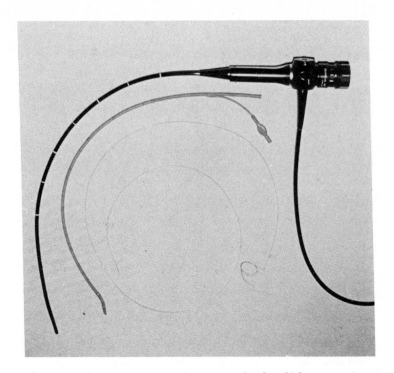

Fig. 2.   19F Metras catheter and Flexible Bronchoscope

Resulting volume of centrifuged white layer and brown layer
were recorded.

Eight smokers, average age twenty-seven all with normal
pulmonary function, were compared to eight nonsmokers, average
age twenty-four with normal pulmonary function.

RESULTS

Table 1 gives the recovery of the volume of saline recovered,
white and brown layers, in the smokers and nonsmokers. The
recovery of saline was slightly greater in the nonsmokers.
There was a seven fold increase in white layer recovered from
nonsmokers and over twice the volume of brown layer recovered
in smokers.

RECOVERY of SALINE and BROWN and WHITE
LAYER in SMOKERS and NON-SMOKERS (cond.)

NON-SMOKERS:

Subject	saline intake;	rec;	total White	total Brown.
D.E.	300	250	0.10	0.10
D.R.	300	240	0.10	0.10
S.G.	300	220	0.20	0.05
L.C.	300	210	0.20	0.13
L.E.	300	200	0.10	0.15
R.M.	300	200	0.15	0.30
E.V.	300	200	0.20	(Trace)
W.D.	300	140	0.05	0.30

(Mean $\pm$ SD) 207 ± 33* 0.14 ± 0.16** 0.14 ± 0.11**

* $p > 0.05$
**$p > 0.01$

RECOVERY of SALINE and BROWN and WHITE
LAYER in SMOKERS and NON-SMOKERS.

SMOKERS: Subject	saline aliquot intake;	rec;	total White	total Brown.
M.M. (20-30)*	300	250	(trace)	0.20
P.L. (30-40)	300	180	0.05	0.40
M.T. (20-40)	300	175	0.01	0.18
J.R. (20)	300	175	0.05	0.50
J.D. (30-40)	300	160	0.01	0.20
J.G. (20)	300	150	0.02	0.30
M.S. (20-40)	300	150	0.04	0.50
A.I. (60)	300	140	0.0	0.80

(Mean$\pm$ SD) 173 ± 34 0.02 ± 0.02 0.38 ± 0.22

* No. of cigarettes smoked/day.

Table 1.

Table 2 gives the weight per volume and total calculated
lipid of the lipid components of the white layer and the
brown macrophage layer from smokers and nonsmokers. (Because
of the lack of white layer in smokers, only two of the smokers
had sufficient white layer for measurement of volume.)

Table 3 gives the various classes of neutral lipids and
phospholipids. Table 4 gives the volumes of the brown and the
white layers and the time in months for the three subjects who
were lavaged before and after cessation of smoking. There was
an increase in the white layer of these subjects two weeks after
they stopped smoking that reached nonsmoker levels in one month.

301

LIPID COMPOSITION of PACKED White and Brown
LAYERS of SMOKERS and NON-SMOKERS.

Lipid	Smokers		Non-smokers	
	mg/ml*	mg.	mg/ml*	mg.[a]
White layer;	N = 2		N = 6	
Neutral lipid	21 + 9	0.4	24 + 12	3.1
Phospholipid	40 + 2	0.8	40 + 13	5.6
Phosphatidyl choline	27 + 2	0.5	26 + 8	3.6
Brown layer;	N = 5		N = 6	
Neutral lipid	16 + 4	6.0	14 + 2	1.8
Phospholipid	18 + 4	6.4	25 + 6	3.2
Phosphatidyl choline	8 + 2 [x]	3.1	14 + 2	1.8

* + SD.
a = based on average packed vol of 8 smokers & 8 non-smokers.
x p < 0.01

Table 2.

VARIOUS CLASSES of LIPIDS and PHOSPHOLIPIDS
IN WHITE and BROWN LAYERS OF SMOKERS and
NON-SMOKERS.

LIPID	WHITE LAYER (%)		BROWN LAYER (%)	
	Smokers (7)	Non-smokers (6)	Smokers (9)	Non-smokers (4)
Neutral lipids:				
Cholesterol	14.9 + 7.2	31.3 + 16.3	21.9 + 15.8	20.7 + 15.0
Free fatty acid	14.9 + 12.2	11.8 + 11.8	9.9 + 4.5	9.3 + 7.4
Triglyceride	12.3 + 8.3	18.7 + 8.7	14.9 + 7.1	17.7 + 18.3
Cholesterol esters	55.1 + 14.6	38.1 + 12.7	54.0 + 8.4	52.8 + 5.1
Phospholipids:				
Phosphatidyl choline	64.1 + 3.6	65.0 + 2.8	48.0 + 2.7*	55.9 + 1.1
Phosphatidyl ethanol- amine.	15.4 + 2.5	13.0 + 1.65	15.8 + 1.1	14.1 + 4.1
Phosphatidyl inositol & " serine.	6.6 + 1.3	6.7 + 1.4	10.5 + 2.1	9.0 + 3.0
Shingomyelin	2.9 + 1.9	1.9 + 0.7	11.9 + 1.2	9.1 + 4.5
Phosphatidyl dimethyl ethanolamine	2.8 + 0.2	6.2 + 0.2	8.4 + 1.2	7.0 + 1.0

* Mean + SD.

Table 3.

VOLUMES of SALINE and PACKED WHITE
and BROWN LAYERS IN 3 SUBJECTS,
BEFORE and AFTER CESSATION of SMOKING

Subject	Saline intake (ml)	Saline recovered (ml)	Time (Mo.)	White layer (ml)	Brown layer (ml)
M.T.	300	175	0	0.01	0.18
	300	190	5	0.15	0.15
	300	210	16	0.12	0.10
M.S.	300	150	0	0.04	0.50
	300	160	½	0.09	0.32
J.G.	300	150	0	0.02	0.30
	300	220	1	0.15	0.42

Table 4.

To support the hypothesis that pulmonary surfactant can be
removed by alveolar lavage, we did studies involving dogs using
electron microscopy. By very rapid dehydration with alcohol
we preserved the alveolar lining in situ and then comparing the
appearance of this material and alveolar lining to that obtained by endobronchial lavage in dogs. (2) The striking
similarity of the white layer in vitro and the alveolar lining
material in situ was shown in Figure 3 and Figures 4-6.

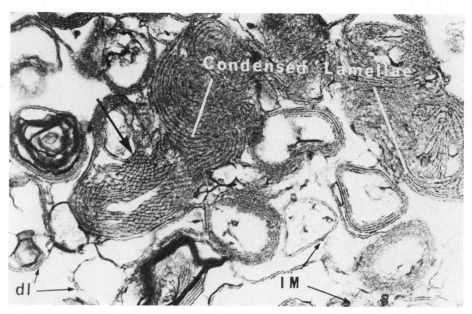

Fig. 3. Electron micrograph of a portion of the white layer.
Thin lines, interpreted as the cut edges of lamellae, occur as
large whorls. Within these whorls, the lines are roughly parallel to each other or form irregular squares and rectangles.
Outside the whorls, irregularly oriented material (IM) resembling
membranes occurs as dense lines of various thicknesses (dl)
which often run into broader amorphous areas.

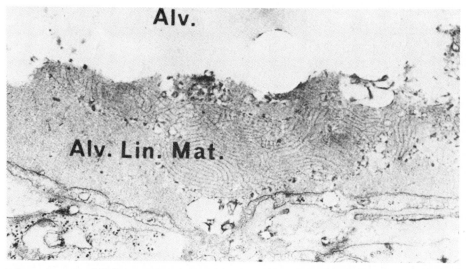

Fig. 4. Acellular material lining the alveolar epithelium (Alv.)
in a lung biopsy sample. To the left and far right, the material
consists of a granular substance. In the center, thin lines or
lamellae occur in regular arrays, either as parallel lines or, in
a few places, as squares and rectangles.

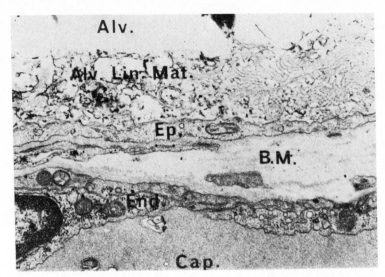

Fig. 5. Alveolar lining material (Alv. Lin. Mat.) in an alveolar space closely associated with the epithelium (Ep). The lining material at the left consists mostly of irregularly oriented membranes. At the right, more regularly arranged thin lines or lamellae are present. End., endothelium; End. Nuc., endothelial nucleus; Cap., Capillary; BM, basement membrane.

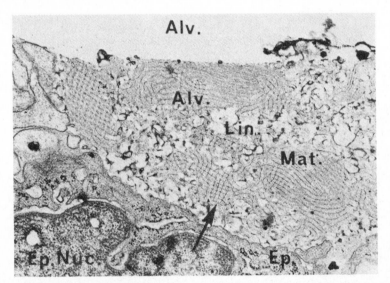

Fig. 6. A depression in an alveolar wall (Alv.) filled with alveolar lining material (Alv. Lin. Mat.) Regular arrays of parallel lines are mixed with less regularly arranged membranous structures. In some regions, the thin lines form squares or rectangles (arrow). Ep., epithelium; Ep. Nuc., Epithelial nucleus.

DISCUSSION

Material obtained by endobronchial lavage in normal humans consists primarily of two layers, a non-cellular white layer which has the physical characteristics of pulmonary surfactant and a brown layer which is predominantly cellular. The data presented here showed a marked increase in alveolar macro- phages and a decrease in surfactant obtained by lavage in smokers. The source of these macrophages was presumably the alveoli. It is possible that some of the macrophages are lining airways rather than alveoli. More detailed study in this regard is necessary. The former observation is not remarkable in view of the effect of increased alveolar macrophages in a variety of experimental conditions induced by inhaling foreign material (6-8). The reduction in pul- monary surfactant however, remains unexplained. The possible explanations are (1) difficulty in harvesting alveolar material in smokers, (2) reduced production or (3) in- creased elimination.

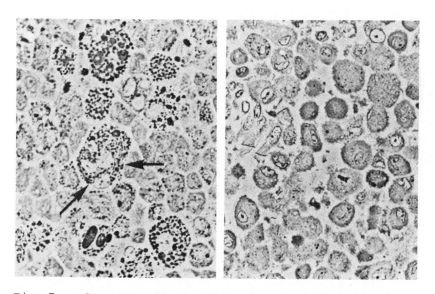

Fig. 7. Lft. A portion of a brown layer from a smoker. Some cells are filled with dense inclusions; other cells contain only a few inclusions. Arrows indicate a possibly multi- nucleate cell. Rt. A portion of a brown layer from a nonsmoker. The cells contain only a few inclusions. Some ciliated cells can be seen at the middle left of the micrograph.

The comparison of alveolar macrophages obtained from
smokers and nonsmokers (Fig. 7) shows that the inclusions in
nonsmokers are mostly round oval measuring from .1 to .2
microns in diamter. (Fig. 8).

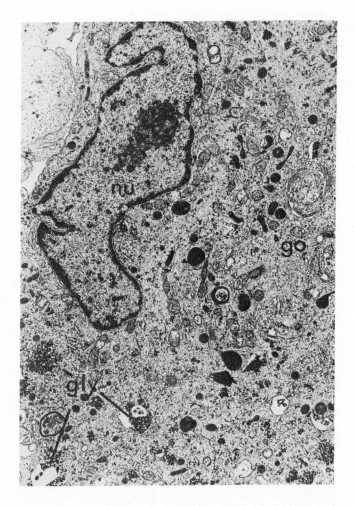

Fig. 8. Alveolar macrophage from nonsmokers.

In smokers, the inclusions measure .1 to 20 microns in diameter
and are pleomorphic in shape. (Fig. 9)

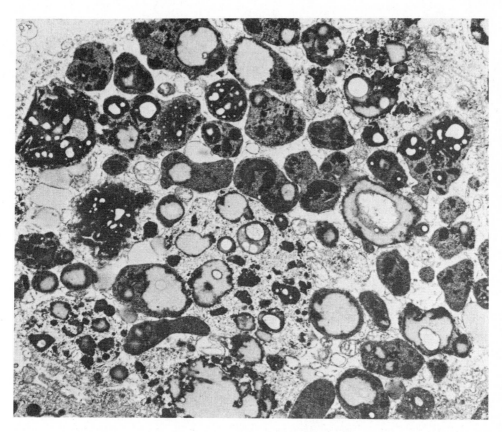

Fig. 9. Alveolar macrophage   from smoker.

They contain the structure seen in the inclusions of nonsmokers
but lipid like zones are more abundant. Moreover; dense,
angular, neddlelike structures were observed only in the
inclusions of smokers and may represent undigested smoke
products possibly kaolin. (Fig. 10)

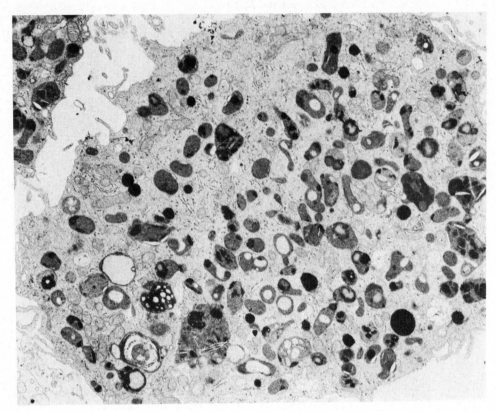

Fig. 10

HYPOTHESIS

It would appear reasonable that the large increase in
alveolar macrophage as seen in smokers is the response to
the foreign material contained in cigarette smoke and that
much of this has been phagocytosed by the alveolar macrophages. The process of phagocytosis may involve pulmonary
surfactant as illustrated in Figure 11.
Figure 8 shows a particle at the air surface interface. As
it passes through, it is coated with surfactant. Pulmonary
surfactant, theoretically half a cell membrane, would then

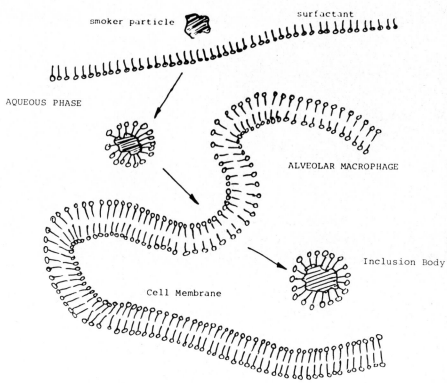

AIR PHASE

smoker particle

surfactant

AQUEOUS PHASE

ALVEOLAR MACROPHAGE

Inclusion Body

Cell Membrane

Fig. 11. Model of air surface and alveolar macrophage interface.

arrange itself around the particle with its polar heads
extending into the aqueous phase. This could allow transport
of the particles to the alveolar macrophage which would then
ingest the particle as well as the half cell membrane of
pulmonary surfactant. (Fig. 12) Figure 12 shows an inclusion
body in smoker's alveolar macrophage.

The explanation for the reduced surfactant in smokers could be
explained by its coating the smoke particles and through ingestion into the alveolar macrophage by the process of phagocytosis. This hypothesis could be tested in vitro. Certainly
more work needs to be done in this regard.

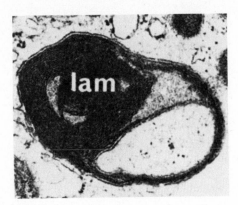

Fig. 12

REFERENCES

1. Pratt, S.A., Finley, T.N., Smith, M.H., et al: (1969)
    A comparison of alveolar macrophages and pulmonary surfactant
    obtained from the lungs of human smokers and nonsmokers by
    endobronchial lavage. Anat. Rec. 163:497-507.

2. Finley, T.N., Pratt, S.A., Ladman, A.J., et al: (1968)
    Morphological and lipid analysis of the alveolar lining mat-
    erial in dog lung, Jour. Lipid Res. 9:357-365.

3. Finley, T.N., Swenson, E.W., Curran, W.S., et al: (1967)
    Bronchopulmonary lavage in normal subjects and patients
    with obstructive lung disease. Ann. Intern. Med. 66:651-8.

4. Low B., Davis, G.S., Giancola, M.S., (1978) Biochemical
    analyses of bronchoalveolar lavage fluids of healthy human
    volunteer smokers and nonsmokers. Am. Rev. Respir. Dis.
    118:863-9.

5. Reynolds, H.Y., Fulmer, J.D., Kasimierowski, J.A., et al:
    (1977) Analysis of cellular and protein content of broncho-
    alveolar lavage fluid from patients with idiopathic pulmon-
    ary fibrosis and chronic hypersensitivity pneumonitis.
    J. Clin. Invest. 59:165-72.

6. Labelle, C.W., Brieger, H., (1960) The fate of inhaled par-
    ticles in the early postexposure period II. The role of
    pulmonary phagocytosis. Arch. Environ. Health 1:423-427.

7. Ferin, J., Urbankova, G., Vickova, A., (1965) Pulmonary
    clearance and the function of macrophages. Arch. Environ.
    Health. 10:790-795.

8. Guarneri, J.J., Laurenzi, G.A.: (1968) Effect of alcohol
    on the mobilization of alveolar macrophages. J. Lab. Clin.
    Med. 72:40-51.

THE MUCOCILIARY APPARATUS

ALVEOLO-BRONCHIOLAR CLEARANCE MECHANISMS

GARETH M. GREEN

Department of Environmental Health Sciences, The Johns Hopkins University
School of Hygiene and Public Health, 615 North Wolfe Street, Baltimore,
Maryland 21205 (U.S.A.)

THE PROBLEM OF ALVEOLAR CLEARANCE

Alveolo-bronchiolar clearance mechanisms comprise a complex of secretory,
cellular, and transport systems that remove endogenous cells and secretions
and exogenous deposited particulates from the respiratory membrane to the
mucociliary systems of regional bronchioli, or to subpleural, paraseptal,
and perivascular lymphatic channels. Although the respiratory membrane is
well protected from environmental particulates by effective aerodynamic filtration mechanisms in the bronchi and upper respiratory tract, so-called
"respirable size" particles between 0.3 and 3.0 μ penetrate these systems
and are selectively deposited by gravitational forces on the respiratory
membrane in the respiratory bronchioles and alveoli. These particles are
rapidly phagocytosed and transported intracellularly from the respiratory
membrane.

The respiratory membrane has a large surface area, approximately the size
of a tennis court in the adult. The mechanisms for clearing that membrane,
the pathways taken by cells and secretions moving from the membrane to drainage sites, the volume of fluids transported, and the source of energy required to move the secretions and cells are poorly understood problems of
physical clearance. Assuming that these clearance mechanisms function at
the level of the primary anatomic unit of the lung, the pulmonary lobule,
the relative distances covered from peripheral alveoli in the lobule to the
closest mucociliary system in the lobule's terminal bronchiole are large with
reference to the size of transporting cells and the speed of cellular motion.
Observations on the rate of clearance suggest that it is too rapid for dependence on the motility of macrophage cells, and there are no cilia to ener-
gize this system.

The ciliary system commences at the junction of the respiratory portion of
the lung and the terminal bronchiole, where both the architecture of the lung
and the epithelial elements change dramatically. The bronchioles are lined
with a continuous epithelium of ciliated and secretory cells. While the
secretory and ciliary components of the epithelium become sparser toward

the periphery of the bronchiolar system, the ciliary mechanism remains intact to the termination of this membrane at the respiratory bronchiole.

The alveolar structure, by contrast, is perforated by the interalveolar communications of the pores of Kohn. While these structures assist the passage of gaseous molecules during respiration, they may also serve a vital function in the transport of cells and fluid between the alveoli and the terminal bronchioles. Although the kinetics of this form of interalveolar transport is not understood, macrophages can be seen occupying these pores as though in transit from one alveolus to another. The epithelium lining the alveolar membrane comprises three principal cell types: the squamous type I barrier cell, the large granulated secretory type II cell, and the phagocytic alveolar macrophage. The cellular contents may be augmented by inflammatory and immune cells from the systemic circulation and cellular pool of the bone marrow.

CHARACTERISTICS OF THE PULMONARY LOBULE

A study of alveolo-bronchiolar clearance mechanisms must begin with an understanding of the characteristics of the pulmonary lobule. The pulmonary lobule comprises that portion of the lung parenchyma that receives its primary ventilation from a single terminal bronchiole, although collateral ventilation occurs from neighboring bronchiolar systems. This unit is perfused by a terminal branch of the pulmonary artery and is drained centrally by peripheral branches of the bronchiolar lymphatics that commence at the terminal bronchiole. Fluid drainage is augmented by perivascular, subpleural, and paraseptal lymphatics. Calculations made from observations in the literature suggest that approximately two-thirds of particulate clearance occurs centripetally via the bronchiolar system, with perhaps one-third passing to paraseptal, perivascular and subpleural points. However, no precise measurement of this distribution has been made.

While the pulmonary lobule receives its air and arterial blood supply centrally, venous drainage and accompanying perivenous lymphatic drainage takes place peripherally in the lobule. While lobules at the periphery of a segment or lobe may be bounded by pleura or septal tissue, the anatomic distinctions between adjacent lobules are not distinct and abundant communication through collateral airway, vascular, and lymphatic channels undoubtedly occurs; these connections serve to diminish the liabilities of a lobular structure which depends for its function on airway, lymphatic and vascular channels at some distance from portions of the alveolar membrane. Although a considerable amount of information exists for collateral ventilation, little is available on collateral alveolo-bronchiolar clearance channels between neighboring pulmonary lobules. The extent to which alveolar cells and secretions such as surfactant follow these interlobular channels is likewise poorly understood.

The kinetics of interstitial solute and water transport is the subject of a great deal of research at the present time. Vascular fluids enter the interstitial space under hydrostatic pressure through the vascular endothelium of the capillaries, and by active solute and water transport by alveolar epithelium from the alveolar surface. The controlling mechanisms of intracellular pores and intercellular junctions are rapidly being clarified but are beyond the scope of this discussion. Studies of interstitial fluid transport focus primarily around mechanisms of pulmonary edema; these studies debate the pathways and direction of fluid flow along the interalveolar septae to drainage via perivascular, peribronchiolar, and subpleural lymphatics. It is highly likely that particle and cellular clearance occurring along these interstitial pathways follows these fluid transport mechanisms passively.

OBSERVATIONS ON PARTICLE CLEARANCE

Studies of alveolo-bronchiolar clearance mechanisms can be conveniently made by observation of the deposition and translocation of microscopically visible materials inhaled as respirable micronic and submicronic particulates. We have made a number of observations over the years using small particle aerosols of inert coal dust particulates because of their visibility on light microscopy, and of radiotracer-tagged bacterial particulates because of the ease with which phagocytic and physical transport events can be quantified *in vivo*. Light microscopic studies of carbon dust particulates, and light and immunofluorescent observations of inhaled bacterial particulates indicate that both of these agents are handled similarly as particulates by alveolar macrophages. Our studies have been confined to the early post-exposure periods, focusing on the first four to twenty-four hours, with a few observations made over longer periods of time. Animal studies include rats, mice, and rabbits. Although these species show differences as to detail, general mechanisms of alveolo-bronchiolar clearance seem to be consistent.

Within an hour after short-term exposures, bacterial or carbon particulates can be found widely scattered throughout the pulmonary lobule, located primarily in an intracellular position within alveolar macrophages. Particulates may also be found unphagocytosed on the alveolar surface and in the interstitium. When highly chemotactic bacteria or high dose levels are used, polymorphonuclear leukocytes may be seen infiltrating the interstitial and alveolar spaces. Phagocytosed particulates are also found in interstitial pericapillary positions. Whether these particles are phagocytosed *in situ* in the interstitium or are carried there within phagocytes that have taken up the particles on the alveolar surface is a longstanding uncertainty; I favor the *former* explanation. Transport of these interstitial cells through the lung probably takes place along interstitial pathways. While many, and perhaps most, particle-laden cells appear to be transported to bronchiolar locations where they exit from the lung along the mucociliary pathway, a significant number of particle-laden cells can be found in perivascular positions where no ready exit pathway is available. The long-term fate of these particulates is not known. Particle-laden cells appear both on the alveolar surface and in interstitial locations, but in either event seem to concentrate primarily in bronchiolar locations and on the mucociliary surface of the terminal bronchioles. There is little particulate found in peribronchiolar lymphatics.

The inescapable conclusions from these observations are that particle-laden cells migrate from both alveolar and interstitial pathways onto the surface of the mucociliary system at the alveolo-bronchiolar junction. Careful study of this region in the early post-exposure hours confirms that peribronchiolar and perilymphatic channels are essentially free of particle-laden macrophages and that these cells exit from the interstitium onto the bronchiolar epithelium at a number of points at the alveolo-bronchiolar junctional area. Close study of this junctional area reveals the presence of minute channels at the very terminus of the bronchiolar epithelium through which particle-laden cells appear to pass from the interstitium. These channels ring the bronchiolar area and provide multiple points for the exit of cells onto the bronchiolar epithelial surface. The location of draining peribronchiolar and perivascular lymphatics at these points suggests that the lymphatic fluid is picked up and drained along these lymphatic channels, while the cells are excreted onto the surface of the bronchiolar epithelium. The mechanism of this bifurcation of fluid and cellular flow pathways is unknown.

The kinetics of alveolo-bronchiolar clearance is likewise poorly understood. We have studied the clearance of radiotracer-labeled bacterial particulates which, being of respirable size, predominantly deposit in the peripheral lung distal to the mucociliary stream. Any particles deposited on the bronchiolar epithelial surface are cleared rapidly in thirty to sixty minutes by the ciliary system. Any radioactivity remaining beyond that time can be considered to represent particulates deposited in the peripheral lung on the respiratory membrane. Alveolar clearance begins at about two hours; much or all of the

subsequent clearance--at least over the first two to three days--probably
represents the action of the alveolar bronchiolar clearance mechanisms. If
that assumption is correct, our measurements would suggest that the half-time
for near-term alveolar bronchiolar clearance is twenty-four to thirty-six
hours, a time period in close agreement with the thirty-hour rapid phase
clearance time found by others.

HYPOTHESES OF ALVEOLO-BRONCHIOLAR CLEARANCE

We believe that our observations allow several hypotheses to be formulated
regarding alveolo-bronchiolar clearance mechanisms. Inhaled and deposited
particulates are phagocytosed in the lung both on the surface of the alveolus
and in pericapillary interstitial positions. These particulates are cleared
in intracellular positions in two directions: centripetally to the terminal
bronchiole supplying ventilation at the center of the pulmonary lobule, and
centrifugally to perivascular, subpleural, and paraseptal positions. The
cells which reach the alveolo-bronchiolar junction area of the pulmonary lobule by either surface or interstitial interalveolar pathways then exit onto
the bronchiolar epithelium where they are rapidly removed by the mucociliary
apparatus of the bronchial tree. Under low-level particulate dose and non-
inflammatory conditions relatively little of the particulate material enters
the lymphatic system. Exit of particle-laden phagocytes onto the bronchial
surface occurs through multiple channels apparent at the bronchoalveolar junctional region. The mechanism by which these cells achieve this excretory pathway is not apparent from these studies. Distinct mechanisms may be involved
in the surface transport and the interstitial transport systems.

Observations of the surface transport of particle-laden cells suggest that
the cells move from the unfixed regions of the pulmonary lobule to the relatively fixed structures of the terminal bronchioles and vascular structures.
Since the unfixed structures presumably change dimensions during the process
of ventilation, transport is perhaps related to the expansion and contraction
of the surfactant film that occurs during ventilation. Other investigators
have reported that binding the chest so as to interfere with ventilation of a
lobe or region of the lung impairs alveolo-bronchiolar clearance. Those observations would suggest that the energy for the surface transport is ultimately generated from the muscular and elastic energy associated with
ventilation.

The mechanism of the intraseptal transport pathway along interstitial tissue
spaces suggests strongly that transport occurs passively with tissue fluid

flow to perilymphatic and peribronchiolar lymphatic positions and subpleu-
rally. Energy for this pathway of transport may similarly depend on the elastic squeezing forces induced by expansion and contraction with respiration,
although capillary hydrostatic pressures and oncotic gradients may also play a
role. In either case, the primary energy source rests in the respiratory muscles being transmitted to the fluid transport pathways by the elastic tissues
of the lung and the energies resident in surface tension gradients.

IMPLICATIONS AND PREDICTIONS

The above hypotheses allow the following predictions, which, if verified by
experiment, would strengthen our understanding of alveolo-bronchiolar clearance
mechanisms.

1. Surfactant anomalies, by interfering with the transmission of surface tension forces, should interfere with alveolo-bronchiolar clearance. Such
   appears to be the case in alveolar proteinosis.

2. Factors impairing cell exit at the alveolo-bronchiolar junctions would result in the peribronchiolar accumulation of phagocytes. Such is the case
   in smokers, early asbestosis, bronchopneumonia, and bronchiolar fibrosis.

3. Since undamaged peribronchiolar clearance allows the exit of particle-
   laden macrophages while perivascular pathways do not, long-term accumulation of inert particulates should occur in perivascular positions. Such
   appears to be the case with coal dust macules.

4. Since the energy of alveolo-bronchiolar clearance depends on the transmission of the muscular energy of ventilation, any impairment of local expansion or contraction of the lung should lead to cellular fluid accumulation. Such is the case with atelectasis and thoracic immobilization.

5. From the considerations given above, it should be possible to enhance
   alveolo-bronchiolar clearance by:
   a. hyperventilation, such as with exercise;
   b. increased pulmonary fluid flows such as in pulmonary congestion or
      edema; and
   c. enhanced volume or quality of surfactant secretion.

These predictions might form useful models for testing the stated hypotheses
by future planned experimentation.

RHEOLOGY OF BRONCHIAL FLUIDS ASSESSED BY FORCED OSCILLATIONS

LUIGI ALLEGRA[1], ROBERTO BOSSI[1], AND PIERCARLO BRAGA[2]

[1]Institute of Respiratory Diseases (II chair) and [2]Institute of Pharmacology (chair of Chemotherapy), Milan (Italy)

INTRODUCTION

Rheology is the science of the study of the deformation of bodies when subjected to mechanical stress. "Bodies" in this sense may be solids, liquids or gases. An ideal solid is deformed elastically, that is, the energy required for the deformation can all be recovered when the stress applied returns to zero. Fluids (liquids and gases) are irreversibly deformed, which is to say, they flow.

Real bodies are neither ideal solids nor ideal fluids. Real solids undergo permanent creep when the stress applied is great. There are very few liquids of practical importance that behave as ideal or quasi-ideal fluids. Most of them, from the rheological point of view, are at the boundary between liquids and solids. They can be either viscous or elastic, which is to say "viscoelastic". While solids can be subjected to both tensile and tangential forces (shearing stress), liquids can only be subjected to shearing stress. The resistance of a fluid to irreversible alteration of its shape is called viscosity (1,2,3).

In 1687 Isaac Newton discovered the fundamental law of flow for an ideal fluid $\tau = \eta \cdot D$ $[1]$.

The flow between two parallel planes is useful for measuring both the shear stress (or tangential stress) τ and the velocity flow gradient D.

The flow of the liquid layers is due to the movement of the upper plane, of Area A, to which a tangential force F is applied. The resulting velocity depends on the ratio of F to A and on the internal resistance, the viscosity, of the fluid: $\tau = \dfrac{F \text{ (force)}}{A \text{ (area)}} = \dfrac{N \text{ (Newton)}}{m^2} = [\text{Pa (Pascals)}]$ $[2]$. We call laminar flow the type of flow in which infinitely thin layers of liquid are in movement with respect to each other (Fig. 1).

The strict definition of the gradient D is given in terms of a differential: $D = \dfrac{dv}{dy} = \dfrac{cm/s}{cm} = \dfrac{1}{s} = [s^{-1}]$ $[3]$. When the decrease in velocity along the thickness y is linear, the gradient becoms $D \simeq \dfrac{Vmax}{y}$ $[s^{-1}]$ $[4]$.

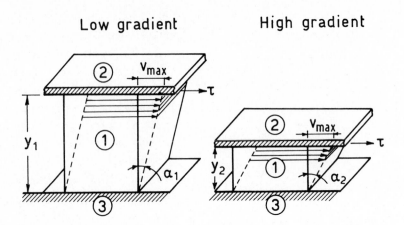

Fig. 1 . Flow between parallel planes. ① Flowing liquid, ② moving plane (whose area is A), ③ stationary plane.

The gradient is indicated as $\dot{\gamma}$, in which the dot above indicates that it is derived from the deformation γ as it varies in time $D = \frac{d\gamma}{dt} = \dot{\gamma}$ [5] . It can be shown that equation [3] and equation [5] are equal and equation [1] can be rewritten as equation [6] $\tau = \eta \cdot \frac{d\gamma}{dt} = \eta \cdot \dot{\gamma}$ [6] .

From equation [1], the viscosity η of a fluid is: $\eta = \frac{\tau}{D} = \frac{N}{m} \cdot s = $ [Pa.s] [7] . The unit of measure is the Pascal-second (Pa.s).

1. Newtonian Fluids (curves [1] in Fig. 2)

According to Newton's Law (equation 1), for an ideal fluid the flow curve is a straight line with slope tan α that passes through the origin of the axes. The viscosity, η is the ratio between τ and D (equation 7) that is the ratio between the ordinate and abscissa at any point along the line. There are several newtonian fluids, including water and mineral oils. However, the bronchial secretions are non-newtonian fluids, viscoplastic, thixotropic (4).

2. Non-newtonian Fluids

There are many fluids that do not follow Newton's law which have viscosity dependent on the gradient of the flow rate D. Their flow behaviour depends on the "flow curve" and not on some "intrinsic viscosity property". According to the values of D, their viscosity may be any of the infinite values within the defined limits.

Pseudoplasticity(curves [2] in Fig. 2) . To understand the concept of

Flow curves

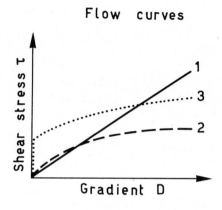

Viscosity curves

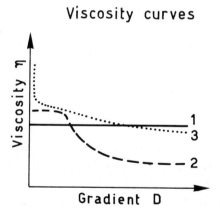

① **Newtonian fluids**
② **Pseudoplastic fluids**
③ **Pseudoplastic fluids with yield point = plastic fluids**

Fig. 2 . Common types of rheological behaviour.

plasticity, it is helpful to define pseudoplasticity. Many non-newtonian fluids have viscosity that decreases as the gradient increases. This dimension of viscosity at the increase of flow rate, implies that when certain pressures or certain shear stresses are applied, certain types of non-newtonian fluids will flow at faster rates than would have been predicted if their viscosity remained constant.

For many fluids the decrease in η with increase of D is reversible.

Plastic behaviour (curves [3] in Fig. 2). Pseudoplastic fluids with yield points are called plastic fluids. Pseudoplastic and plastic liquids are actually both solid and liquid (so that they share properties of both kind of bodies, such as elasticity as well as viscosity). These are usually dispersions that at rest maintain a three-dimensional network of dispersed particles aggregated between thamselves so that mobility within the complete system is severely restricted, the viscosity high, and under low stress they behave like solids.

Many substances can behave like visco-plastics or sometimes as pseudoplastics, among these the bronchial secretions.

<u>Thixotropy</u> (Fig. 3) . Thixotropy is a rheological phenomenon, which is complex and associated with molecular or supermolecular interactions. In the pseudoplastic systems the decrease in viscosity that occurs with increasing gradient depends above all on the orientation of the particles or molecules, an orientation that disappears the moment flow stops.

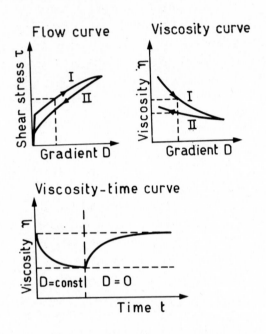

Fig. 3 . Thixotropy

Thixotropic behaviour is presented graphically in Fig. 3. The "rising" curve does not coincide exactly with the "descending" curve, but is above it. The area A between the two curves is a measure of the degree of thixotropy. At the same values of gradient, there are two different viscosities (points I and II, corrisponding viscosities η 1 and η 2), and the second is lower because the corresponding "rheological history" effect is greater. The viscosity-time curves show the characteristic decrease in η when gel is transformed into sol and the increase in η when flow ceases (unless, of course as is the case with bronchial secretions, there are enzyme-induced changes in the material while it is kept for a certain period of time).

PATIENTS AND METHODS

Patients

Selection of subjects . The secretion of 10 patients has been examined who
were all males of the age between 54 and 70 years (mean $\pm$ standard error =
62.5 $\pm$ 1.5), weight between 62 and 76 kg (mean $\pm$ standard error = 63 $\pm$ 6), 5
smokers and 5 ex smokers (they had stopped smoking not more than 5 years ago),
with a total number of > 30 pack-years of smoked cigarettes.

All the subjects had chronic bronchitis, none ot them showed clinical
or radiological signs of bronchiectasis. All showed functional signs of airways
obstruction and hyperdistention of the airspaces (basic conditions: FEV_1 ,
m $\pm$ se=69 $\pm$ 5% predicted; Raw, m $\pm$ se = 3.9 $\pm$ 0.7 cm $H_2O/l/s$; RV, m $\pm$ se =
156 $\pm$ 16%. The functional tests were carried out before the beginning of the
pharmacological treatment.

Method of research and treatment

The chosen patients suffered of a chronic bronchitis according to the
definition of the working group SEPCR - WHO (5), were in steady conditions,
without any exacerbation. All the patients have been chosen from those who
could be kept for three days without any therapy except for physiokinesitherapy
and postural drainages. After these three days of wash-out, the patients were
submitted for seven days to a monopharmacological therapy with ambroxol per os
(180 mg/day subdivided into three daily administration at 9 a.m., 4 p.m. and
11 p.m.). In all patients the sputum, in basic conditions, appeared serous or
mucous, never purulent. It was collected in the morning of the first day
between 8 and 9 a.m. and immediately afterwards the treatment began. Then the
sputum was collected once more in the morning of the 8th day at 8 to 9 a.m.

The rheological tests on the just collected sputum were carried out within
90" - 120" from emission. The body temperature of the patients never passed
36.5°C. The constant room temperature was between 20 and 22°C at the moment of
the collection of the sputum.

Method of collecting the sputum

The sputum has been collected after having invited the patient to lie
alternatively on the two sides while in the meantime for 5' clapping manoeuvres
on the two hemithoraxes have been practised. After these manoeuvres, the
patient was invited to cough strongly. The first collected sample was eliminated.

Immediately afterwards a rinsing of the oral cavity was done and gargarisms
with water. Then between the cheeks and the dental archs as well as between the

inferior dental archs and the tongue, small rolls of compressed cotton, of the odontological type, were placed. Then again the patient was invited to cough strongly and a sample of at least 1 ml was collected and submitted to the rheological test.

Under these conditions, the risk of salivary contamination and of enzymatic degradation of the sample of sputum is sensibly reduced compared to the samples of a spontaneous expectoration (6) and the measures employed at precise times on samples of fresh material result as being quite well reproducible.

Rheological assessment on bronchial secretions

Rotational viscosimeter for apparent viscosity and thixotropy. For the study of viscosity and thixotropy of the secretion samples in question we used a viscosimeter with coaxial cylinder, type Couette (Rotovisco, model RV 100/CV100 /LV100, Haake, Karlsruhe, Federal Republic of Germany). If the rotative viscosimeter is constructed in the "right" way, it is possible to obtain the cutting force = τ as well as the gradient of the sliding velocity D with strict mathematic equations.

The relation between τ and D, i.e. the flow curve, can be considered as the rheological "fingerprint" of the sample which is under study.

As to non-newtonian fluids, each couple of values τ - D obtained from the flow curve gives a different viscosity value, therefore function of the gradient.

In the case of non-newtonian fluids, η is called "apparent" viscosity because it caracterizes the fluid only at a certain gradient D, without referring to the η-values which are obtained at higher and lower gradients of D (3).

However, as to the viscoelastic fluids submitted to sliding, the response of the fluid to the force field is partly viscous and partly elastic and it is technically difficult to separate the two parts in order to obtain the "absolute" values of viscosity and elasticity. Some instruments permit the evaluation of some elastic parameters. Particularly, in a rotative viscosimeter, type Couette, the container, instead of rotating at a constant speed, can oscillate periodically with sinusoidal movement of the speed. This periodical movement can also be placed on a normal rotative stationary movement. If the speed of the external cylinder varies sinusoidally in time, the same happens to the gradient. The fluid transmits to the inner cylinder a sinusoidal solicitation having the same frequency, but a phase difference which depends on the elastic component of the response of the sample to its imposed movement.

Moreover, when the material is thixotropic, this type of measure permits to define the "grades of thixotropy" through the hysteresis area.

Many works have been carried out with viscosimeters of various types on the rheology of the sputum. The use of rotative viscosimeters has allowed a further progress in this type of investigation. But, while the viscosity has been investigated like this during the last 20 years under numerous physiological(7) and pathological (8,9,10) conditions, there were only few scientific contributions regarding the studies on the elasticity (11) performed with viscosimeters or viscoelastometers (12). In fact, only during the last years certain rotative viscosimeters have been modified in order to permit the execution of investigations on rheologic aspects which are more tied to the elastic properties of the secretions (13). Only a very short time ago, someone even tried to measure the viscoelastic properties of the secretions even in situ with a capillary rheometer which was introduced through a fibroscope (14).

Oscillation tests for elasticity and viscoelasticity . The Rotovisco RV 100 /CV100/LV100 controls the measuring system CV100 to obtain either a defined rotational speed or a forced oscillation. In rotational mode, a certain voltage is maintained over a period of time and fed to the motor to give a rotational speed.

In oscillation mode, the same relationship is valid, except the motor is fed with a sine voltage.

The beaker will move out of phase (by 90°) to the voltage or speed because the traveled distance S is: $s = \int v dt = \omega v_0 \cos (\omega t + c)$.

In rheology, the speed of a sensor system is proportional to shear rate $\dot{\gamma}$ and the displacement proportional to shear strain γ . Strain and rate of strain are out of phase by 90° which is identical to one being a sine wave, and the other a cosine wave, $\sin (90° . \omega t) = \cos (\omega t)$.

It is now easy to understand that in the Rotovisco RV 100/CV100, the present motor voltage $U_m = U_0 . \sin (\omega t)$ gives the beaker speed $v = v_0 . \sin (\omega t)$ with a defined geometry $\dot{\gamma} = \dot{\gamma}_0 . \sin (\omega t)$ whereas the displacement is $s = s_0 . \cos (\omega t)$ with the resulting deformation or strain $\gamma = \gamma_0 . \cos (\omega t)$.

When we have liquid in the sensor system, in rotational mode we know that with increasing speeds (shear rates) we get higher torque (shear stress) values. Measuring the same material in dynamic mode, we have to expect a similar result. But when the strain is actually recorded on the RV 100 at the X-axis, we will get the results of Figure 4 (example 1 : viscous fluid).

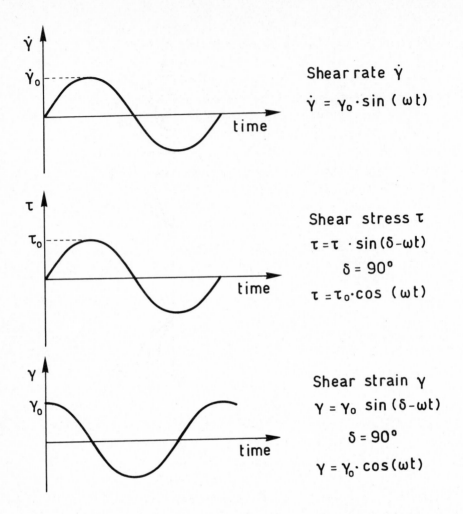

Shear rate $\dot{\gamma}$

$\dot{\gamma} = \gamma_0 \cdot \sin(\omega t)$

Shear stress τ

$\tau = \tau \cdot \sin(\delta - \omega t)$

$\delta = 90°$

$\tau = \tau_0 \cdot \cos(\omega t)$

Shear strain γ

$\gamma = \gamma_0 \sin(\delta - \omega t)$

$\delta = 90°$

$\gamma = \gamma_0 \cdot \cos(\omega t)$

Fig. 4 . $\dot{\gamma}$, γ, τ = Example 1: relationship for a viscous fluids.

When we plot shear stress versus shear strain on the XY-recorder of the RV100, we end up with the so-called Lissajous figures or circle-like figures for pure viscous fluids (Fig. 5).

The conclusion from this graph is that we can expect circles, or circles-like figures for viscous fluids with the RV100. A pure circle is relatively rare, but the main axis of an ellipse is usually identical to the X-axis or at least parallel to it (Fig. 6).

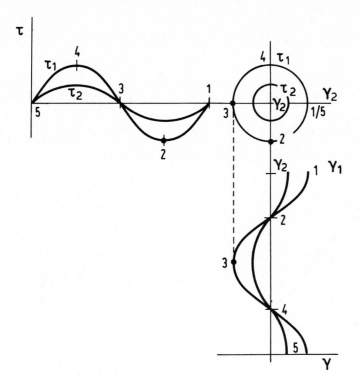

Fig. 5 . Lissajous figures for 2 viscous fluids (shear stress versus strain)

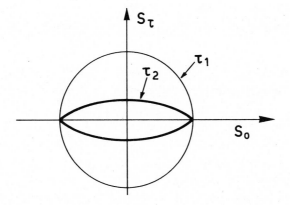

Fig. 6 . Results of two different viscous fluids (oils) from the RV100-recorder

The contrary to a pure viscous liquid is a pure elastic body which shows different results (Fig. 7, example 2).

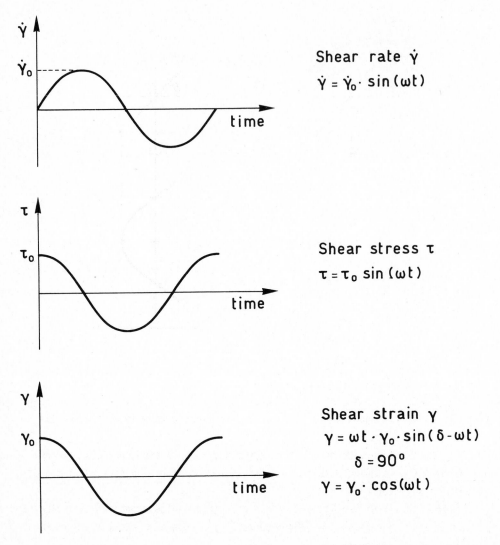

Shear rate $\dot{\gamma}$
$$\dot{\gamma} = \dot{\gamma}_0 \cdot \sin(\omega t)$$

Shear stress τ
$$\tau = \tau_0 \sin(\omega t)$$

Shear strain γ
$$\gamma = \omega t \cdot \gamma_0 \cdot \sin(\delta - \omega t)$$
$$\delta = 90°$$
$$\gamma = \gamma_0 \cdot \cos(\omega t)$$

Fig. 7 . $\dot{\gamma}$, γ , τ = Example 2: relationship for an elastic body.

Now, we see that the shear stress signal is out of plase by 90° to the shear rate $\dot{\gamma}$, but in phase with the strain. This means that an elastic body reacts with deformation (strain) rather than deformation speed (rate of strain = $\dot{\gamma}$). Plotting the results of figure 7 by means of an XY-recorder as done with the RV100, we get figure 8.

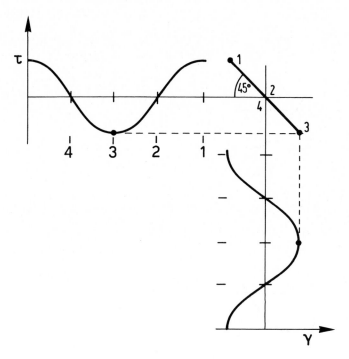

Fig. 8 . Lissajous figure for an elastic body.

As it can be seen, the result for a pure elastic body is a straight line with an angle of 45°.

We must also remind that water, assumed as non viscous, non elastic (non-viscoelastic) liquid, results in a non Lissajous figure, a straight line, but with on angle of 0°.

The majority of the liquids we experience (and also bronchial secretions), in reality are very seldom pure viscous or pure elastic, but are a mixture of both, called viscoelastic.

Mathematically, it means they show a phase shift between 0° and 90° in a dynamic test (Fig. 9, example 3) with one part being elastic (in phase with strain) and the other viscous (in phase with shear rate).

330

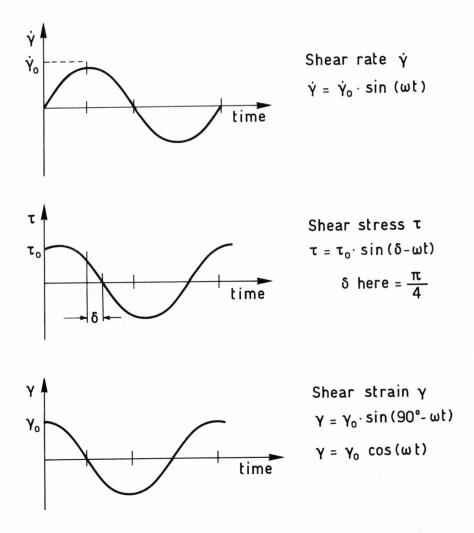

Shear rate $\dot{\gamma}$

$$\dot{\gamma} = \dot{\gamma}_0 \cdot \sin(\omega t)$$

Shear stress τ

$$\tau = \tau_0 \cdot \sin(\delta - \omega t)$$

$$\delta \text{ here} = \frac{\pi}{4}$$

Shear strain γ

$$\gamma = \gamma_0 \cdot \sin(90° - \omega t)$$

$$\gamma = \gamma_0 \cos(\omega t)$$

Fig. 9 . $\dot{\gamma}$, γ , τ = Example 3: relationship for a viscoelastic fluid.

   The phase shift between strain γ and shear stress characterizes the amount of elasticity. Another suggestion for better understanding was given by Ferry (15).

   He divides the stress response in two waves:
- one part in phase with the shear rate   = viscous part
- one part in phase with the shear strain = elastic part

Coming back to the XY-plot of the two functions, we end up with an ellipse with its main axis twisted against the X-axis (Fig. 10).

Measuring two liquids in a dynamic test which have the same viscous behaviour but are different in elasticity gives figure 11. Normally, the questions come up of how to see that liquid (1) is more elastic than liquid (2) of the example in figure 11.

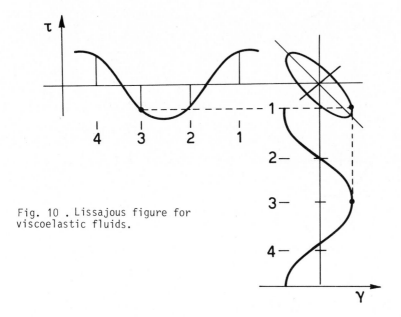

Fig. 10 . Lissajous figure for viscoelastic fluids.

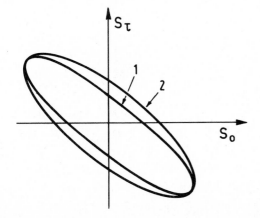

Fig. 11 . Result of two liquids with (1) being more elastic than (2)

When we recall that a pure viscous fluid approaches a circle we see that liquid (2) gives a more circle-like result than liquid (1) which is closer to a straight line as occurs for a pure elastic body. We can quantify this relation by calculating the phase shift δ for this example knowing that a circle (viscous fluid) has a 90° shift to strain (Fig. 12).

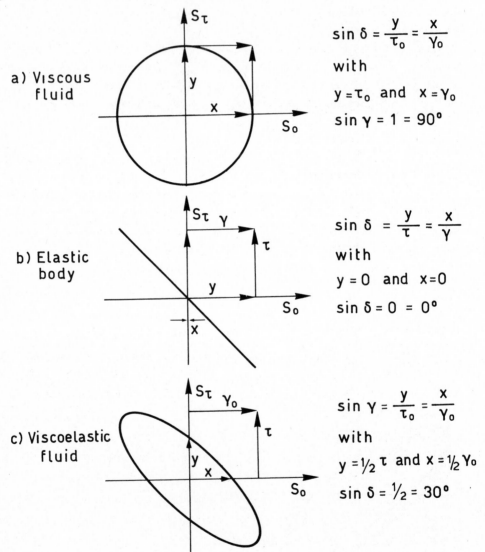

a) Viscous fluid

$$\sin \delta = \frac{y}{\tau_0} = \frac{x}{Y_0}$$

with

$$y = \tau_0 \text{ and } x = Y_0$$

$$\sin \gamma = 1 = 90°$$

b) Elastic body

$$\sin \delta = \frac{y}{\tau} = \frac{x}{Y}$$

with

$$y = 0 \text{ and } x = 0$$

$$\sin \delta = 0 = 0°$$

c) Viscoelastic fluid

$$\sin \gamma = \frac{y}{\tau_0} = \frac{x}{Y_0}$$

with

$$y = \frac{1}{2}\tau \text{ and } x = \frac{1}{2}Y_0$$

$$\sin \delta = \frac{1}{2} = 30°$$

Fig. 12 . Evaluation of the phase shift with $\delta = \arcsin \frac{y}{\tau_0} = \frac{x}{Y_0}$.

RESULTS

The results concerning the changes of the apparent viscosity, thixotropy and coefficient of elasticity observed in the secretion of 9 out of the 10 patients chosen for the trial with ambroxol are given in table 1. One of the subjects was withdrawn from the trial because, during the 7-day treatment, he suffered from bronchitic exacerbation so that his bronchial secretion, originally mucous, appeared frankly purulent at final control.

Apparent viscosity . The pharmacological treatment did not induce uniform changes of apparent viscosity η evaluated for each curve τ-D (see fig. 2) at 25, 50 and 100% of the applied velocity gradient (which was kept constant for each patient before and after treatment). In fact, η increased in 6 patients and diminished in 3 patients after treatment (table 1), with unimportant mean changes (table 2: reports only η-values at 50% of D).

Thixotropy . The pharmacological treatment did not induce uniform changes of the index of the index of thixotropy η_1/η_2 evaluated for each curve τ-D at 50% of the applied velocity gradient, where η_1 was the apparent viscosity during the "rising" curve and η_2 the apparent viscosity during the "descending" curve (see fig. 3). In fac η_1/η_2 increased in 4 patients and diminished in 5 after treatment (table 1), with unimportant mean changes (table 2).

TABLE 1

RHEOLOGY AFTER AMBROXOL IN 9 PATIENTS AFFECTED WITH CHRONIC BRONCHITIS

Initials	Age (ys)	Tendency of Lissajous major axis to 45°	Area of the Lissajous figure	Apparent viscosity η (at 50% of applied SD)	Thixotropy index η_1/η_2 (at 50% of applied SD)
S.A.	54	+	+	+	+
B.V.	61	+	+	+	-
M.C.	66	+	+	+	-
B.G.	60	+	+	+	-
D.P.	68	+	+	+	+
R.F.	62	+	+	+	+
F.C.	60	+	-	-	-
L.F.	70	+	-	-	+
C.G.	60	-	-	-	-

(+) means increase and (-) decrease of the considered variable after treatment as compared to base value.

Elasticity . The pharmacological treatment induced a non significant increase (table 2) of the area contained in the Lissajous figure proper of the viscoelastic fluid (see figures 10,11,12),in 6 out of 9 cases (table 1).

On the contrary, in all cases except one, the pharmacological treatment induced the correction of the major axis of the Lissajous figure (table 1), so enhancing its tendency to 45° (see figures 8,10,12). In other words, the angle formed by the major axis (which in 8 cases was < 45° and in one case > 45°) changed at the end of the treatment so that its mean value was closer to the "ideal" 45°: this happened when both started from low values (in 7 out of 8 cases with an initial angle < 45°) or from high values (in the 9th case that had an initial angle > 45°). In spite of this trend, the changes were not statistically significant (table 2).

TABLE 2

RHEOLOGIC VALUES BEFORE AND AFTER TREATMENT (M + SE)

Variables	Base values	After treatment	Variance analysis
η (Pa.s)	5.14 ± 2.12	5.17 ± 1.24	N.S.
η_1/η_2	1.43 ± 0.28	1.69 ± 0.31	N.S.
Major axis (Lissajous figure)	$24.8° \pm 5.0°$	$32.1° \pm 5.3°$	N.S.
Area in mm^2 (Lissajous figure)	1531 ± 240	1670 ± 366	N.S.

DISCUSSION

The rheological properties of the mucus being transported directly affect mucociliary clearance. On the whole, bronchial secretions behave rheologically like viscoelastic non-Newtonian fluids, flowing like viscous liquids but at the same time becoming deformed like solid elastic bodies. When compressed by ciliary beating, the secretions store energy during the deformation process and dissipate it when they flow.

For ciliary transport the elasticity of the mucus is more important than its viscosity (4). For example, egg white, which is elastic, if placed on a ciliated epithelial surface, flows in a manner similar to that of mucus. On the other hand, purely viscous substances such as oils are not moved along by ciliary beating. For correct mucociliary transport, expectorate with a shear rate of 0.3/s must have a viscosity between 25 and 200 poises and a elasticity of 4 to 13 SR units (9). In chronic bronchitis, the inflammation and the decreased

protein synthesis of the bronchial mucosa act together to change the
rheological properties of the secretions and to make their transport more
difficult, decreasing the mucociliary clearance(10,16).

From what we have been saying, it is clear that it is possible to modify
pharmacologically the excessive viscosity and also, with mucus-thickening drugs,
to modify the excessive fluidity which is characteristic of the secretion in
certain forms of watery bronchorrhea (10,17,18).

What we know less about is how to modify the elasticity of the secretions.
In fact, we do not know in what pathological conditions of mucociliary function
the secretions should be classified as hypo- or hyper-viscous or hypo- or
hyper-elastic. It would be worth studying those substances that act on mucociliary clearance considered to be active by rheological effects separately in
patients carefully classified into subgroups.

For the elasticity, finally, there is the problem of how to measure it.
Using a particular type of rotational viscosimeter, one can obtain not only
the rotational velocity (useful for measurement of viscosity), but also forced
oscillations, and with these latter one can obtain Lissajous figures useful for
evaluation of the elasticity. The area of the Lissajous figure (see Figs. 11
and 12) is influenced by both the viscosity and the elasticity, and we think
it is important to measure the angle of the major axis of the Lissajous figure
itself, since for an ideal elastic body this is 45° (see Fig. 8).

With this background, we think that ambroxol though it has no effects on
viscosity or thixotropy of the secretions of chronic bronchitis when given
alone, has interesting activity on the elasticity of the secretions. This
cannot be seen so clearly by measuring the area of the Lissajous figure, which
the analysis of the data shows to be due, perhaps prevalently, to the viscosity.
It is rather clear, however, that even though the change is not statistically
significant, there is a trend with the drug for the secretions to assume the
characteristics of elasticity, which tends to shift the major axis of the
Lissajous figure toward the 45° of the ideal elastic body. This seems to us to
be a positive sign, whatever the rest of the rheological pattern is. At the
present state of our knowledge, we must emphasize, however, that we can not
definitely state that increased elasticity of a secretion will always improve
its mucociliary transport, but we also cannot say definitely that it will not.

Ambroxol has been known for some time to favor the production and the
release of surfactant (19). According to some investigators there is an
interaction between bronchial mucus and surfactant, apparently important in all
parts of the respiratory tree (20, 21), and especially in the more peripheral

airways (22,23), for transport of the secretions. This transport appears to be favored by ambroxol, under experimental conditions (24). It remains to be seen if the presumed effects on the elasticity of the secretion are in some way correlated with the increased surfactant effect that the drug has on the secretions, especially in the more peripheral bronchioles, which are likely to collapse and in which there is always the possibility that excessively gluey secretions could tend to favor their adhesiveness and their tendency to collapse (25,26).

It also remains to be clarified whether the surfactant acts only to decrease the adhesiveness of the secretion droplets at the interface between the periciliary sol layer and the mucus gel layer or whether it also, by decreasing the tension on the entire surface of the gel droplets, contributes to the development of more effective elastic behaviour when the droplet is stretched or compressed.

SUMMARY

Viscosity and elasticity of secretions can be studied at the same time by a rotative viscosimeter with coaxial cylinder where either defined rotational speeds or forced oscillations can be obtained. The rheological changes of serous and mucous secretions of 10 male patients (mean age 62.5 ± 1.5) suffering from chronic bronchitis in stability stage have been assessed. Evaluations were performed before and after treatment with ambroxol at the dose of 180 mg/day for 7 days, monotherapy. The treatment did not cause changes of viscosity (before treatment 5.14 ± 2.12 Pa.s, after treatment 5.17 ± 1.24 mPa.s, N.S.) nor of thixotropy (1.43 ± 0.28 and 1.69 ± 0.31 respectively, N.S.). From the analysis of the resulting Lissajous figures, though the areas seem perhaps more related to viscosity than to elasticity, the angle of the major axis tends after treatment to the 45° which are characteristic of an "ideal" elastic body, 0° being the angle of the water ($24.8° \pm 5.0°$ before treatment, $32.1° \pm 5.3°$ after treatment): the last behaviour was present in 8 out of 9 patients, an interesting, though not yet significant trend, which anyhow looks as a positive event. One patient was drop-out.

REFERENCES

1. Van Wazer, J.R., Lyons, J.W., Kim, K.Y. and Colwell, R.E. (1963) Viscosity and flow measurement, Wiley and Sons, New York and London .

2. Sherman, P (1970) Industrial rheology, Academic Press, London and New York.

3. Schramm, G. (1981) Introduzione alla viscosimetria pratica, Gebruder Haake GmbH, Karlsruhe (Ital. Ed.).

4. Puchelle, E. (1979) Qualitées fonctionnelles des sécrétions bronchiques. Etude rhéologique, biochimique et transport mucociliaire, Thèse Doctorat Sciences Pharmaceutiques, Nancy.

5. Nomenclature and definitions in respiratory physiology and clinical aspects of chronic lung diseases (1975), Bull. Physio-path. Resp., 11, 937-959.

6. Pham, Q.T., Peslin, R., Puchelle, E., Salmon, D., Caroux, G. and Benis, A.M. (1973) Bull. Physio-path. Resp., 9, 293-311.

7. Denton, R. (1965) Ann. N.Y. Acad. Sci., 106, 746-754.

8. Palmer, K.N.V., Ballantyne, D., Diament, M.L. and Hamilton, W.F.D. (1970) Brit. J. Dis. Chest., 64, 185-191.

9. Puchelle, E., Girard, F. and Zahm, J.M. (1976) Bull. Physio-path. Resp., 12 771-779.

10. Puchelle, E., Zahm, J.M., Girard, F., Bertrand, A., Polu, J.M., Aug, F. and Sadoul, P. (1980) Eur. J. Resp. Dis., 61, 254-264.

11. Charman, J. and Reid, L. (1972) Biorheology, 9, 185-199.

12. Puchelle, E. and Benis, A.m. (1971) Bull. Physio-path. Resp., 7, 673-712.

13. Benis, A.M., Puchelle, E. and Sadoul, P. (1972) in: Rheology of Biological Systems, Litt, M. and Gabelnick, H. Eds., C.C Thomas, Springfield (Illinois).

14. Kim, C.S., Berkley, B.B., Abraham, W.M. and Wanner, A. (1982) Bull. Europ. Physio-path. Resp., 18, 915-927.

15. Ferry, J.D. (1970) Viscoelastic properties of polymers, J.W. Ley ans Sons.

16. Litt, M. (1970) Arch. Intern. Med. 120, 417-423.

17. Allegra, L., Bossi, R. and Braga,P.C. (1981) Respiration, 42, 105-109.

18. Braga, P.C., Bossi, R. and Allegra, L. (1981) Curr. Ther. Res. 29, 738-744.

19. Curti, P.C. (1972) Pneumologie, 147, 62-74.

20. Morgenroth, K. (1982) Bronchitis, Pharmazeutische Verlagsgesellshaft mbH, München.

21. Morgenroth, K. and Bolz, J. (1983) Morphological findings regarding the interaction between mucus and surfactant, Abstract book, Intern. Symp. on the Surfactant System of the Lung, Rome, p. 70.

22. Reifenrath, R. (1983) Surfactant action in bronchial mucus transport, Abstract book, Intern. Symp. on the Surfactant System of the Lung, Rome, p. 92.

23. Rensch, H., Gebhardt, K.F., Weiss, J.M. and von Seefeld,H. (1983) Transport properties of surface-active films, Abstract book, Intern. Symp. on the Surfactant System of the Lung, Rome, p. 71.

24. Von Seefeld, H., Gebhardt, K.F., Ziegler, H. and Rensch, H. (1983) Transport properties of bronchial lavage fluid from rat lungs, Abstract book, Intern. Symp. on the Surfactant System of the Lung, Rome, p. 72.

25. Pasargiklian, M. and Allegra, L. (1968) Il tensioattivo alveolare in pneumologia, Minerva Medica, Torino.

26. Scarpelli, E.M. (1968) The surfactant system of the lung, Lea and Febiger, Philadelphia.

SURFACTANT ACTION IN BRONCHIAL MUCUS TRANSPORT

RAINER REIFENRATH
Berlinerstrasse 42, 3104 Unterlüß (FRG)

Over more then two decades, surfactant function has been related
to the lungs alveoli almost exclusively. This might be underlined
by the commonly used term "lung alveolar surfactant". However, the
material lining the bronchial wall must be of crucial significance
to the mechanical stability of the bronchial system and therefore
to pulmonary ventilation.

Before discussing bronchial surfactant action, let us recall a
few morphological and histological facts. It is well known, that
the pharynx, trachea and bronchi are carrying goblet cells. Their
frequency is decreasing with decreasing bronchial diameter. Within
the upper part of the bronchial tree they are sometimes arranged
to larger groups which are called "intraepithelial glands". Below
an inside bronchial diameter of 0.8mm, the goblet cells are
getting rare and are always single ones. They disappear at a diameter of 0.5mm (inside diameter, determined on human autopsy
lungs). With further decreasing diameter, down to 0.1 to 0.2mm, a
new type of cells, the Clara cell, appears. The terminal and
respiratori bronchi, which are free of cartilage, are characterized by this cell type. The terminal bronchi still have some
ciliated cells, the respiratori bronchi do not.

The Clara cells are secretory cells like the goblet cells, but
their secretions are different in their physicochemical nature.
This has been realized by Max Clara himself. He wrote: "It is for
sure, that neither within the granules nor within the secretory
extensions, a mucus-like substance can be demonstrated by any of
the so called mucus specific stains. The secretion is not a mucus-
like substance". (1)

To this observation Max Clara's, made in 1938, I may add a personal observation, made in 1976. While I was trying to sample
bronchial lining fluid from isolated rat lung bronchi, I realized
the decreasing viscosity of this material with decreasing
bronchial diameter. Within the small bronchi, let say below 1-2mm
outside diameter, the fluid was rather watery while it was

plugging my capillary at the tracheal level and at the level of the larger bronchi.

This change from a watery to a viscous lining fluid is a strong argument for the critical role of:
1. Surface forces determining the mechanical stability of small bronchi and 2. The physical state of the lining fluid determining the ciliae-independent transport capacity. With other words:
1. To part wetted surfaces, distanced in capillary dimensions, requires considerably higher forces if the wetting fluid is viscous. With a viscous wetting fluid, the very small bronchi, if closed, would possibly never be opened again by physiological forces. 2. The ciliae-independent transport capacity within and onto the linings surface is larger in a more watery system simply by the higher fluidity.

Considering surfactant action related to transport phenomenons, one has to clarify its biochemical, ultrastructural and physico-chemical nature. Here, only ultrastructural transformations will be discussed. At least four distinct ultrastructural types are known: Lamellar bodies (L.B.), tubular myelin (T.M.), common myelin (C.M.) and the interfacial or surface film (I.F.). The existance of an amorphous state is possible but hypothetic.

The L.B.'s are the site of storage and secretion. The T.M. represents the first step of structural transformation, i.e. the desintegration of L.B. The formation of T.M. may be dependent upon divalent cations (2). The mode of formation of C.M. is not known. They might be created from L.B.'s directly, from T.M. or from both. However, structural transformation observed in rat fetal pulmonary fluid suggests a sequence L.B.-T.M.-C.M. (Fig. 1). L.B. and T.M. are made of bimolecular phospholipid leaflets. According to Haydon and Taylor, this bimolecular leaflet structure will ultimately become unstable and small globular micelles of lipid might then be formed, if the cholesterol ratio increases in the sheet (3). A rapid uptake and temporary storage of cholesterol in Type I but not Type II cells has been observed as well as the presence of cholesterol within the extracellular linig layer (4,5). This suggests an extracellular interaction between surfactant phospholipids and cholesterol. A cholesterol dependent breakdown of bimolecular L.B. and/or T.M. leaflets to globular micelles

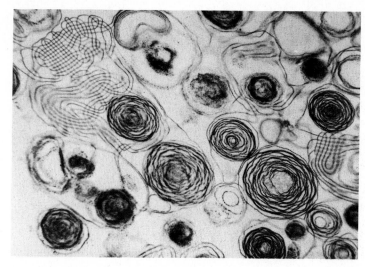

Fig. 1. Lamellar bodies, tubular myelin and common myelin structures in pulmonary fluid of a mature rat fetus. Fixation via airways after sectio caesarea. The fetus was not allowed to breath
air. The direct transformation of L.B. to T.M. was observed
repeatedly and more impressive with higher magnification. The mode
of C.M.-formation still is a matter of speculation.

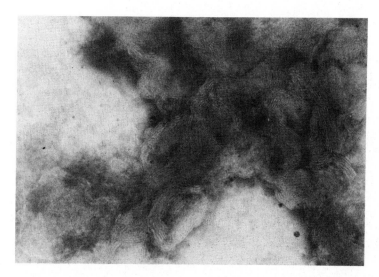

Fig. 2. Common myelin structures in a sample obtained by alveolar
micropuncture technique (rat lung). Undiluted alveolar fluid was
transferred directly on a grid. Note the dense packing of multilamellated lipid.

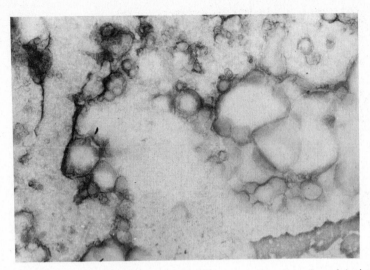

Fig. 3. Common myelin structures in a sample obtained by alveolar micropuncture rinsing technique (rat lung). In contrast to Fig. 2, due to surfactant dilution by rinsing liquid, individual C.M.-vesicles are clearly separated.

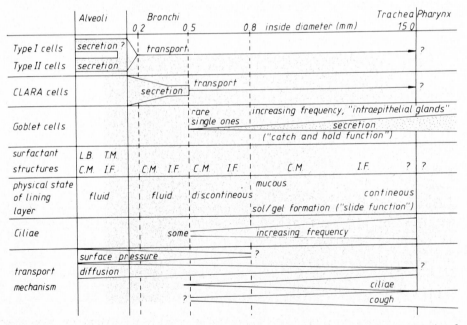

	Alveoli	Bronchi 0.2 0.5 0.8 inside diameter (mm)	Trachea 15.0	Pharynx
Type I cells	secretion ?	transport		?
Type II cells	secretion			
CLARA cells		secretion transport		?
Goblet cells		rare single ones — increasing frequency, "intraepithelial glands" / secretion ("catch and hold function")		
surfactant structures	L.B. T.M. C.M. I.F.	C.M. I.F. / C.M. I.F.	C.M. I.F. ?	?
physical state of lining layer	fluid	fluid / discontineous mucous / sol/gel formation ("slide function")	contineous	
Ciliae		some — increasing frequency		
transport mechanism	surface pressure / diffusion	? / ciliae / ? cough		?

Fig. 4. Histological, ultrastructural, physical and morphological parameters involved in fluid and mucus transport. Compare text. L.B. = Lamellar bodies; T.M. = Tubular myelin; C.M. = Common myelin; I.F. = Interfacial or surface film.

and a rearrangment of the latter to C.M.-structures can be
postulated. However, C.M.-structures are the predominating extracellular type and are found from the alveolar septum to the
larger bronchi (Figs. 2 and 3) (7,8). The I.F. has been observed
at the alveolar surface (6) and the bronchial interface (7).It
very likely is originated from the above mentioned structures or
from a hypothetic amorphous surfactant.

Less is known about the contribution of Clara cells to the biochemical and ultrastructural nature of surfactant.

The conditions described so far are the morphological, histological and ultrastructural background for the following concept
of surfactant supported transport phenomenons. This concept is
summarized in Figure 4.

Transport along the non-mucus zone

Surfactant secretion at the alveolar level produces a concentration gradient directed to the trachea. A static and dynamic
surface transport must result. The static surface transport is
due to the surface film pressure, i.e. the movement of film molecules along the gradient in an open system. The dynamic surface
transport during continued compression and decompression of the
surface results from surface pressure hysteresis. If during
decompression film molecules are adsorpt from the subphase, i.e.,
the adsorption kinetic is superior to the kinetic of respreading,
the "backward movement" of particles floating on top of the surface must be less than the "forward movement" during compression.
A directed net-movement of particles results. This has been
demonstrated recently in a model system by Rensch et al. (9).
Inspiration and expiration are asymmetric changes of the total
alveolar area, always beginning at the periphery and progressing
to the hili. That is, why the movement of the pleura can be
compared with the barrier movement in the trough model in this
respect.

Along the non-mucus zone of airways, surfactant transport within
the subphase simply arises from concentration gradients.

Transport along the mucus zone

The mucus transport usually is attributed to ciliae function.

More recently, the interaction between mucus transport and surfactant has attracted attention. In 1976, the presence of structured surfactant within the sol-phase (C.M.) and between sol- and gel-phase has been demonstrated (7). Morgenroth also demonstrated C.M.-structures (vesicles and multilamellated figures) within the sol-layer (8). We do not know, whether C.M.-vesicles act directly like "biological ball-bearings" or, more likely, indirectly by donating molecules to surfaces and interfaces. However, the presence of surfactant at the bronchial wall can be interpreted as "soft soap function", enabling the mucus and/or the sputum to slide on top of the ciliae (10). This would imply the importance of surfactant for an effective cough-mechanism ("slide-function", see Fig. 5). In Fig. 5, the adhesive surfaces are represented by zig-zag lines and comparable with an adhesive fastener. In case this bronchus is getting closed, (see number 1 in Fig. 5), the wall very likely would stick together, because the outer surface of these cells is composed of a layer of mucopolysacharides, 200-1000 A thick (11,12). This layer of mucopolysaccharides is intimately associated with the cell membrane. Number 4 in Fig. 5 refers to the contact between the mucopolysaccharide surface of the cells and the mucus. Here, depending upon the nature of the molecules, high adhesive forces may result. The mucus or the sputum would not slide but stick to the wall as they stick to themselves.

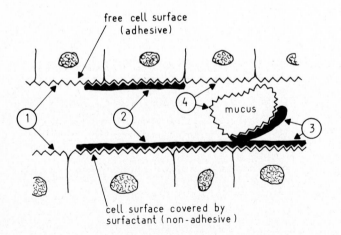

Fig. 5. Schematic representation of interaction between cell surface, surfactant and mucus. Compare text.

The situation changes significantly if one introduces a surface active substance (numbers 2 and 3 in Fig. 5). The surfactant always tends to spread and to cover the entire surface. The adhesive forces disappear as long as sufficient amount of surf- actant is available. Concerning the interaction with sputum, surfactant now becomes an abhesive material. This would be the case if the spreading coefficient of sputum is negative, i.e., sputum adhears to itself much more than to the surfactant layer.

The conclusion is, that the interfacial tension tissue/lining layer is not necessarily extremely small as it was stated in the literature, but may take on values unusually high for biological interfaces if sufficient amount of surfactant is absent!

Summarizing the concept illustrated in Fig. 4, the following conclusions are suggested:

1. Type I and Type II cells and possibly the Clara cells are the source of surfactant material. Structured surfactant (C.M. and I.F.) is transported up to the large airways by surface pressure, diffusion and later in addition by ciliar movement. The finally active surfactant structures are C.M. and I.F. and/or a hypo- thetic amorphous material.

2. The mucus, not present at the alveolar level and the final branches of the bronchial tree, appears above an inside bronchial diameter of 0.5mm, at first sliding on top of the surfactant layer in a focal and later in a contineous distribution ("slide- function of surfactant"). Because of its sticky nature, the mucus is supposed to have a "catch and hold function" for clearence mechanism.

3. The transport mechanism for mucus and materials which have to be removed from airways is different at different morpho- logical levels. Static and dynamic surface pressure properties are determining particle transport from the alveoli to the small bronchi, presumably up to an inside bronchial diameter between 0.5 to 0.8mm. With increasing diameter, the ciliae itself increasingly represent the driving force for mucus transport. Here, surfactant acts like an excellent lubricant, promoting either ciliar movement itself or their efficiency by reduction of adhesive forces (sol/gel formation). Concerning the cough mechanism, surfactant also becomes involved as an anti-glue material allowing separation of sputum from the bronchial wall.

4. Care should be taken not to underestimate the contribution of bronchi below 0.8mm diameter to mucus and fluid transport. According morphometric data, these bronchi (generations 14-23) account for 99.9% of total airway number (13). The corresponding bronchial surface area, calculated from Weibels data, account for 85,8 % of total tracheobronchial area.

5. The alveolo-bronchial transport system is able to move everything up to the pharynx - but not water. The accumulated volume from trachea and bronchi generation 1 to 13 is for an adult human lung at about 75 % maximal inflation 106 cm^3 (13). The liquid volume corresponding to the bronchial area of generation 14 to 23 would be 12 cm^3 and that of alveolar area (80 m^2) 80 cm^3 with 10 μm thickness of liquid layer. This volume is large enough to flood the central airways if moved trachealwards. Indeed, water instilled into central bronchi normally is sucked up by the lung rapidly by capillary forces.

6. The airways are not only conducting air in and out of lungs. They have highly specialized features preventing bronchi from beeing contaminated, glued and flooded contineously.

ACKNOWLEDGEMENTS
 The specimen for figure 1 was prepared and photographed by Dr. A. Vatter, Denver/Colo. Figures 2 and 3 were obtained by help of Dr. J. Gil, then Bern/Switzerland. I gratefully acknowledge the excellent cooperation with these scientists.

REFERENCES

1. Clara, M. (1937) Zur Histologie des Bronchialepithels,
   Z. mikr.-anat. Forsch. 41, 321

2. Sanders, R.L., R.J. Hassett and A.E. Vatter (1980) Isolation
   of lung lamellar bodies and their conversion to tubular
   myelin figures in vitro, The Anatomical Record 198, 485-501

3. Haydon, D.A. and J. Taylor (1963) The stability and properties
   of bimolecular lipid leaflets in aqueous solutions,
   J. Theoret. Biol. 4, 281-296

4. Darrah, H.K. and J. Hedley-Whyte (1971) Distribution of
   cholesterol in lung, J. Appl. Physiol. 30, 78-90

5. Reifenrath, R. (1973) Chemical analysis of the lung alveolar
   surfactant obtained by alveolar micropuncture,
   Resp. Physiol. 19, 35-46

6. Weibel, E.R. and J. Gil (1968) Electron microscopic demonstration of an extracellular duplex lining layer of alveoli,
   Resp. Physiol. 4, 42

7. Yoneda, K. (1976) Mucous blanket of rat bronchus, Am. Review
   of Respir. Disease 114, 837-842

8. Morgenroth, K. (1982) Bronchitis, PVG Pharmazeutische Verlags-
   gesellschaft mbH, 8000 München 40, Türkenstraße 106

9. Rensch, H., H. von Seefeld, K.F. Gebhardt, D. Renzow and
   P.-J. Sell (1983) Stop and Go particle transport in the
   peripheral airways? A model study, Respiration, in press

10. Reifenrath, R. (1978) Open airways - an engineering achievement
    of nature, Bull. Europ. Physiopath. 14, 79-81

11. Brandt, P.W. (1962) A consideration of the extraneous coats of
    the plasma membrane, Circulation 26, 1075

12. Groniowsky, J. and W. Biscyskowa (1964) Structure of the
    alveolar lining film of the lungs, Nature (London) 204, 745

13. Weibel, E.R. (1963) Morphometry of the human lung, page 139,
    Table XI.2. and Table XI.3., Springer-Verlag OHG, Berlin -
    Göttingen - Heidelberg

ACTION OF AMBROXOL ON MUCOCILIARY CLEARANCE

L. BERTOLI[1], G. RIZZATO[1], F. BANFI[2], M. POSSA[2], G. MAGRI[2],
S. LO CICERO[1]

[1]Divisione Medica Vergani and [2]Servizio di Medicina Nucleare,
Ente Ospedale Niguarda Cà Granda, Milano, Italy

SUMMARY

In a previous open study (3) on clearance rates of inhaled
[99m]Tc labelled human serum albumin minimicrospheres we had
shown that ambroxol given by aerosol is active on the mucociliary
transport of the peripheral regions of lung in a group of patients with chronic obstructive lung disease (COLD). We have now
repeated the same study on 20 other patients with COLD, in double
blind conditions(10 patients treated with ambroxol 22.5 mg in 3
ml saline solution and 10 with placebo aerosol). Additionally,
after this study all patient underwent 15 days double blind
treatment with oral ambroxol (3o mg three times daily) or placebo
and penetration and distribution indexes (PI and DI) were re-eva-
luated at the end of this period. Due to high standard deviation
of the mucociliary clearance rates, no significant actin of ambroxol vs placebo could be shown in the acute study by aerosol;
nevertheless, the drug induced a significant improvement of PI
($P < .001$) and of DI ($P < .05$) , that we think due to improvement
of the mucus rheology.

INTRODUCTION

For many years the efficacy of mucolytics and expectorant agents has been studied in the man evaluating qualitative and quantitative changes on the sputum or on hystochemical and viscoelastic properties of the secretions; yet, in the last few years,
the measurement of mucociliary clearance has been possible following the transport of inhaled monodisperse aerosols labelled with
radioisotopes: this technique can provide a direct evaluation in
vivo of the activity of these drugs (1). By this approach we have
shown that :
                                        slowed
 1) mucociliary clearance is noteably down in patients suffering
from COLD (2), and
 2) in an open study on 10 patients with COLD ambroxol was active
on the mucociliary transport on the peripheral regions of lung in
 the first thirty minutes after aerosol and this activity was
significantly higher (P < .05) in respect of inhaled saline solution (3).
The aim of this study was to evaluate if this action of ambroxol
is confirmed in patients with COLD also in a double blind study
using the same technique on a wider number of patients.

METHODS AND PATIENTS

It is well known that the deposition pattern of inhaled radioactive markers influences the measured clearance rate and that
in patients with remarkable obstruction of airways excessive central accumulation of the inhaled particles and incomplete visualization of the peripheral lung zones occurs : with this in mind,
only patients with FEV_1 over 60% in respect of predicted values
and $Pa\,O_2$ over 60 mm Hg were choosen for the study, in order to
avoid unreliable clearance rates and also because precise definition of the outer lung margins would have been impossible under
these conditions. In order to exclude also patients with asthma,

FEV_1 was also studied after Fenoterol inhalation (2 puffs) and patients showing FEV_1 increase exceeding 15% in respect of basal value were rejected. All patients were in steady state conditions, without infections and antimicrobial treatments in the last month, and none of them had assumed mucolytics in the last ten days.

Following all the above criteria of exclusion, we studied 20 stable patients with COLD (15 males and 5 females), aged 22 to 68 (mean age 53 $\pm$ 13): their respiratory function data are presented in Table 1 .

Twelve of them were smokers, 4 ex smokers, 4 non smokers.

When the double blind was opened, mean values of the two groups (Ambroxol and Placebo) were calculated and no statistical differences were found between the two groups, except TLC. The ambroxol group included 3 non smokers, 2 ex smokers and 5 smokers; the placebo group 1 non smoker, 2 ex smokers and 7 smokers. In a double blind study between drug and placebo patient were examined in the nuclear medicine laboratory on two occasions . In the first day, 20 mCi of the ^{99m}Tc labelled albumin particles were administered to the patients via aerosol for ten minutes . The average diameter of these particles was 1μm, as described elsewhere. At the end of the administration the patient was positioned sitting against a large field gamma camera interfacied with a minicomputer. Radioactivity was continuously recorded for 100'. After obtaining in the first 30' the basal clearance of the patient, he received, under double blind conditions, the drug (Ambroxol 22.5 mg in 3 ml saline solution) or a placebo (isotonic saline solution 3ml) during 10 minutes aerosol. Radioactivity was then recorded for 60 minutes. The study was first preprocessed to correct for the motions of the patient and to mask gastric radioactivity, if needed; according to Weiss et al (4), regions of interest (ROI_s) were then outlined as follows: the whole lung, the hilar

TABLE 1

AGE AND RESPIRATORY FUNCTION DATA OF OUR PATIENTS WITH COLD

	All patients	Ambroxol 10 patients	Placebo 10 patients	P
Age ys	53.00±13.49	49.40±15.57	58.25± 8.73	n.s.
FEV_1 ✗	77.05±14.81	79.20±14.28	76.66±15.88	n.s.
FVC ✗	96.05±12.73	98.01±15.31	94.30±17.01	n.s.
RV ✗	138.15±44.42	125.3 ±38.92	145.00±47.68	n.s.
TLC ✗	110.78±15.93	105.70±15.25	116.44±15.53	< .02
FRC ✗	128.57±31.52	120.70±26.42	137.33±35.67	n.s.
RAW ✗	181.15±26.26	160.10±25.06	194.05±23.15	n.s.
PaO_2 mmHg	81.05± 8.01	82.3 ± 5.01	79.66±10.59	n.s.
$PaCO_2$ "	39.42± 2.77	40.30± 2.21	38.44± 3.12	n.s.

LEGEND : FEV_1 : forced expiratory volume in the first second

FVC : " vital capacity

RV : residual volume

TLC : total lung capacity

FRC : functional residual capacity

PaO_2 $PaCO_2$: arterial blood O_2 and CO_2 partial pressure

RAW : airways resistance

P : statistical difference between patients treated with Ambroxol and Placebo

n. s. : non significant.

✗ : in percent of predected value

region, the lung periphery, the upper, middle and lower thirds
of the lung (Fig 1) .

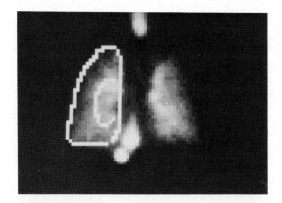

Fig. 1

Outlining the regions
of interest (ROI$_s$).
Top panel: hilar region
and lung periphery.
Bottom panel: upper,
middle and lower thirds
of the left lung.
Same ROI$_s$ were delimi-
ted on right lung.

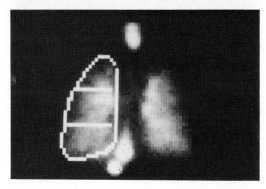

According to Fazio and Lafortuna (5) the hilar region is defined
as a region comprising 30% of the total area of the lung. The
degree of aerosol penetration into the lung periphery was assessed by computing on the first frame of each study the penetration index (PI) which was calculated by dividing the peripheral
by the total counts. Also an aerosol distribution index (DI) was
calculated computing the standard deviation of the radioactivity
of each ROI divided by the mean radioactivity of each lung :
this index is a measure of dispersion of radioactivity in the
five lung zones, and high values indicate uneven aerosol distri-

bution, while low values show more even distribution (4). Time/ Activity curves obtained from each ROI were first corrected for decay of ^{99}Tc and then plotted and fitted in the intervals : 1-30', 40-70', 70-100'. The corresponding half times of decay of radioactivity (T/2) were computed and compared in order to provide reliable statistical study; clearance rate (λ) was calculated according to the formula $\lambda = \dfrac{.693}{T/2}$. In order to test the efficiency of the chronic therapy, in the same patients radioaerosol was repeated after 15 days oral assumption of the drug (30 mg t.i.d.) or the placebo, and PI and DI were determined in the same way as above.

When analysing the data obtained, three patients were rejected (1 placebo, 2 ambroxol) because their data were unreliable owing to cough (1 patient) or too low PI (2 patients).

RESULTS AND DISCUSSION

1- <u>Giving the drug by aerosol</u> . Figures 2 and 3 show that there is no significant difference between clearance patterns of the patients treated with ambroxol in respect of placebo. In the patient treated with ambroxol statistical study failed also to show statistical significance between the basal clearance and its values after drug.

Nevertheless the standard deviation of the mucociliary clearance rates is so wide in our patients with COLD (see values at 30 minutes in respect of healty subjects, Fig 2 and 3) that the demonstration of a statistically significant action of ambroxol vs. placebo appears a priori very difficult indeed. Yet in single patients the drug has shown a very good action on mucociliary clearance (Fig.4). The study of action of any drug (vs placebo) on the mucociliary clearance by this tecnique shoud probably start with a more even population of patients with COLD, but this is very difficult if we consider that mucociliary clearance has been found reduced, or unchanged, or increased by various autors (Table 2)

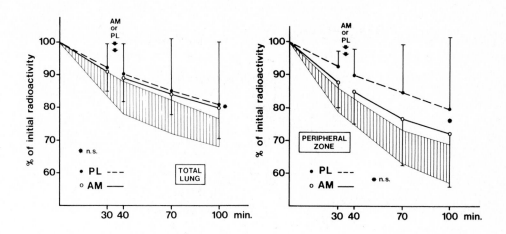

Fig. 2.   Clearance curves (mean and SD) for peripheral lung
zones of left lung in patients with COLD treated with aerosol
of ambroxol (AM) or of placebo (PL).
Shaded area shows clearance patterns of healthy subjects, given
from Weiss et al (4).
 The standard deviation of the mucociliary clearance rates is
so wide in patients with COLD (see values at 30 minutes in
respect of healty subjects) that the demonstration of a statistically significant action of ambroxol vs placebo appears a
priori very difficult indeed.
In fact no statistically differences were found between ambroxol
and placebo.
 Clearance curves for peripheral lung zone of right lung were
quite similar.

Fig. 3.   Clearance curves (mean and SD) for total left lung in
the same patients as in fig. 2 .
 Shaded area shows clearance patterns of healthy subjects, given
from Weiss et al (4). Clearance curves for total right lung were
quite similar.
 No statistical differences between ambroxol and placebo.

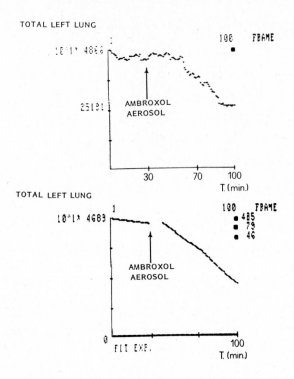

Fig. 4 . Clearance curve of total left lung in a patient with
COLD treated with aerosol of ambroxol.
Top panel : original recording.
Bottom panel : semilogarithmic fit elaboration.
In single patients this drug may show a very good action on muco
ciliary clearance.

TABLE 2

RESULTS OF MUCOCILIARY CLEARANCE IN COLD PATIENTS

REDUCED

1- Toigs A. et Al   : Am. Rev. Resp. Dis. 87,487,1963

2- Camner P.   : Scand.J. Resp. Dis. 54,272,1973

3- Lourenco R.   : Am. Rev. Resp. Dis. 101,450,1970

4- Weiss T.   : Chest   80, 881,1981 (suppl.)

5- Bertoli et Al   : Giorn. It. Mal.Tor. 1983 in press

UNCHANGED

1- Luchsinger P.   : Am. Rev. Resp. Dis. 97,1046,1968

INCREASED

1- Thomson L.   : Arch. Environ Healt 29,214,1974

2- Sauchis J.   : Bull. Physiopat. Resp. 9, 325,1973

2- <u>Giving the drug per os</u> - The results of aerosol penetration
index (PI) and of distribution index (DI) are grafically represented in Fig. 5 and 6 : using T statistic evaluation (paired

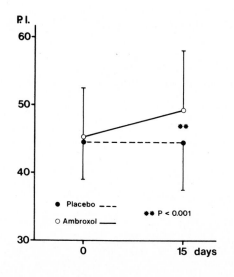

Fig. 5.Aerosol pe-
netration index (PI)
(m±sd) in patients
with COLD: in respect
of placebo, ambroxol
(given 15 days per
os) improved signifi-
cantly (P< .001) the
PI

358

observation), ambroxol given 15 days per os, induced a statistically significant improvement for both (Fig.7).

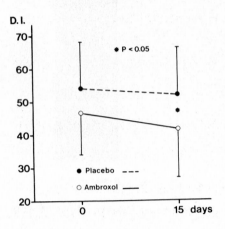

Fig.6. Aerosol distri-
bution index, DI (m+ds)
in patient with COLD: in
respect of placebo, am-
broxol (given 15 days
per os) improved signi-
ficantly (P < .05) the DI

The reason for this behaviour is matter of discussion; such indexes provide an objective measure of airway patency and our results suggest that tracheobronchial particle transport might depend
on rheologic behaviour of the mucus (the other component of the
mucociliary apparatus) more than up to now suspected. These results are according to the previous data given from Weiss et al
(4) and to the known qualitative and quantitative improvement
induced from Ambroxol on bronchial secretions in patients with
COLD (7).

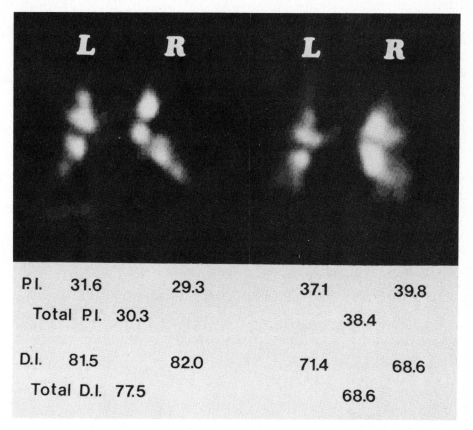

Fig. 7. Deposition pattern before (left panel) and 15 days after (right panel) treatment with ambroxol per os in one of the most impaired patients. Both penetration and distribution indexes are clearly improved (in both lungs) after the treatment.
L : left lung; R : right lung

REFERENCES

1. Matthys, H. (1982) Mucociliary clearance of the bronchial tree
   Newsletter S.E.P. pp 10-15

2. Bertoli,L. Banfi, F. Camisasca, E. Lo Cicero, S. Possa,M.
   Magri,G. Rizzato, G. (1983) La clearance mucociliare, studiata
   con microsfere di albumina marcata nella bronchite cronica e
   nel soggetto normale Gior. It.Mal.Tor. In press

3. Rizzato,G. Banfi,F. Magri,G. Possa, M. Vercelloni,M.
   Lo Cicero,S. Bertoli,L. (1983) Studio preliminare dell'at-
   tività dell'ambroxol sulla clearance mucociliare Med.Tor.
   In press

4. Weiss, T. Darrow,P. Felix, R. (1981) Effects of beta-adrenergic drug and a secretolytic agent in regional mucociliary
   clearance in patients with COLD. Chest 80, 881-5 (suppl.)

5. Fazio,F. and La Fortuna,C. (1981) Effect of inaled salbutanol
   on mucociliary clearance in patients with chronic bronchitis
   Chest 80, 827-30 (suppl.)

6. W.H.O. (1975) Nomenclature and definition in respiratory
   physiology and clinic aspects of chronic lung disease
   Bull. Europ. Physiopat. Resp. 11, 937

7. Morgenroth,K. and Schlake, W. (1975) Wien. Med. Wschr. suppl.
   23, 34-43

© 1983, Elsevier Science Publishers B.V.
Pulmonary Surfactant System, E.V. Cosmi
and E.M. Scarpelli eds.

BIOMEDICAL AND FUNCTIONAL CHANGES IN BRONCHOALVEOLAR PARAMETERS
INDUCED BY AMBROXOL TREATMENT OF CHRONIC BRONCHITIS

CARLO GRASSI[1],MAURIZIO LUISETTI[1],VIRGINIA DE ROSE[1],ANNA FIETTA[1],
FULVIO SACCHI[1],MAURO GENGHINI[2] AND ERNESTO POZZI[1]
[1]Institute of Phtisiology and Respiratory Disease,University of
Pavia and[2]"E.Morelli"General Hospital,Sondalo (Italy)

INTRODUCTION
   Chronic bronchitis is characterized by hyperactivity of the
bronchial structures which secrete mucus.As is well known,this is
a consequence of chronic inhalation of irritants.
   The patients shows cough and an abnormal production of sputum,
which is also physicochemically modified.Changes in the rheologic
characteristics of the bronchial secretion concur to the inef-
fectiveness of the mucociliary apparatus,whose epeithelial component is already damaged.
   That is why under such circumstances mucolytic agents are so
widely employed.Hower,the true mechanism of action of many of
them has not yet been clarified,in spite of their well known clinical efficacy.Among the most recently mucolytics,Ambroxol,accor-
ding to literature reports,seems to favour the elimination of
sputum by stimulating surfactant synthesis and secretion at bron-
chiclar-alveolar level (1-2-3),thus aiding the flow of the gel
and sol phases of mucus (4),the normalization of mucus production
by tubuloalveolar glands (5) and an increase in ciliary beat rate
(6).Since however these results were obtained under different
experimental conditions,some in man and some in the animal,we
thought it appropriate to carry out a controlled study in patients
with chronic bronchitis,also including an investigation of drug-
induced changes in the biochemical and functional activities of
bronchi and alveoli.

MATERIALS AND METHODS
   Choice of subjects. Our series included 15 male patients,aged
45 to 60 years (mean age 53.3 years)diagnosed as suffering from
chronic bronchitis,stage I or II,according TO WHO criteria (stage
I:prevalent involvement of small airways;stage II:involvment also

of larger airways,with modification of blood gases.

Choice was restricted to these patients for the following reasons:

1)to avoid the use of drugs capable of affecting the parameters studied;

2)to avoid that too severely impaired functional conditions advised against broncho-alveolar lavage.

Informed consent was obtained by each subject.All were smokers and were asked not to change their habits during the study.

Treatment carried out.Following simple randomization,10 subjects were treated with Ambroxol for 15 days,120 mg/day fractionated into two administrations.Five subjects were given a placebo according to the same schedule.

Parameters evaluated.At the beginning and at the end of treatment the following checks were performed:

1.0) Spirometric tests($VC,RV,FEV_1,MMEF,MEF_{75}$) and arterial gases analysis.

2.0) Characteristics of sputum.0,5 ml samples of initial sputum and of that collected after 7 days and at the end of treatment were examined for rheologic characteristics with a Biclot-Elvi thromboelastograph 816(Logos S.p.A.,Milan) equipped with cuvettes and small pistons modified according to Grassi et al.(7).The mucorheogram areas so obtained were measured with an Areo compensation polar planimeter (STI,Milan).

3.0) Rate of mucociliary transport with the fluoroscopic method of Friedman et al.(8).the method involves observation by fluoroscopic image intensifier of the motion of teflon particles 0.7 mm in diameter and 0.2 mm thick,made radiopaque by bismuth trioxide and laid into the trachea by fibrobronchoscopy.

4.0) Morfological appearance of the bronchial mucosa.Fragments of mucosa from the origin of the upper right lobar bronchus obtained by biopsy with fibrobronchoscope forceps were examined at the ultramicroscope following fixation in 1% osmium in 0.1 M phosphate buffer and staining with uranyl acetate and lead citrate.

5.0) Material obtained by broncho-alveolar lavage(BAL).Using a fibrobronchoscope introduced into a segmental bronchus of the lingula or middle lobe,three 80 ml fractions of sterile saline

at 37°C were instilled and then gently aspirated.The recovered liquid was then additionated with heparinized PBS(1:1,
V/V),filtered through sterile gauze and centrifuged at 1,500
rpm.

5.1)In the supernatant,the following were determined:

    5.1.1)Phospholipids,extracted with the method of Folch et
al.(9)following centrifugation at 40,000 g,and measured with the combined technique of thin layer chro-
matography(TLC)and flame ionization detector(Iatro-
scan,MKIII),recording being carried out by a Hewlett
Packard 3390A recorder-integrator.Lecithins were do-
sed in order to detect the phospholipidic fraction.
To eliminate possible fluctuations due to the lavage
technique,we thought it more correct to express results as ratio with transferrin,evaluated by laser
nephelometric method.

    5.1.2)Immunoglobulins(IgG,S-IgA,IgM),evaluated by laser ne-
phelometric method.Also in this case,we report the
ratio of immunoglobulins to transferrin concentration
instead of the absolute values,to avoid inaccuracy
due to the technique.

5.2)Alveolar macrophages,recovered from the pellet obtained
following low speed centrifugation.The cells were washed
twice with PBS and made to stick to the bottom of tissue
culture plates,in order to measure:

    5.2.1)phagocytosis,expressed as phagocytosis frequency(PhF)
i.e.the fraction of macrophages wich had phagocyti-
zed the opsonized yeasts;

    5.2.2)metabolic activation,as deduced by the reduction of
NBT to formazan by phagocytizing macrophages (NRF)

RESULTS

1.0)The results of spiromtric tests are reported in Table 1.A
comparison of the mean values obtained in the ambroxol treated
subjects showed no significant changes of VC,RV and FEV_1.On the
contrary,a highly significant improvement was obtained for MMEF
and MEF_{75}.No changes were found in the placebo group.With regard
to blood gases tests,PaO_2,$PaCO_2$ and pH were not significantly modified both in the treated and in the placebo groups.

TABLE 1

MEAN CHANGES IN PULMONARY FUNCTION TESTS BEFORE (B) AND AFTER (A) TREATMENTS

TREATMENT		PULMONARY FUNCTION TESTS				
		VC	RV	FEV_1	MMEF	MEF_{75}
AMBROXOL	B	4,045.8 ± 372.9	2,626.8 ± 461.9	2,900.2 ± 245.1	1.315 ±0.358	0.480 ±0.125
	A	4,117.8 ± 404.2	2,493.1 ± 389.7	3,064.5 ± 256.2	2.055 ±0.476	0.967 ±0.112
PLACEBO	B	4,210.0 ± 397.5	2,582.5 ± 400.8	2,932.2 ± 306.1	1.186 ±0.453	0.487 ±0.005
	A	4,142.0 ± 390.0	2,564.3 ± 522.2	2,896.1 ± 340.7	1.170 ±0.447	0.510 ±0.079

Δ MMEF with Ambroxol $p < 0.001$; with placebo N.S.

Δ MEF_{75} with Ambroxol $p < 0.001$; with placebo N.S.

2.0)The rheologic characteristics of sputum,as evaluated with the modified thromboelastograph,were unchanged in the placebo group(mean area of mucorheograms:basal value $3,105 \pm 1,105$ mm^2;day 7: $3,010 \pm 732$;end of treatment: $3,031 \pm 974.9$).

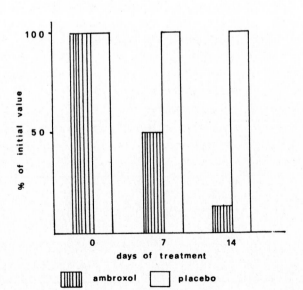

Fig. 1. Mean changes in mucorheograms areas

On the contrary, in the Ambroxol group the initial mean area of 2,831±306.1 was reduced to 1,475±781.5 at day 7 and to 314± 279 at the end of treatment. Fig. 1 shows a comparison of the mean percent variations of the mucorheogram areas: while no changes were found in the placebo group, in the Ambroxol group the mucorheogram area was reduced on the average by 50% at the first check and by 80% at the end of treatment.

3.0) Table 2 reports the mean behavior of the mucociliary transport rate in the two groups of patients. The motion rate of the teflon disks was unmodified in the placebo group, while it was significantly increased in the Ambroxol group.

TABLE 2

Changes in mucociliary-transport mean rate (mm/min)

	AMBROXOL		PLACEBO	
	B	A	B	A
mucociliary	6.27	8.11	6.32	6.32
transport	±1.21	±0.89	±1.47	±1.22
	└ $p < 0.05$ ┘		└ N.S. ┘	

4.0) The morphological investigations carried out on the bronchial mucous membrane demonstrated a similar damaging of the bronchial epithelium in all the examined subjects. The predominant lesion, typical of this disease, was squamous metaplasia of the epithelium. In particular, electron microscopy (Fig. 2 a) showed, as a trait common to all patients, a marked disorganization of the epithelium, whose cells had pratically lost the intercellular junctions, were multistratified, were positively undergoing regeneration, as shown by the presence of large nucleoles, and were poorly differentiated, with regard to both cilia and secretory structures; also, the basement membrane was thickened, due to irregular deposition of collagen fibers.

In the placebo group this picture was unchanged, while in the Ambroxol group (Fig. 2 b) the epithelium appeared perfectly orga-

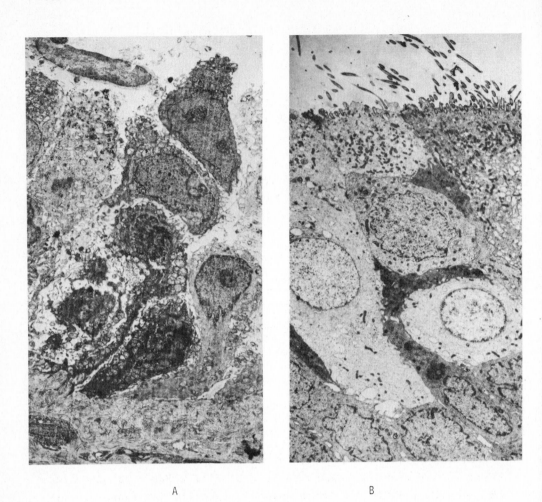

A   B

Fig. 2. Ultramicroscopical aspects of the bronchial epithelium
from a patient with chronic bronchitis. (A) before, (B) after Ambroxol treatment. (x 4,750)

nized, with well preserved cell junctions. From the bottom to the
surface the epithelium, which was still multistratified, exhibi-

ted clear signs of cell differentiation, with increase of cyto-plasmic organelles and normally structuredcilia.

5.1.1. In the liquid portion of the material obtained by bron-cho-alveolar lavage, Table 3 shows that no changes in the concen-tration of phospholipids occurred in either group.

TABLE 3
Mean changes of the phospholipids in B.A.L.

	AMBROXOL		PLACEBO	
	B	A	B	A
LECITHINS	0.157	0.168	0.166	0.156
TRANSFERRIN	±0.046	±0.039	±0.054	±0.090
	└ N.S. ┘		└ N.S. ┘	

5.1.2. The mean concentration of immunoglobulins in the broncho-alveolar lavage liquid of the two groups is reported in Table 4. As compared with the control group, the Ambroxol group showed a significant increase of the SIgA/TF ratio, the mean concentration of transferrin being in all cases 52.5 ± 7.9 γ/ml.

TABLE 4
Mean changes of the immunoglobulin levels in B.A.L.
(Values are expressed as immunoglobulin/transferrin levels ratio)

		IgG/TF	SIgA/TF	IgM/TF
AMBROXOL	B	5.493 ±2.350	3.658 ±2.622	0.637 ±0.378
	A	5.942 ±1.979	4.578 ±2.508	0.750 ±0.635
PLACEBO	B	5.700 ±0.708	2.538 ±0.490	0.558 ±0.141
	A	5.688 ±0.714	2.477 ±0.448	0.582 ±0.200

SIgA/TF with Ambroxol: $p < 0.001$

5.2. The percentage of phagocytizing and phagocytizing-dependent metabolic activation alveolar macrophages appeared normal in both group, with respect to healthy controls. Following either Ambroxol or placebo, no significant modifications were observed (Table 5).

TABLE 5

Mean values of macrophage phagocytosis (PHF) and phagocytosis-dependent metabolic activation (NRF) before (B) and after (A) treatments

		PHF (%)	NRF (%)
AMBROXOL	B	92.3 ±3.7	95.0 ±2.6
	A	91.4 ±5.6	92.8 ±6.6
PLACEBO	B	93.6 ±2.6	93.8 ±3.7
	A	93.6 ±2.6	93.4 ±3.8

CONCLUSIONS

Our controlled study in patients with chronic bronchitis, marked by hypersecretion of mucus, showed that Ambroxol administered for 15 days caused:

1) a marked mucolytic action on expectoration which, at the end of treatment, had rheologic characteristics quite close to the physiologic ones;

2) a significant increase in tracheal mucociliary transportrate;

3) a dramatic modification of the morphological characteristics of the epithelium of large bronchi, as if the drug had stimulated maturation or had exerted a protective action on epithelial cells.

As a consequence of the improved mucociliary clearance, the patency of large bronchi was increased, as shown by the improved flow of the most peripheral airways.

The broncho-alveolar lavage liquid also revealed:
1) an increase of SIgA, suggesting a tendency to the restoration of the bronchial epithelium secretory activity by Ambroxol;
2) the lack of important changes in the phospholipidic fraction;
3) a phagocytizing and metabolic activity of the alveolar macrophages similar to thet of the control group.

On the other hand before the treatment both phospholipid concentration and macrophagic function were previously normal and therefore no effect were noted.

It is suitable to complete our studies with researches in patients with chronic bronchitis at 3rd stage in which, of course, the alveolus is morphologically and functionally involved.

In the light of these findings, Ambroxol seems to be a promising tool in the treatment of chronic bronchitis since, in addition to acting as a mucolitic, it apparently protects the bronchial epithelium from the damaging effects of air contaminants.

This is a totally new aspect, wich deserves to be further investigated.

REFERENCES

1. Cerutti, P. and Kapanci, Y. (1979) Respiration, 37, 241.

2. Elmer, G. and Kapanci, Y. (1981) Prog.Resp.Res., 15, 234.

3. Curti, P.C. (1972) Pneumologie, 147, 62.

4. Macklem, P.T. (1978) Am.Rev.Physiol., 40, 157.

5. Noak, W. and Elbrecht, B. (1975) Wiem.Med.Wschr., 125,26.

6. Iravani, J. and Melville, G.N. (1974) Arzneim.Forsch., 24, 849.

7. Grassi, C., Morandini, G.C., Pernice, A., Puglisi, M. (1977) Respiration, 34, 100.

8. Friedman, M., Stott, F.D., Poole, D.O., Dougherty, R., Chapman, G.A., Watson, H., Sackner, M.A. (1977) Am.Rev.Resp.Dis.,115, 67.

9. Folch, J., Lees, M., Sloane-Stanley, G.H. (1957) J.Biol.Chem., 226, 497.

10.Morgenroth, K., Hoerstebrock, U. (1978) Arzneim.Forsch., 28, 911.

11. Nakamura, M., Sosaki, H., Takishima, T. (1979) J.Appl.Physiol. 47, 692.

12. Pozzi, E. and Pilatti, M. (1979) Med. Tor., 1, 213.

13. Prevost, M.C., Soula, G., Douste-Blazy, L., Gutleben, C.(1978) Bull.Europ.Physiopath.Resp., 14, 53.

© 1983, Elsevier Science Publishers B.V.
*Pulmonary Surfactant System, E.V. Cosmi
and E.M. Scarpelli eds.*

EFFECTS OF SECRETOLYTIC AGENT (AMBROXOL) ON REGIONAL MUCOCILIARY
CLEARANCE IN PATIENTS WITH CHRONIC OBSTRUCTIVE LUNG DISEASE

PETER DOROW, M.D., THOMAS WEISS, M.D., ROLAND FELIX, M.D.
Pulmonary Division and Department of Radiology, Klinikum
Charlottenburg, Free University Berlin, Spandauer Damm 130,
1000 Berlin 19, West-Germany

INTRODUCTION

The rate of clearance of inhaled radioactive particles from the
lung offers an objective means of assessing the efficiency of
drugs supposed to influence the mucociliary system. There is
little information available concerning clearance patterns at
different levels of the human respiratory tract. To apply this
approach to the study of drug effects in clinical disease, we
used a procedure in which regional clearance measurement in five
pulmonary zones of interest are performed. Additionally, we
introduced an index for quantitative analysis of pulmonary
aerosol distribution patterns in order to detect any possible
changes in the site of radioaerosol deposition caused by the drug.
We studied 30 patients with chronic obstructive lung disease and
its response to the secrotolytic agent ambroxol (mucosolvan).

MATERIALS AND METHODS

We studied 30 stable patients with COLD. The COLD patients were
devided in three groups:
chronic obstructive bronchitis (13)
asthma (8)
obstructive emphysema (9)

Sympathicomimetic and secretolytic-mucolytic agents were stopped
giving 12 hours before measurement. The patients received over
4 days double-blind either placebo or 3 x 30 mg ambroxol. Tracheobronchial clearance and pulmonary aerosol deposition patterns were
studied after the subjects inhaled a radioaerosol of 0.5 to 3.5 m
of human serum albumin minimicrospheres (HAMM) at normal tidal
volume in a sitting position. The jet nebulizerproduced aerosol
was administered for radioactivity data were recorded using an
online gamma camera-computer system as an uninterrupted series of

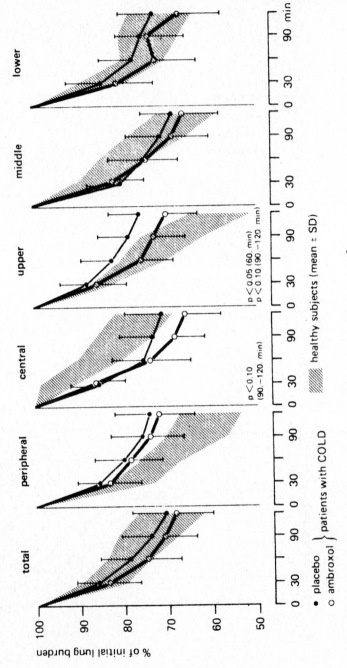

Fig. 1. Regional clearance curves for peripheral, central, upper, middle, and lower lung zones including total right lung in 30 patients with COLD before and after giving ambroxol. For comparison (shaded areas), regional clearance patterns without evidence of obstructive lung disease.

60 second frames with a 64 x 64 matrix cell resolution.
Measurements continued for at least 120 minutes from an anterior
camera position in the supine subject.

RESULTS

While ß-adrenergic agonists are known to be affective in stimulating the mucociliary transport system (1, 2, 5, 6, 9, 10),
little information is available concerning efficacy of secretolytic drugs on the human tracheobronchial transport capacity (3,
7, 8, 10).

In most of the 30 patients, the highest clearance rate was
achieved during the first 60 minutes, a tendency which remained
after drug administration. In the healthy subjects, regular
continuous particle flow was observed in nearly all lung zones
evaluated, with only the lower ROI exhibiting a slowing down of
particle transport after 60 minutes (Fig. 1).

The placebo runs in both patient groups provide especially
convincing evidence that upper and peripheral clearance delay seem
to compensate for a faster activity decrease seen in the more
central lung regions, resulting in a whole lung clearance curve
hardly distinguishing in a whole lung clearance curve hardly
distinguishable from the one encountered in the healthy subjects.

Ambroxol was associated with definite ($p < 0.05$) improvement of
lung aerosol homogen eity, expressed in terms of ADI, in emphy-
sematous patients in the current study.

In these patients epithelial lesions with loss of cilia may
occur (4). Under these circumstances, more than under normal
conditions, tracheobronchial particle transport might be even more
dependent on rheologic behavior of mucus, the other componen of
the mucociliary apparatus.

REFERENCES

1. Camner P., Strandberg K., Philipson K. (1976) Increased mucociliary transport by adrenergic stimulation. Arch Environ
   Health 39:79-82

2. Felix R., Hedde JP., Zwicker HJ., Winkler C. (1978) Mucociliary clearance during beta-adrenergic stimulation with
   fenoterol. Prax. Pneumol. 32:777-82

3. Iravani J., Melville GN. (1974) The effects of the bromohexine
   metabolite 8 and a new adrenergic agent on mucociliary
   function of the airways. Drug.Res. 24:849-55

4. Matsuba K., Thurlbeck WM. (1973) Disease of the small airways in chronic bronchitis. Am Rev.Respir.Dis. 107: 552-58

5. Mossberg B., Strandberg K., Camner P. (1976) Tracheobronchial clearance and beta-adrenoceptor stimulation in patients with chronic bronchitis. Scand.J.Respir.Dis. 57:281-89

6. Sackner M. (1978) Effect of respiratory drugs on mucociliary clearance. Chest 73:958-66

7. Thomson ML., Pavia D., Gregg I., Stark JE. (1974) Bromhexine and mucociliary clearance in chronic bronchitis. Br.J.Dis. Chest 68:21-27

8. Thomson ML., Pavia D., Jones CJ., Mc-Quiston TAC (1975) No demonstrable effect of S-carboxymethylcysteine on clearance of secretions from the human lung. Thorax 30:669-73

9. Wanner A. (1977) Clinical aspects of mucociliary transport. Am Rev.Respir.Dis. 116:73-125

10. Weiss Th., Dorow P., Felix R. (1981) Effects of a beta adrenergic drug and a secretolytic agent on regional mucociliary clearance in patients with COLD. Chest 80:881

PROTECTIVE EFFECT OF AMBROXOL AGAINST DRUG-INDUCED MODIFICATIONS OF LUNG SURFACTANT

PIER COSTANZO CURTI AND MAURO GENGHINI

Ospedale Generale Regionale - 23039 Sondalo (SO) Italia

INTRODUCTION

Many drugs influence alveolar surfactant production (1,7) and Ambroxol has stimulating effect on Type II pneumocytes (8). Therefore it seemed justified to study the possible protective effect of Ambroxol on the surfactant alterations produced by a number of commonly used drugs. The study presented here includes previous investigations carried out by Curti and Renovanz (8).

MATERIAL AND METHODS

The experiments were carried out on white mice CRL:CD-1(DCR)BR. For each drug 140 animals were used, in two groups: 70 animals were treated with Ambroxol and control group of 70 animals were treated with placebo. Normal mice were used as a reference for judging the adverse effects of the drugs on alveolar surfactant.

Surfactant alterations were estimated by means of the following tests:

a) Pressure/volume diagrams of the excised lung in air (20 Ambroxol and 20 control mice)

b) Tension/area diagrams of bronchoalveolar washings on the Langmuir-Wilhelmy balance (10 Ambroxol and 10 control mice (9,10)

c) Quantitative determination of total phospholipids and thin-layer chromatographic fractions of bronchoalveolar washings of the all lung (30 Ambroxol and 30 control mice). Total lecithins were estimated by the enzymatic method (11) or from phosphorus (2). Lysolecithin was added in known quantity to the extracts as an internal reference. Thin-layer chromatography of Folch's extract (3) was done using Merck-60-F plates developed with chloroform-methanol-water-acetic acid (65/25/4/8, v/v). Dipalmitoyl lecithin and phosphatidyl glycerol were added for identification of the spots, which were colored by phosphomolybdic acid and iodine vapor. Quantitative determination of the chromatographic spots was done by flame ionization detection (4)

d) Histochemical study of the lung by the Bracco and Curti method (12) using 10 Ambroxol and 10 control mice.

Ambroxol was given by mouth in a dose of 6 mg per kg body weight in 0.15 ml of saline twice daily from five days before the administration of the drug to be tested until the killing of the animal. The control mice received saline alone. The means used for producing the surfactant alterations were: vincristine, amphotericin B, diazepam, bromocarbamide, pilocarpine, phentermine, O_2 inhalation and anaesthetics. The method of killing the animals must avoid terminal lung edema and associated surfactant alterations. Our method was during pentothal anaesthesia to cannulate the trachea and connect it with an air reservoir at the pressure of 30 cm H_2O, then quickly inject i.v. tubocurarine and cut the abdominal aorta. Statistical analysis was done with Student's t test.

RESULTS

Vincristine (6). Vincristine was given in a single i.v. dose of 0.15 mg per kg b.w. The animals were killed 3-6 days later. The P/V diagram of the excised lung is significantly modified by vincristine: the curve is inclined on the pressure axis and the hysteresis area is decreased (Fig. 1). The differences in the means of the deflation volumes between the control group and normal mice are significant at P values of 0.05-0.001. The P/V diagram alterations are less in the Ambroxol group than in the control group. The differences of the means of the deflation volumes are significant at P values of 0.02.

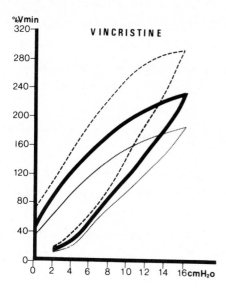

Fig. 1. Vincristine.
P/V diagram of excised
lungs: ---normal, ——
Ambroxol,····· control.

The phospholipid content of
bronchoalveolar washings in
comparision with normal mice
decreased in both the control
and Ambroxol groups, but in
the latter the amount of
phospholipid is significantly greater (Table I). The
histochemical findings correspond with these results.
The pneumocytes are depleted
of surfactant granules, but
evidently less in the Ambroxol group (Fig. 2A) than in
the control one (Fig. 2B).

Amphotericin B (13). Am-
photericin B was given in a
single i.v. dose of 1 mg per
kg b.w. The animals were killed 3-5 days later. The P/V

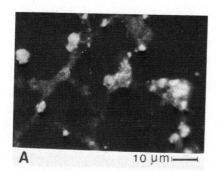
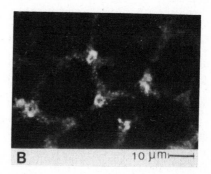

Fig. 2. Lung of mouse treated with vincristine. Bracco
and Curti method. A Ambroxol, B control.

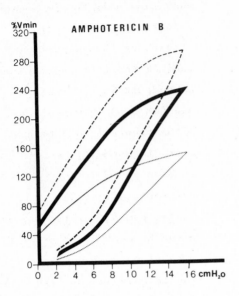

%Vmin

AMPHOTERICIN B

Fig. 3. Amphotericin B.
P/V diagram of excised
lungs: ---normal, ——
Ambroxol,······ control.

diagram of the excised lungs reveals a marked decrease in lung compliance in control mice, while the deviation from normal in the Ambroxol group is fairly significant (Fig. 3). The differences of the means of the deflation volumes between the Ambroxol and control groups are highly significant at P values of 0.001. Lecithin contents of the bronchoalveolar washings are much more decreased in the controls than in the Ambroxol group (Tab. I). Histochemistry showed a clear depletion of surfactant granu-

les (Fig. 4B) in alveolar Type II cells in control mice while the differences between the Ambroxol mice (Fig. 4A) and the normal

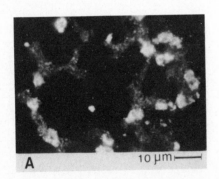
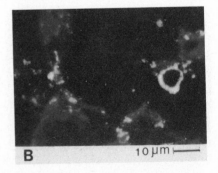

Fig. 4. Lung of mouse treated with amphotericin B. Bracco and Curti method. A Ambroxol, B control.

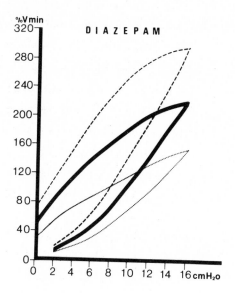

Fig. 5. Diazepam.
P/V diagram of excised
lungs: ---normal, —
Ambroxol,...... control.

ones were only fairly significant. In conclusion, the
results of this experiment
confirm those previously reported; it is advisable to
use Ambroxol in association
with amphotericin B treatment. Encouraging results have been found in one case of
cryptococcosis (13).

Diazepam (14). Diazepam was
given by mouth in a single
dose of 0.72 mg per kg b.w.
The animals were killed within 8-10 hours of diazepam administration. Diazepam produces in the control marked alterations of the P/V diagrams
of the excised lung (Fig. 5), only slightly less severe than with
bromocarbamide. Ambroxol gave a good protective action against dia-

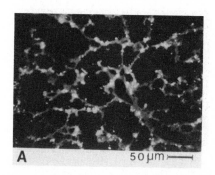

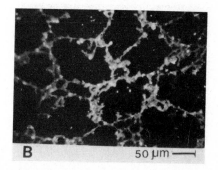

Fig. 6. Lung of mouse treated with diazepam. Bracco and
Curti method. A Ambroxol, B control.

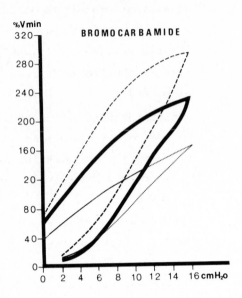

%Vmin

BROMOCARBAMIDE

Fig. 7. Bromocarbamide.
P/V diagram of excised
lungs: ---normal, ———
Ambroxol, ...control.

zepam damage (Fig. 5). The difference in the means of the deflation volumes are highly significant between the control group and normal mice (P 0.001). In the Ambroxol group the P/V diagram alterations are less pronounced than in the control group. The differences in the means of the deflation volumes between Ambroxol and control groups are significant at P values of 0.001. The phospholipid content of bronchoalveolar washings compared with normal mice is decreased in both the control and Ambroxol groups, but in the latter the phospholipid amount is significantly greater (Tab. I). Histochemistry gives concordant results. The

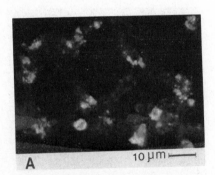

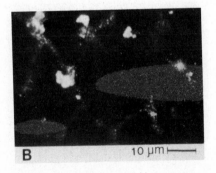

Fig. 8. Lung of mouse treated with bromocarbamide.
Bracco and Curti method. A Ambroxol, B control.

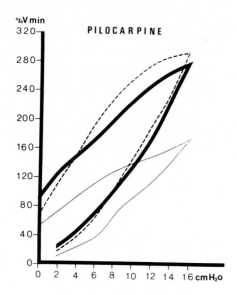

Fig. 9. Pilocarpine.
P/V diagram of excised
lungs: ---normal, ———
Ambroxol, ...control.

surfactant granule depletion is evidently more severe in the control group (Fig. 6B) than in the Ambroxol group (Fig. 6A).

<u>Bromocarbamide</u> (1). Bromocarbamide was given in a single dose of 0.33 g per kg b. w. by mouth. The animals were killed within 3-6 hours after bromocarbamide administration. In the control group the alterations of the P/V diagram of the excised lungs are highly significant (Fig. 7). In the Ambroxol group the protective effect is evident and the differences of the means of relaxation volumes between Ambroxol and control groups are significant at P values of 0.001. The histochemical observations are

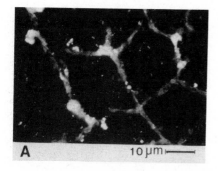
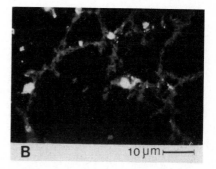

Fig. 10. Lung of mouse treated with pilocarpine. Bracco and Curti method. A Ambroxol, B control.

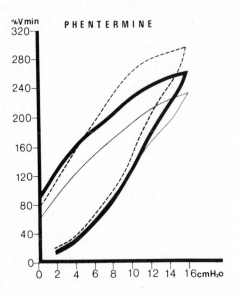

Fig. 11. Phentermine.
P/V diagram of excised
lungs: ---normal, ——
Ambroxol, ...control.

in agreement with the physiological data (Fig. 8A,B). In
the control group the type II
pneumocytes appear depleted
oɪ surfactant (Fig. 8B), whereas in the animals treated
with Ambroxol have a clearly
higher surfactant content
(Fig. 8A). The phospholipid
content of bronchoalveolar
washings is reduced to a less
severe degree in the Ambroxol
than in the control mice
(Tab. I).

Pilocarpine (15). Pilocarpine was given by mouth five
times at a dose of 2 mg per
kg b.w. every 12 hours. In

control mice the P/V diagram is inclined on the pressure axis indicating a decrease in efficiency. In the Ambroxol group the pilocarpine effect is less pronounced and the P/V diagram is closer to

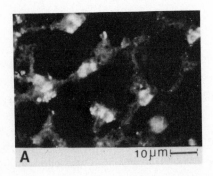
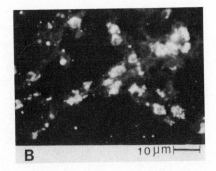

Fig. 12. Lung of mouse treated with phentermine. Bracco
and Curti method. A Ambroxol, B control.

normal (Fig. 9). The differnces in the means of the relaxation volumes between the animals treated with Ambroxol and normal are
small. The differences in the relaxation means between the control
and Ambroxol groups are significant at P values of 0.05. Because
pilocarpine enhances surfactant excretion from pneumocytes we propose that in the control group there is an exhaustion of surfactant
production while the animals treated with Ambroxol withstand the
effect of pilocarpine because of a greater production of surfactant. Histochemical findings agree with this hypothesis. In the
control group the type II pneumocytes look pale and contain few
granules, while an unusual amount of liposomes appears free in the
alveolar spaces (Fig. 10B). In the Ambroxol group free liposomes
are also present in the alveoli, but the granular pneumocytes still
have a good quantity of surfactant in their protoplasm (Fig. 10A).
The phospholipid content of bronchoalveolar washings approaches
normal values in the Ambroxol group but it is decreased in the control group. The differences between the two groups are significant
at P values of 0.02.

Phentermine (16). Clorphentermine was given by esophageal cannula in a daily dose of 0.1 mg for 12-16 days. The P/V diagram of
excised lungs (Fig. 11) shows in the control group a peculiar pattern: while the inflation curve is close to normal, the deflation
curve is flattened and the means of the deflation volumes are significantly decreased at P values of 0.01. In the Ambroxol group
the diagram does not differ significantly from normal. The phospholipid content of the bronchoalveolar washings in the Ambroxol
group approaches the normal values, while in the control group it
is significantly decreased (Tab. I). A study of the fatty acids of
lecithins seemed indicated. Histochemistry does not show remarkable differences between the two groups if the greater number of
free liposomes in the alveolar spaces in the control group is dis-
regarded (Fig. 12A,B).

384

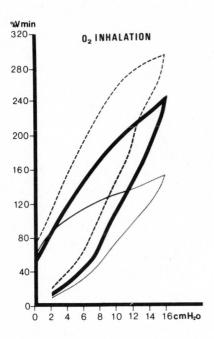

%∆V min

320

280

240

200

160

120

80

40

0

O₂ INHALATION

0 2 4 6 8 10 12 14 16 cmH₂o

Fig. 13. O₂ inhalation.
P/V diagram of excised
lungs: ---normal, ——
Ambroxol, ...control.

O₂ <u>inhalation</u> (5). Mice were exposed to a high concentration (93-95%) of O₂ for
48-70 hours. In the control
group the P/V diagram of the
eₓcised lungs is significantly altered in the sense of
reduced compliance (Fig. 13).
The differences in the means
of the relaxation volumes are
significant at P values 0.001.
The total phospholipids of
the bronchoalveolar washings
are increased, while the lecithins are clearly decreased
(Tab. I). Histochemistry
shows large quantities of liposomes in the alveolar spaces with progressive depletion of surfactant granules

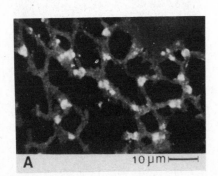

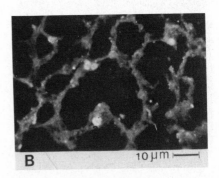

Fig. 14. Lung of mouse treated with O₂ inhalation.
Bracco and Curti method. A Ambroxol, B control.

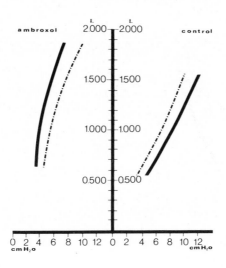

Fig. 15. Mean pulmonary compliance curves at ---start and ——end of operation. *left*, cases treated with Ambroxol; *right*, control.

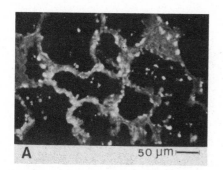

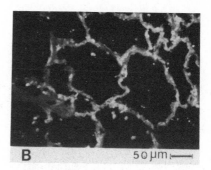

Fig. 16. Lung exeresis in man. Bracco and Curti method. A case treated with Ambroxol, B case control.

TABLE I

PHOSPHOLIPIDS OF BRONCHOALVEOLAR WASHINGS

Total phospholipids (1), lecithins (2) and phosphoglycerol (3) µg.
Ambroxol group (A), control group (C), normal mice (N).
Standard deviation (SD), means $\bar{m}$.

		N	A	C	Diff.N-A	Diff.N-C	Diff.A-C
	1)	398 (49)	391 (20)	278 (29)	7	120***	113***
I	2)	361 (48)	356 (35)	259 (26)	5	102***	97**
	3)	37 (5)	43 (4)	29 (4)	8	6**	14***
	1)	398 (49)	241 (17)	146 (25)	157***	252***	95***
II	2)	361 (48)	214 (15)	132 (22)	147***	229***	82**
	3)	37 (5)	27 (3)	17 (2)	10**	20***	10**
	1)	398 (49)	355 (11)	270 (12)	43	128***	85***
III	2)	361 (48)	320 (10)	243 (11)	41	118***	77***
	3)	37 (5)	36 (3)	26 (2)	1	11***	10***
	1)	398 (49)	335 (30)	239 (11)	63*	159***	96**
IV	2)	361 (48)	297 (28)	216 (14)	64*	145***	81**
	3)	37 (5)	32 (4)	28 (3)	5	9**	4
	1)	398 (49)	284 (19)	208 (8)	114**	190***	76**
V	2)	361 (48)	256 (18)	192 (8)	105**	169***	64**
	3)	37 (5)	29 (2)	20 (2)	8*	17***	9**
	1)	398 (49)	395 (30)	266 (25)	3	132***	129**
VI	2)	361 (48)	352 (25)	235 (33)	9	126***	117**
	3)	37 (5)	51 (7)	31 (6)	14	6	20*
	1)	398 (49)	477 (29)	607 (31)	79	209***	130**
VII	2)	361 (48)	308 (12)	253 (10)	53	108***	55***
	3)	37 (5)	36 (2)	28 (2)	1	9**	8*

I Vincristine, II Amphotericin B, III Diazepam, IV Bromocarbamide,
V Pilocarpine, VI Phentermine, VII O_2 inhalation.
$P \leq 0.001$ *** $P \leq 0.01$ ** $P \leq 0.05$ *.

in Type II pneumocytes (Fig. 14B). The tension-area diagram shows a faster slope on the compression branch, probably caused by a decreased percentage of unsaturated lecithin fatty acids. In the Ambroxol group the same alterations are detectable to a minimal degree, and the lecithin content of bronchoalveolar washings is much greater than in both control and normal groups (Tab. I).

Anaesthetics (16,17). A protective effect of Ambroxol has been found in man on the surfactant alterations produced by liposoluble anaesthetics, as was reported in animals (18). Twenty seven patients undergoing thoracic surgery were divided between two groups: fourteen patients were treated before, during and after operation with high doses of Ambroxol, and thirteen patients were kept as control with no treatment. The pulmonary compliance values (Fig. 15) at the beginning of the operation are already greater in the Ambroxol group than in the control. At the end of the operation the pulmonary compliance decreases in the control group while it increases in the Ambroxol group. The difference in the means between the two groups are statistically highly significant. The histochemical patterns indicate a remarkably lesser depletion of surfactant in the Ambroxol group (Fig. 16A,B).

CONCLUSION

Ambroxol is a useful adjuvant for the prevention and treatment of alveolar surfactant alterations induced by many drugs, including the chemiotherapeutic agents of neoplastic diseases and anaesthethics, and sedatives.

REFERENCES

1. Curti, P.C. and Renovanz, H.D. (1981) Therap. Woche. 31: 5633--5648.

2. Fiske, C.H. and Subbarow, Y. (1925) J. Biol. Chem. 66: 375.

3. Folch, J., Lees, J.M. and Sloane Stanley, G.H. (1957) J. Biol. Chem. 226: 497-509.

4. Itoh, T., Tanaka, M. and Kaneko H. (1980) in: Thin-layer Chromatography. John Wiley & Sons, New York.

5. Morgan, T.E., Finley, T.N., Huber, G.L. and Fialcow, H. (1965) J. Clin. Invest. 44: 1737-1744.

6. Pozzi, E. and Pilatti, M. (1979) Medicina Toracica 1: 213-220.

7. Renovanz, H.D. (1979) Med. M. Pharm. 2: 361-367.

8. Curti, P.C. and Renovanz, H.D. (1981) Ann. Med. Sondalo. Special number Mucosolvan June 1981.

9. Abrams, M.E. (1966) J. Appl. Physiol. 21: 718-720.

10. Bracco, M. and Curti, P.C. (1969) Ann. Forlanini 29: 209-220.

11. Takayama, M.N., Ito, S., Nagasaki, T. and Tanimizu, I. (1977) Clin. Chim. Acta 79: 93-98.

12. Bracco, M. and Curti, P.C. (1969) Ann. Forlanini 29: 221-227.

13. Curti, P.C. (1978) Atemwgs. n. Lungenkrank 4: 68-70.

14. Whitelaw A.G.L., Cummings, A.J. and McFadyen, I.R. (1981) Brit. Med. J. 282: 1106-1108.

15. Curti, P.C. and Renovanz, H.D. (1981) Klin. Manatshlat f. Augenheilk 179: 113-115.

16. Brody A.R., Clay, M.F., Collins, M., Eden, A.A. and McDermott, M. (1975) J. Appl. Physiol. 245: 105-106.

17. Curti, P.C., Camerota, G., Bianchini, C. and Rizzi, A. (1981) Ann. Med. Sondalo. Special number Mucosolvan June 1981.

18. Curti, P.C. and Bracco, M. (1969) Ann. Forlanini 29: 253-265.

SUMMARY AND CONCLUDING REMARKS OF THE CHAIRMAN

(Abstracted are portions of the concluding statement which provide a summary of the presentations given during the Symposium).

The founder of the surfactant system, the late R.E. Pattle, would rejoice to know that surfactants have spread throughout the world. Some of the mysteries have been solved and we are gratified to have had the privilege of receiving the "state of the art" from our speakers. The enigmas that remain are the solutions we expect from the researchers of tomorrow. From birth to adulthood, and from bronchi to alveoli there is the surfactant system. Its absence can now be diagnosed and treated in a fashion that is comparatively primitive but holds great promise for achievement of sophistication in the not-too-distant future.

Our meeting opened with the report of Scarpelli which gave us a new definition of how surfactants operate. His display of bubble production by the mature lung at birth and also by the normal adult lung resolves a number of unanswered questions for the physiologists, as it explains the mechanisms by which immature lungs fail and surfactant supplementation succeeds.

Doctor Baritussio separated fractions of lung lavage from rabbits and found that one fraction has the characteristics of purified alveolar surfactant. Moreover, his studies of incorporation of tritium-labelled palmitate into these fractions suggest that surfactant-related structures undergo sequential transformations within the alveolar space.

I was pleased to discuss the diagnosis of fetal lung maturity in utero by biochemical and biophysical analyses of amniotic fluid. This approach is recommended for the timing of delivery prior to elective cesarean section, for complicated pregnancies and for the institution of a pharmacological prevention of RDS in utero and after birth. The most reliable method is, at present, evaluation of the lung profile, i.e., the identification of PG, PI, L/S, and disaturated L. Moreover, as pointed out by Luerti, fluorescence polarization is a relatively simple method for predicting fetal lung maturity and should become a practical tool in the future.

RDS is still a leading cause of neonatal morbidity and mortality. Bucci discussed the epidemiology of the syndrome including those factors that increase risk (such as male sex, cesarean section, diabetes, perinatal asphyxia and familial predisposition) and those that seem to reduce risk (such as prolonged rupture of membranes and chronic fetal distress). Happily mortality rate is declining with the improvement of peri- and neonatal care and with judicious use of prophylactic and specific therapy.

Walters showed that in the mature fetus beta-mimetics initiate surfactant release and reduce lung water, that the release of surfactant during labour is associated with beta-adrenergic stimulation and that the response of the immature fetus is restricted. The full implication of beta-adrenergic stimulation and its role in the adaptive changes at birth is sure to be the subject of continued research.

The vulnerability of the diaphragm of the neonate to the stress of overwork (for example in RDS) puts the baby at greater risk to respiratory failure than the adult. Milic-Emili introduced the concept of monitoring "diaphragmatic pressure" (Pdi) and showed how this parameter comes perilously close to the "zone of fatigue" in the newborn infant.

Experimental models for the study of RDS and the mechanisms which regulate surfactant production have been presented and critically analyzed by various speakers. Van Golde reported his vast experience with the use of type II cells isolated from adult rat lung and of organotypic cultures of fetal lung epithelial cells. Understanding of the biochemical pathways of surfactant synthesis is clearly improved by these models. An animal model for the study of experimental RDS in rabbits, with features very similar to those of the human, was presented by Nilsson, who discussed the pathological and biochemical features of RDS in the premature rabbit compared to the human. He pointed out that the mechanisms for development of epithelial lesions are probably the same in both species. Lachmann, who has pioneered the development of laboratory models of respiratory distress, reported his current work with adult guinea pigs and dogs. This included evaluation of lung function in vivo; histological and biochemical aspects of surfactant deficiency; and the use of Ambroxol as a prophylactic and therapeutic agent. He reported that the latter improves pulmonary function, increases phospholipid concentration, and enhances alveolar aeration. Saitto reviewed the mechanism by which bilateral pulmonary lavage may produce an RDS-like condition in adult laboratory animals. He showed that significant cardiovascular changes occur after lavage, in addition to water retention within alveoli, and hence respiratory insufficiency. Three general models were reviewed including those that produce distress by altering the vascular system, the airspaces or by producing systemic derangements. Clearly there is no single precise model and additional research is needed.

The session on clinical and therapeutic aspects was opened by Hills on the biophysical properties of the surfactant system. The benefits of antifoaming agents in preventing edema were related to their hydrophobic properties. Moreover, the problem of discontinuity of the liquid lining at the air/liquid interface of the lung and its effect on surface tension was discussed.

Following this lecture, the clinical aspects of RDS were developed. The work of Giuntini on the radiographic features that characterize RDS shows that the chest xray is still a focal point for diagnosis and prognosis. The work of Bryan, presented by Milic-Emili, revealed that high frequency ventilation is an effective method for preventing experimentally-induced RDS lesions and blood gas deterioration. However, it has not proved to be of equal effectiveness when used in the clinical setting. The same conclusions were arrived at by Marini from his work with the "jet" high-frequency ventilator.

The effectiveness of Ambroxol for prevention and treatment of RDS was suggested by a number of investigators during the symposium, including Doctors Lowemberg, Wauer, Luerti and others. The surfactant-stimulating effects of

Ambroxol have been shown by morphologic, biochemical and biophysical analyses, as well as in clinical trials. These studies indicate that Ambroxol may become a drug of choice for the prevention and treatment of RDS. Indeed, the randomized study of Wauer provides convincing evidence for the effectiveness of Ambroxol in the treatment of neonatal RDS and these findings are consistent with the work of Kapanci which reveals, in adult rats, that Ambroxol stimulates incorporation of radioisotope-labelled palmitate into pulmonary lecithin and into the lamellar bodies of type 2 cells.

Another approach to the prevention and treatment of RDS, is endotracheal instillation of supplementary surfactant as pointed out by Robertson. In animal models, the therapeutic effect of exogenous surfactant is more impressive and more long-standing when the material is administered before the onset of spontaneous or artificial ventilation. Recent trials have shown that babies with RDS can be treated effectively by tracheal administration of mixtures of synthetic surfactants. The results were discussed by Robertson with a view to establishing guidelines for the preparation of a more effective synthetic substitute for natural surfactant. The potential of exogenous replacement therapy in deficiency states such as neonatal RDS, is an area of intense clinical interest today. At present, a fundamental problem with any type of exogenous replacement is that there is still uncertainty about the nature of the physiologically critical components of pulmonary surfactant in vivo. Continued basic research may well provide relatively simple, well defined "artificial" surface-active mixtures which will replicate the primary surface properties of the complex natural system. However, no such simple mixture has yet been proved to be as efficacious as replacement with the natural surfactant. Sources of natural surfactants have included extracts from animal lungs and also from human amniotic fluid. Finally, a number of basic questions remain about the optimal delivery route, the time course of therapy, and the method of preparation of the replacement mixture.

Our conference was equally active on another important aspect of surfactant function, i.e., its role in airway dynamics. Doctor Olivieri began the deliberations with his report on bronchoalveolar clearance mechanisms in normal and pathological conditions. In certain disease states, such as chronic bronchitis and pulmonary emphysema, he found that the surface activity of bronchoalveolar lavage fluid was reduced, but that it could be modified by therapeutic means. It was also shown by Valenti that drugs such as Ambroxol and bromhexine tend to increase phospholipid content (mainly disaturated lecithin) in bronchoalveolar and bronchial lavage as shown by an increase of the ratio of lecithin to albumin.

In smokers, lung surfactant is reduced, whereas it returns to normal following cessation of smoking as shown by the work of Finley. The reduction during smoking could be due to reduced production or to increased removal of surfactants. The large number of cytoplasmic inclusion bodies in alveolar macrophages of smokers may account for the diminution of lung surfactant. This hypothesis is impressive but needs further study. Mineral particles were also found by Richards to affect lung surfactant. Although the effect of many minerals is only transient, at least two, quartz and asbestos (which are generally agreed to cause fibrosis), produce an elevation of surfactants that persists and may reach levels 20 times greater than normal. Richards concluded that the striking increase in lung surfactant helps prevent the onset of fibrosis in the mineral-treated lung.

Many challenges in the experimental animal may result in significant changes in surfactant production. Among these are such diverse factors as chemotherapeutic agents, tranquilizers, liposoluble anaesthetics and O_2 inhalation in high concentrations. These effects, as shown by Curti, could be prevented by the administration of Ambroxol. Similarly, tests of the drug in chronic bronchitis by Grassi also showed improvement of biochemical and biophysical parameters. Less definitive results were reported by Catena, who analyzed the ratios among phospholipids in a number of diseases.

Our speakers also provided a good deal of material on the role of surfactants in the mucociliary system of the bronchial tree. Understanding that function of surfactant is probably not restricted to the alveoli, it has become apparent that the original suggestion of the Mendenhalls and Scarpelli (that surfactants are swept from alveoli to airways) requires further investigation. This general theme was discussed by Reifenrath in his comprehensive lecture. Doctor Green's most provocative talk embraces these possibilities in hypotheses that lead to predictions that surfactant dysfunction can result in impaired bronchiolar clearance (e.g., alveolar proteinosis), peribronchiolar accumulation of phagocytes (e.g., asbestosis), perivascular accumulation of inert particles (e.g., coal dust), and cellular fluid accumulation (e.g., atelectasis). As the speaker said, these predictions might be the basis for future experimentation.

Studies of the rheological characteristics of mucociliary clearance were presented by Allegra, who tested the effect of Ambroxol in patients affected by chronic bronchitis. Ambroxol was shown to increase elasticity but not viscosity of bronchial secretions. This study, along with the one presented by Rizzato, shows an improvement of mucociliary clearance rate evaluated before and after inhalation of the drug in chronic obstructive lung disease, but that the effects of the drug (although clearly positive) are not yet completely understood, as emphasized by Dorow.

At this point there is no question that the decade of the '80s will see further applications of the principles of basic biology and biophysics to the problems of clinical medicine and that this will lead to new insights into the etiology and treatment of lung diseases related to alteration of the surfactant system. From what we have seen and heard at this Symposium it is obvious that one can safely predict nothing less.

E.V. Cosmi

SUBJECT INDEX